Symbolic
Logic

THIRD EDITION

Irving M. Copi

University of Michigan

THE MACMILLAN COMPANY

COLLIER-MACMILLAN LIMITED, LONDON

FOR AMELIA

THE MACMILLAN COMPANY
COLLIER-MACMILLAN CANADA, LTD., TORONTO, ONTARIO

PRINTED IN THE UNITED STATES OF AMERICA

PREFACE TO
THIRD EDITION

The third edition of *Symbolic Logic* differs from the second in several minor respects and one major respect. Some of the minor revisions involve mere changes in wording for greater clarity. The major change is due to Professor William Tuthill Parry, who discovered that the quantification rules set forth in Chapter 4 of the second edition were incorrect.[1] Those rules were originally published early in 1956,[2] and appeared to offer some advantages in simplicity and ease of application over the quantification rules presented in the first edition of this book. When no objections to them had come to my attention by the end of 1964, I decided to include them in the second edition, which was published in the spring of 1965. Its appearance was followed shortly by the publication of Professor Parry's article.

[1] William Tuthill Parry, 'Comments on a Variant Form of Natural Deduction', *The Journal of Symbolic Logic*, vol. 30 (June 1965), pp. 119–122. See also Hugues Leblanc, 'Minding One's *X*'s and *Y*'s', *Logique et Analyse* (September 1965), and John G. Slater's 'The Required Correction to Copi's Statement of UG', *Logique et Analyse* (June 1966).

[2] Irving M. Copi, 'Another Variant of Natural Deduction', *The Journal of Symbolic Logic*, vol. 21 (March 1956), pp. 52–55.

In the third edition new quantification rules replace the unsatisfactory old ones. The changes are in Existential Instantiation (**EI**) and Universal Generalization (**UG**). They now represent a closer approximation to Gentzen's original version of these rules, though modified to conform to the general approach of the present volume.[3] I have received a good deal of help in preparing this new edition. Professor Dag Prawitz of Stockholm University has corresponded with me about the needed change in rules, and offered very sound advice. Professors William Tuthill Parry of The State University of New York at Buffalo, Hugues Leblanc of Bryn Mawr College, Henry W. Johnstone of The Pennsylvania State University, and Donald Kalish of The University of California at Los Angeles have been kind enough to examine an earlier formulation of my new rules and to give me the benefit of their judgment on them. If any mistakes remain, however, the responsibility is mine alone.

Other minor revisions were required by that major one. These include changes in some of the sample proofs set forth in Chapters 4 and 5, changes in some of the solutions at the end of the book for exercises in those chapters, and changes in Section 4 of Chapter 9, where the 'Natural Deduction' techniques of Chapter 4 are shown to be derivable within the first-order function calculus RS_1 developed in Chapter 9.

Again, warm thanks are offered to Mr. John Dennis Moore and Mr. Joseph Falzone of The Macmillan Company for their help, and to my wife and daughter for assistance in reading proof.

IRVING M. COPI

Honolulu

---

[3] The new phrasing of **EI** is similar to, and the new phrasing of **UG** is the same as, rephrasings of Gentzen's rules suggested by Professor Hugues Leblanc. I am indebted to Professor Leblanc for permission to borrow his new formulations, which he plans to substitute in the second edition of his *Techniques of Deductive Inference*, Englewood Cliffs, N.J.: Prentice-Hall, 1966, for the rules now employed there.

PREFACE TO
SECOND EDITION

The second edition differs from the first in several respects.

There are three changes in organization. First, the material on Normal Forms and Boolean Expansions from the end of Chapter 2 has been made into Appendix A at the back of the book. It was a digression from the orderly development of logical techniques in the first five chapters. But because of its intrinsic interest and importance it should be included in a textbook of this type. Placing it in an appendix seems to me to improve the organization of the book.

The second organizational change is the division of Chapter 3's nineteen Rules of Inference (elementary valid argument forms) into two groups. The first nine are discussed separately, and are followed by exercises intended to help the student master the first group before going on to the second. This change should help make the student's progress more gradual and more secure.

The third organizational change is the earlier appearance in Chapter 3 of the method of proving invalidity by assigning truth values to the simple components in an argument or argument form. The addition of a proof of incompleteness of the nineteen Rules of Inference makes it desirable to present techniques for proving invalidity before rather than after the rules of conditional and indirect proof.

There are two substantive changes in the materials of the first edition. The new quantification rules presented in Chapter 4 are both easier to understand and easier to apply in the second edition. They permit simpler proofs of validity to be given for some arguments, as I pointed out in 'Another Variant of Natural Deduction'[1].

The other substantive change in the first edition's material is in its proofs and demonstrations. Many of the proofs of theorems and meta-theorems are both simpler and shorter in the second edition. Some of these improvements were suggested by colleagues at other colleges and universities; others were devised by interested and able students.

Besides the organizational and substantive changes already mentioned, the second edition contains significant new materials. An alternative way of writing out truth tables is given in Chapter 2. The original nineteen Rules of Inference in Chapter 3 are *proved* to be incomplete. The independence of the R.S. axioms is proved in Chapter 7. Solutions to selected exercises are given in the back of the book, which should make the text more useful for independent study and should diminish the amount of class time required for drill. Finally, the second edition contains over two hundred new exercises, although most of them are replacements rather than additions to the study materials included.

Many teachers of logic have been kind enough to write me suggestions for improving this book. I have given earnest consideration to the advice offered, even though I have not been able to incorporate all of the changes that were proposed. For their helpful communications I am particularly indebted to Professors Alan Ross Anderson of the University of Pittsburgh, Richard B. Angell of Ohio Wesleyan University, Sidney Axinn of Temple University, Robert W. Beard of Florida State University, Mario Bunge of University of Buenos Aires, Charles E. Bures of the California Institute of Technology, Robert E. Butts and Kaith Emerson Ballard of Bucknell University, George A. Clark of Lafayette College, Filippo Costa of the University of Pisa, Kendall B. Cox of the University of North Dakota, Haskell B. Curry of the Pennsylvania State College, Richard Gale of the University of Pittsburgh, Theodore Hailperin of Lehigh University, John van Heijenoort of New

---

[1] *The Journal of Symbolic Logic*, vol. 21, no. 1 (March 1956), pp. 52–55.

York University, Donald Kalish of the University of California at Los Angeles, E. D. Klemke of De Pauw University, Hugues Leblanc of Bryn Mawr College, Charles R. Magel of Moorhead State College, Robert McNaughton of the University of Pennsylvania, Rene S. Meyer of the University of South Africa, Douglas N. Morgan of the University of Texas, C. Mason Myers of Northern Illinois University, W. T. Parry of the University of Buffalo, J. Porte of the Centre National de la Recherche Scientifique, Ruth Mathers Putnam of Wellesley College, Peter Remnant of the University of British Columbia, William Rowe of Purdue University, Leo Simons of the University of Tennessee, Avrum Stroll of the University of California at San Diego, J. F. Thomson of Brandeis University, and Rollin Workman of the University of Cincinnati.

I am enormously indebted to my friend and former student Mrs. W. L. Barbee for a great deal of help in preparing the manuscript of this new edition. The staff of The Macmillan Company have been unfailingly helpful throughout the long process of preparing this new edition. Warm thanks are especially due to Mr. John Dennis Moore and Mr. Joseph Falzone for their wise counsel and expert professional advice. I should like to express my appreciation also to my cousin, Peggy Fingard Roffe, for help with the index, and to my wife for many hours shared in the onerous chore of reading proof.

IRVING M. COPI

Belsize Park, Hampstead

PREFACE TO
FIRST EDITION

This book has been written to serve as a first textbook of symbolic logic for undergraduate and graduate students. It presupposes no earlier training in either classical or modern logic. The topics covered in this book are those studied in the author's two-semester course in symbolic logic at the University of Michigan. In this book, as in my teaching, I have attempted to combine two distinct approaches to the subject.

Logic was discussed by its ancient founder, Aristotle, from two quite different points of view. On the one hand, he regarded logic as an instrument or organon for appraising the correctness of reasoning; and on the other, he saw the principles and methods of logic as interesting and important topics to be themselves investigated more or less systematically. Modern symbolic logic can also be viewed from the same two perspectives. Through the development of its special symbols logic has become an immeasurably more powerful instrument for analysis and deduction. And the principles and methods of symbolic logic can be very fruitfully investigated in their own right through the construction and examination of *logistic systems*. The present book combines these two approaches to the study of symbolic logic.

The first half of the book, comprising Chapters 1 through 5, presents the standard notations, methods, and principles of symbolic logic for *use* in determining the validity or invalidity of arguments. It takes up successively more complex modes of argumentation: beginning with those which involve truth-functionally compound statements, it goes on to arguments containing singly general and then multiply general propositions, and finally relational arguments. The standard methods of truth tables, of Boolean Expansions,[1] and the method of deduction are introduced, the latter including both conditional and *reductio ad absurdum* proofs. Next propositional functions and quantifiers are introduced, with 'natural deduction' rules for working with them. The logic of relations is developed in a separate chapter, which includes a discussion of identity theory and definite descriptions. A great many exercises are provided to help the student acquire a practical mastery of the material.

The second half of the book contains a more systematic treatment of the logical principles *used* in the first half. After a brief discussion of deductive systems in general, a propositional calculus is developed according to the highest modern standards of rigor, and proved to be consistent and complete. Alternative notations and axiom systems for the propositional calculus are discussed, and then a first order function calculus is developed. The latter is shown to be equivalent to the 'natural deduction' methods presented in the first half of the book, and is proved to be consistent and complete.

There are two appendices, the first dealing with the algebra of classes, the second with the ramified theory of logical types.

In the first part of the book an attempt is made to achieve maximum clarity by introducing the special symbols in as natural and intuitive a way as possible. Thus the discussion of the horseshoe symbol ($\supset$) for material implication is intended to minimize the arbitrariness and artificiality which too often surround that notion. No novelties are introduced for their own sakes; on the contrary, every effort has been made to conform to standard notations and usages. Although not pretending to be in any sense a 'handbook,' the present volume explains a number of alternative notations, including the stroke and dagger functions, the use of dots as brackets, and the parenthesis-free Polish notation due to Lukasiewicz. Both the simple and the ramified theories of

---

[1] The method of Boolean Expansions is relegated to Appendix A in the second edition.

logical types are explained, and the latter is compared with the object language metalanguage distinction as an alternative method of avoiding the so-called semantical paradoxes. Enough material has been included to enable the student who masters it to go on to read more advanced treatises and even some of the journal articles which report current research in symbolic logic.[2]

The present book is suitable for either a one- or two-semester course in symbolic logic. It is adaptable to courses which stress the informal development of notations and methods for their *use* in appraising arguments, and is equally adaptable to courses whose main emphasis is on the development of systems of symbolic logic. To this end, the chapters are so written as to permit some variation in the order in which they can be read or assigned. Thus Chapters 6, 7, and 8 can be read before Chapters 4 and 5, if it is desired to study the propositional calculus as a logistic system before taking up quantification theory.

Controversial philosophical questions are not allowed to intrude. The entire book is written from what is sincerely intended to be a philosophically neutral point of view.

Some of the material in Chapters 3, 4, 7, and 9 was first communicated to me by my friend and former colleague Professor Atwell R. Turquette of the University of Illinois, and I am happy to acknowledge my indebtedness to him. The logistic systems R.S. and RS_1, which are set forth in Chapters 7 and 9, respectively, are early versions of calculi which appear in revised form in Professor J. Barkley Rosser's *Logic for Mathematicians*, and I am very grateful to Professor Rosser for his permission to include them here. The proof of completeness for the first-order function calculus presented in Chapter 9 is an adaptation to RS_1 of the completeness proof for an alternative first-order function calculus due to Professor Leon Henkin, of the University of California, whose generous permission to reproduce it here is deeply appreciated. I wish to thank Professor J. Barkley Rosser of Cornell University and Professor Gustav Bergmann of the State University of Iowa, who read early versions of the manuscript and made a number of very helpful suggestions. And I am grateful to Professor Martin E. Lean of Brooklyn College for his valuable criticism not only of the manuscript of *Symbolic Logic* but also of the manuscript of my earlier *Introduction to Logic*. My

---

[2] Beginning on page 387 of the third edition is a list of the special symbols of the book with page references to their first occurrence.

thanks to him for the latter are belated only because his identity was not revealed to me by the publisher until the manuscript of the present book was ready for the press. Professor Paul Henle and Dr. Robert McNaughton of the University of Michigan, Professor Nakhnikian of Wayne University, and Dr. Ziff of Harvard University read parts of the manuscript, and I am grateful to them also for helpful suggestions. And I wish to express my gratitude to Mr. Rollin Workman for his expert assistance in the tedious task of proofreading. I also wish to thank Professor Marvin Farber of the University of Buffalo for permission to include in Appendix B some passages which appeared earlier in the journal of *Philosophy and Phenomenological Research.*

I am particularly indebted to my colleague Professor Arthur W. Burks both for his constant encouragement and for his valuable criticisms of my manuscript, of which he read each chapter as it was written. And I wish to acknowledge the help given me by Mr. David M. Copi in preparing the manuscript for publication.

Finally I wish to thank the many students who have participated actively and enthusiastically in the logic classes from which this book developed. I owe a debt to them as well as to the great teachers under whom I studied logic: Rudolf Carnap, C. H. Langford, and Bertrand Russell. I hope this book will not be found too unworthy of the help they have given me.

IRVING M. COPI

Ann Arbor

CONTENTS

Preface to Third Edition   iii

Preface to Second Edition   v

Preface to First Edition   ix

CHAPTER 1

INTRODUCTION: LOGIC AND LANGUAGE   1

1.1   What Is Logic?   1
1.2   The Nature of Argument   2
1.3   Truth and Validity   4
1.4   Symbolic Logic   6

CHAPTER 2

ARGUMENTS CONTAINING COMPOUND
STATEMENTS   9

2.1   Simple and Compound Statements   9

2.2 Implication   14
2.3 Argument Forms and Truth Tables   19
2.4 Tautologies, Contradictions, and Contingencies   27

CHAPTER 3

THE METHOD OF DEDUCTION   33

3.1 Formal Proof of Validity   33
3.2 Proving Invalidity   51
3.3 Incompleteness of the Nineteen Rules   54
3.4 The Rule of Conditional Proof   58
3.5 The Rule of Indirect Proof   62
3.6 Proofs of Tautologies   65
3.7 Shorter Truth Table Technique—*Reductio ad Absurdum*
         Method   68

CHAPTER 4

PROPOSITIONAL FUNCTIONS AND QUANTIFIERS   71

4.1 Singular Propositions and General Propositions   71
4.2 Proving Validity: Preliminary Quantification Rules   80
4.3 Proving Invalidity   91
4.4 Multiply General Propositions   97
4.5 Quantification Rules   103
4.6 Logical Truths Involving Quantifiers   122

CHAPTER 5

THE LOGIC OF RELATIONS   131

5.1 Symbolizing Relations   131
5.2 Arguments Involving Relations   147
5.3 Some Properties of Relations   151
5.4 Identity and the Definite Description   158
5.5 Property Variables and Properties of Properties   169

CHAPTER 6

DEDUCTIVE SYSTEMS   177

6.1 Definition and Deduction   177
6.2 Euclidean Geometry   179
6.3 Formal Deductive Systems   184
6.4 Properties of Formal Deductive Systems   187
6.5 Logistic Systems   190

CHAPTER 7

A PROPOSITIONAL CALCULUS   195

7.1 Object Language and Metalanguage   195
7.2 Primitive Symbols and Well Formed Formulas   198
7.3 Axioms and Demonstrations   211
7.4 Independence of the Axioms   217
7.5 Development of the Calculus   223
7.6 Deductive Completeness   238

CHAPTER 8

ALTERNATIVE SYSTEMS AND NOTATIONS   248

8.1 Alternative Systems of Logic   248
8.2 The Hilbert-Ackermann System   250
8.3 The Use of Dots as Brackets   260
8.4 A Parenthesis-Free Notation   264
8.5 The Stroke and Dagger Operators   265
8.6 The Nicod System   267

CHAPTER 9

A FIRST-ORDER FUNCTION CALCULUS   277

9.1 The New Logistic System RS_1 277
9.2 Development of RS_1 285

9.3 Duality   293
9.4 RS$_1$ and the 'Natural Deduction' Techniques   298
9.5 Normal Forms   302
9.6 Completeness of RS$_1$ 311

**Appendix A: NORMAL FORMS AND BOOLEAN
               EXPANSIONS**   325

Appendix B: THE ALGEBRA OF CLASSES   333

Appendix C: THE RAMIFIED THEORY OF TYPES   345

SOLUTIONS TO SELECTED EXERCISES   357

SPECIAL SYMBOLS   387

INDEX   389

1

INTRODUCTION: LOGIC AND LANGUAGE

1.1 WHAT IS LOGIC?

It is easy to find answers to the question 'What is Logic?' According to Charles Peirce, 'Nearly a hundred definitions of it have been given'.[1] But Peirce goes on to write: 'It will, however, generally be conceded that its central problem is the classification of arguments, so that all those that are bad are thrown into one division, and those which are good into another . . . .'.

The study of logic, then, is the study of the methods and principles used in distinguishing correct (good) from incorrect (bad) arguments. This definition is not intended to imply, of course, that one can make the distinction only if he has studied logic. But the study of logic will *help* one to distinguish between correct and incorrect arguments, and it will do so in several ways. First of all, the proper study of logic will approach it as an art as well as a science, and the student will do exercises in all parts of the theory being learned. Here, as anywhere else,

---

[1] 'Logic', in *Dictionary of Philosophy and Psychology*, edited by James Mark Baldwin, New York, The Macmillan Company, 1925.

practice will help to make perfect. In the second place, the study of logic, especially symbolic logic, like the study of any other exact science, will tend to increase one's proficiency in reasoning. And finally, the study of logic will give the student certain techniques for testing the validity of all arguments, including his own. This knowledge is of value because when mistakes are easily detected they are less likely to be made.

Logic has frequently been defined as the science of reasoning. That definition, although it gives a clue to the nature of logic, is not quite accurate. Reasoning is that special kind of thinking called inferring, in which conclusions are drawn from premises. As thinking, however, it is not the special province of logic, but part of the psychologist's subject matter as well. Psychologists who examine the reasoning process find it to be extremely complex and highly emotional, consisting of awkward trial and error procedures illuminated by sudden—and sometimes apparently irrelevant—flashes of insight. These are all of importance to psychology. But the logician is not interested in the actual process of reasoning. He is concerned with the correctness of the completed process. His question is always: does the conclusion reached *follow* from the premises used or assumed? If the premises provide grounds or good evidence for the conclusion, if asserting the premises to be true warrants asserting the conclusion to be true also, then the reasoning is correct. Otherwise it is incorrect. The logician's methods and techniques have been developed primarily for the purpose of making the distinction clear. The logician is interested in all reasoning, regardless of its subject matter, but only from this special point of view.

1.2 THE NATURE OF ARGUMENT

Inferring is an activity in which one proposition is arrived at and affirmed on the basis of one or more other propositions accepted as the starting point of the process. The logician is not concerned with the *process* of inference, but with the propositions that are the initial and end points of that process, and the relationships between them.

Propositions are either true or false, and in this they differ from questions, commands, and exclamations. Grammarians classify the linguistic formulations of propositions, questions, commands, and exclamations as declarative, interrogative, imperative, and exclamatory sentences, respectively. These are familiar notions. It is customary to distinguish between declarative sentences and what they express, using the word 'proposition' to denote the latter. The distinction is brought out most clearly by remarking that a declarative sentence or statement is always part of a language, the language in which it is enunciated, whereas propositions are not peculiar to any of the languages in which they may be formulated.

Corresponding to every possible inference is an *argument*, and it is with these arguments that logic is chiefly concerned. An argument may be defined as any group of propositions of which one is claimed to follow from the others, which are regarded as supplying evidence for the truth of that one. In ordinary usage the word 'argument' also has other meanings, but in logic it has the technical sense explained. In the following chapters the word 'argument' will be used also in a derivative sense to refer to any collection of statements in which an argument is formulated or expressed. Every argument has a structure, in the analysis of which the terms 'premiss' and 'conclusion' are usually employed. The *conclusion* of an argument is that proposition which is affirmed on the basis of the other propositions of the argument, and these other propositions which are affirmed as providing evidence or reasons for accepting the conclusion are the *premisses* of that argument.

We note that 'premiss' and 'conclusion' are relative terms, in the sense that the same proposition can be a premiss in one argument and conclusion in another. Thus the proposition *All men are mortal* is premiss in the argument

> All men are mortal.
> Socrates is a man.
> Therefore Socrates is mortal.

and conclusion in the argument

> All animals are mortal.
> All men are animals.
> Therefore all men are mortal.

Any proposition can be either a premiss or a conclusion, depending upon its context. It is a premiss when it occurs in an argument which assumes it for the sake of proving some other proposition. And it is a conclusion when it occurs in an argument which purports to prove it on the basis of other propositions which are assumed.

It is customary to distinguish between *deductive* and *inductive* arguments. All arguments involve the claim that their premisses provide evidence for the truth of their conclusions, but only a *deductive* argument involves the claim that its premisses provide *absolutely conclusive* evidence. The technical terms 'valid' and 'invalid' are used in place of 'correct' and 'incorrect' in characterizing deductive arguments. A deductive argument is *valid* when its premisses and conclusion are so related that it is absolutely impossible for the premisses to be true unless the conclusion is true also. The task of deductive logic is to clarify the nature of the relationship which holds between premisses and conclusion in a valid argument, and to provide techniques for discriminating the valid from the invalid.

Inductive arguments involve only the claim that their premisses constitute *some* evidence for their conclusions. Neither the term 'valid' nor its opposite 'invalid' is properly applied to inductive arguments. Inductive arguments differ among themselves in the degree of likelihood or probability which their premisses confer upon their conclusions, and are studied in inductive logic. But in this book we shall be concerned only with deductive arguments, and shall use the word 'argument' to refer to deductive arguments exclusively.

1.3 TRUTH AND VALIDITY

Truth and falsehood are properties of propositions, and may derivatively be said to characterize the declarative sentences or statements in which propositions are formulated. But arguments are not properly characterized as being either true or false. On the other hand, validity and invalidity are properties of arguments rather than of propositions or statements.[2] There is a connection between the validity or invalidity

[2] Some logicians use the term 'valid' to characterize statements which are *logically true*, as will be explained in Chapter 9, Section 9.6. For the present, however, we shall apply the terms 'valid' and 'invalid' to arguments exclusively.

of an argument and the truth or falsehood of its premisses and conclusion, but the connection is by no means a simple one.

Some valid arguments contain true propositions only, as, for example,

> All bats are mammals.
> All mammals have lungs.
> Therefore all bats have lungs.

But an argument may contain false propositions exclusively, and be valid nevertheless, as, for example,

> All trout are mammals.
> All mammals have wings.
> Therefore all trout have wings.

This argument is valid because *if* its premisses were true its conclusion would have to be true also, even though in fact they are all false. These two examples show that although some valid arguments have true conclusions, not all of them do. The validity of an argument does not guarantee the truth of its conclusion.

When we consider the argument

> If I am President then I am famous.
> I am not President.
> Therefore I am not famous.

we can see that although both premisses and conclusion are true, it is invalid. Its invalidity is made obvious by comparing it with another argument of the same form:

> If Rockefeller is President then he is famous.
> Rockefeller is not President.
> Therefore Rockefeller is not famous.

This argument is clearly invalid, since its premisses are true but its conclusion false. The two latter examples show that although some invalid arguments have false conclusions, not all of them do. The falsehood of its conclusion does not guarantee the invalidity of an argument. But the falsehood of its conclusion does guarantee that *either* the argument is invalid *or* at least one of its premisses is false.

There are two conditions that an argument must satisfy to establish the truth of its conclusion. It must be valid, and all of its premisses must be true. The logician is concerned with only one of those conditions. To determine the truth or falsehood of premisses is the task of scientific inquiry in general, since premisses may deal with any subject matter at all. But determining the validity or invalidity of arguments is the special province of deductive logic. The logician is interested in the question of validity even for arguments whose premisses might happen to be false.

A question might be raised about the legitimacy of that interest. It might be suggested that we ought to confine our attention to arguments having true premisses only. But it is often necessary to depend upon the validity of arguments whose premisses are not known to be true. Modern scientists investigate their theories by deducing conclusions from them which predict the behavior of observable phenomena in the laboratory or observatory. The conclusion is then tested directly by observation, and if it is true, this tends to confirm the theory from which it was deduced, whereas if it is false, this disconfirms or refutes the theory. In either case, the scientist is vitally interested in the validity of the argument by which the testable conclusion is deduced from the theory being investigated; for if that argument is invalid his whole procedure is without point. The foregoing is an oversimplified account of scientific method, but it serves to show that questions of validity are important even for arguments whose premisses are not true.

1.4 SYMBOLIC LOGIC

It has been explained that logic is concerned with arguments, and that these contain propositions as their premisses and conclusions. The latter are not linguistic entities, such as declarative sentences or statements, but rather what declarative sentences are typically used to assert. However, the communication of propositions and arguments requires the use of language, and this complicates our problem. Arguments formulated in English or any other natural language are often difficult to appraise because of the vague and equivocal nature of the words in which they are expressed, the ambiguity of their construction, the misleading idioms they may contain, and their pleasing but deceptive metaphorical style. The resolution of these difficulties is not the central problem for the logician, however, for even when they are resolved, the problem of deciding the validity or invalidity of the argument remains.

To avoid the peripheral difficulties connected with ordinary language, workers in the various sciences have developed specialized technical vocabularies. The scientist economizes the space and time required for writing his reports and theories by adopting special symbols to express ideas which would otherwise require a long sequence of familiar words to formulate. This has the further advantage of reducing the amount of attention needed, for when a sentence or equation grows too long its meaning is more difficult to grasp. The introduction of the exponent symbol in mathematics permits the expression of the equation

$$A \times A \times A \times A \times A \times A \times A \times A \times A \times A \times A \times A = B \times B \times B \times B \times B \times B \times B$$

more briefly and intelligibly as

$$A^{12} = B^7$$

A like advantage has been obtained by the use of graphic formulas in organic chemistry. And the language of every advanced science has been enriched by similar symbolic innovations.

Logic, too, has had a special technical notation developed for it. Aristotle made use of certain abbreviations to facilitate his own investigations, and modern symbolic logic has grown by the introduction of many more special symbols. The difference between the old and the new logic is one of degree rather than of kind, but the difference in degree is tremendous. Modern symbolic logic has become immeasurably more powerful a tool for analysis and deduction through the development of its own technical language. The special symbols of modern logic permit us to exhibit with greater clarity the logical structures of arguments which may be obscured by their formulation in ordinary language. It is an easier task to divide arguments into the valid and the invalid when they are expressed in a special symbolic language, for in it the peripheral problems of vagueness, ambiguity, idiom, metaphor, and amphiboly do not arise. The introduction and use of special symbols serve not only to facilitate the appraisal of arguments, but also to clarify the nature of deductive inference.

The logician's special symbols are much better adapted than ordinary language to the actual drawing of inferences. Their superiority in this respect is comparable to that enjoyed by Arabic numerals over the older Roman kind for purposes of computation. It is easy to multiply 148 by 47, but very difficult to compute the product of CXLVIII and XLVII. Similarly, the drawing of inferences and the evaluation of arguments is greatly facilitated by the adoption of a special logical notation. To quote Alfred North Whitehead, an important contributor to the advance of symbolic logic:

. . . by the aid of symbolism, we can make transitions in reasoning almost mechanically by the eye, which otherwise would call into play the higher faculties of the brain.[3]

In view of the importance of the symbols used to formulate arguments, we shall develop our theory in terms of statements rather than propositions.

[3] *An Introduction to Mathematics* by A. N. Whitehead, Oxford, Eng., Oxford University Press, 1911.

2

ARGUMENTS CONTAINING COMPOUND STATEMENTS

2.1 SIMPLE AND COMPOUND STATEMENTS

All statements can be divided into two kinds, simple and compound. A *simple* statement is one which does not contain any other statement as a component part, whereas every *compound* statement does contain another statement as a component part. For example, 'Atmospheric testing of nuclear weapons will be discontinued or this planet will become uninhabitable' is a compound statement that contains as its components the two simple statements 'Atmospheric testing of nuclear weapons will be discontinued' and 'this planet will become uninhabitable'. The component parts of a compound statement may themselves be compound, of course. We turn now to some of the different ways in which statements can be combined into compound statements.

The statement 'Roses are red and violets are blue' is a *conjunction*, a compound statement formed by inserting the word 'and' between two statements. Two statements so combined are called *conjuncts*. The word 'and' has other uses, however, as in the statement 'Castor and Pollux

9

were twins', which is not compound, but a simple statement asserting a relationship. We introduce the dot '·' as a special symbol for combining statements conjunctively. Using it, the preceding conjunction is written 'Roses are red·violets are blue'. Where p and q are any two statements whatever, their conjunction is written $p \cdot q$.

Every statement is either true or false, so we can speak of the *truth value* of a statement, where the truth value of a true statement is *true* and the truth value of a false statement is *false*. There are two broad categories into which compound statements can be divided, according to whether or not there is any necessary connection between the truth value of the compound statement and the truth values of its component statements. The truth value of the compound statement 'Smith believes that lead is heavier than zinc' is completely independent of the truth value of its component simple statement 'lead is heavier than zinc', for people have mistaken as well as correct beliefs. On the other hand, there is a necessary connection between the truth value of a conjunction and the truth values of its conjuncts. A conjunction is true if both its conjuncts are true, but false otherwise. Any compound statement whose truth value is completely determined by the truth values of its component statements, regardless of whether they are true or false, is a *truth-functionally* compound statement. The only compound statements we shall consider here will be truth-functionally compound statements. Therefore in the rest of this book we shall use the term 'simple statement' to refer to any statement that is not truth-functionally compound.

Since conjunctions are truth-functionally compound statements, our symbol is a truth-functional connective. Given any two statements p and q there are just four possible sets of truth values they can have, and in every case the truth value of their conjunction $p \cdot q$ is uniquely determined. The four possible cases can be exhibited as follows:

in case p is true and q is true, $p \cdot q$ is true;
in case p is true and q is false, $p \cdot q$ is false;
in case p is false and q is true, $p \cdot q$ is false;
in case p is false and q is false, $p \cdot q$ is false.

Representing the truth values true and false by the capital letters 'T' and 'F', respectively, the way in which the truth value of a conjunction is determined by the truth values of its conjuncts can be displayed more briefly by means of a *truth table* as follows:

p	q	$p \cdot q$
T	T	T
T	F	F
F	T	F
F	F	F

Since it specifies the truth value of $p \cdot q$ in every possible case, this truth table can be taken as *defining* the dot symbol. Other English words such as 'moreover', 'furthermore', 'but', 'yet', 'still', 'however', etc., are also used to conjoin two statements into a single compound one, and all of them can be indifferently translated into the dot symbol so far as truth values are concerned.

The statement 'It is not the case that lead is heavier than gold' is also compound, being the *negation* (or *denial* or *contradictory*) of its single component statement 'lead is heavier than gold'. We introduce the symbol '$\sim$', called a *curl* (or a *tilde*) to symbolize negation. There are often alternative formulations in English of the negation of a given statement. Thus where L symbolizes the statement 'lead is heavier than gold', the different statements 'it is not the case that lead is heavier than gold', 'it is false that lead is heavier than gold', 'it is not true that lead is heavier than gold', 'lead is not heavier than gold' are all indifferently symbolized as $\sim L$. More generally, where p is any statement whatever, its negation is written $\sim p$. Since the negation of a true statement is false and the negation of a false statement is true, we can take the following truth table as defining the curl symbol:

p	$\sim p$
T	F
F	T

When two statements are combined disjunctively by inserting the word 'or' between them, the resulting compound statement is a *disjunction* (or *alternation*), and the two statements so combined are called *disjuncts* (or *alternatives*). The word 'or' has two different senses, one of which is clearly intended in the statement 'Premiums will be waived in the event of sickness or unemployment'. The intention here is obviously that premiums are waived not only for sick persons and for unemployed persons, but also for persons who are both sick *and* unemployed. This sense of the word 'or' is called *weak* or *inclusive*. A different sense of 'or' is intended when a restaurant lists 'tea or coffee' on its table d'hôte menu, meaning that for the stated price of the meal the customer can have one or the other, but *not both*. This second sense of 'or' is called *strong* or *exclusive*. A disjunction which uses the inclusive 'or' asserts that *at least one disjunct is true*, while one which uses the exclusive 'or' asserts that *at least one disjunct is true and at least one disjunct is false*. The *partial common meaning*, that at least one disjunct is true, is the whole meaning of an inclusive disjunction, and a part of the meaning of an exclusive disjunction.

In Latin, the word 'vel' expresses the inclusive sense of the word 'or', and the word 'aut' expresses the exclusive sense. It is customary to use the first letter of 'vel' to symbolize 'or' in its inclusive sense. Where p and q are any two statements whatever, their weak or inclusive disjunction is written $p \vee q$. The symbol 'v', called a *wedge* (or a *vee*), is a truth-functional connective, and is defined by the following truth table:

p	q	$p \vee q$
T	T	T
T	F	T
F	T	T
F	F	F

An obviously valid argument containing a disjunction is the following Disjunctive Syllogism:

> The United Nations will be strengthened or there will be a third world war.
> The United Nations will not be strengthened.
> Therefore there will be a third world war.

It is evident that a Disjunctive Syllogism is valid on *either* interpretation of the word 'or', that is, regardless of whether its first premiss asserts an inclusive or exclusive disjunction. It is usually difficult, and sometimes impossible, to discover which sense of the word 'or' is intended in a disjunction. But the typical valid argument that has a disjunction for a premiss is, like the Disjunctive Syllogism, valid on either interpretation of the word 'or'. Hence we effect a simplification by translating any occurrence of the word 'or' into the logical symbol 'v'— *regardless of which sense of 'or' is intended*. Of course where it is explicitly stated that the disjunction is exclusive, by use of the added phrase 'but not both', for example, we do have the symbolic apparatus for symbolizing that sense, as will be explained below.

The use of parentheses, brackets, and braces for punctuating mathematical expressions is familiar. No number is uniquely denoted by the expression '$6 + 9 \div 3$', although when punctuation makes clear how its constituents are to be grouped, it denotes either 5 or 9. Punctuation is needed to resolve ambiguity in the language of symbolic logic too, since compound statements may themselves be combined to yield more complicated compounds. Ambiguity is present in $p \cdot q \vee r$, which could be either the conjunction of p with $q \vee r$, or else the disjunction of $p \cdot q$ with r. These two different senses are unambiguously given by different punctuations: $p \cdot (q \vee r)$ and $(p \cdot q) \vee r$. In case p and q are both false and r is true, the first punctuated expression is false (since its first conjunct is false) but the second punctuated expression is true (since its second disjunct is true). Hence a difference in punctuation can mean all the difference between truth and falsehood. In symbolic logic, as in mathematics, we use parentheses, brackets, and braces for punctuation. To cut down on the number of punctuation marks required, however, we establish the symbolic convention that in any expression the curl will apply to the smallest component that the punctuation permits. Thus the ambiguity of $\sim p \vee q$, which might mean either $(\sim p) \vee q$ or $\sim (p \vee q)$, is resolved by our convention to mean the first of these, for the curl can (and therefore by our convention *does*) apply to the first component p rather than to the larger expression $p \vee q$.

Since an exclusive disjunction asserts that at least one of its disjuncts is true and at least one of them is false, we can symbolize the exclusive disjunction of any two statements p and q quite simply as $(p \vee q) \cdot (\sim p \vee \sim q)$. Thus we are able to symbolize conjunctions, negations, and both inclusive and exclusive disjunctions. Any compound statement which is built up out of simple statements by repeated use of truth-functional connectives will have its truth value completely determined by the truth values of those simple statements. For example, if A and B are true statements and X and Y are false, the truth value of the compound statement $\sim[(\sim A \text{ v } X) \text{ v } \sim(B \cdot Y)]$ can be discovered as follows. Since A is true, $\sim A$ is false, and since X is false also, the disjunction $(\sim A \text{ v } X)$ is false. Since Y is false, the conjunction $(B \cdot Y)$ is false, and so its negation $\sim(B \cdot Y)$ is true. Hence the disjunction $(\sim A \text{ v } X) \text{ v } \sim(B \cdot Y)$ is true, and its negation, which is the original statement, is false. Such a stepwise procedure, beginning with the inmost components, always permits us to determine the truth value of a truth-functionally compound statement from the truth values of its component simple statements.

EXERCISES

If A and B are true statements and X and Y are false statements, which of the following compound statements are true?

★1. $\sim(A \text{ v } X)$

★2. $\sim A \text{ v } \sim X$

3. $\sim B \cdot \sim Y$

4. $\sim(B \cdot Y)$

5. $A \text{ v } (X \cdot Y)$

6. $(A \text{ v } X) \cdot Y$

7. $(A \text{ v } B) \cdot (X \text{ v } Y)$

8. $(A \cdot B) \text{ v } (X \cdot Y)$

9. $(A \cdot X) \text{ v } (B \cdot Y)$

10. $A \cdot [X \text{ v } (B \cdot Y)]$

11. $A \text{ v } [X \cdot (B \text{ v } Y)]$

12. $X \text{ v } [A \cdot (Y \text{ v } B)]$

★13. $\sim\{\sim[\sim(A \cdot \sim X) \cdot \sim A] \cdot \sim X\}$

14. $\sim\{\sim[\sim(A \cdot \sim B) \cdot \sim A] \cdot \sim A\}$

15. $[(A \cdot X) \text{ v } \sim B] \cdot \sim[(A \cdot X) \text{ v } \sim B]$

16. $[(X \cdot A) \text{ v } \sim Y] \text{ v } \sim[(X \cdot A) \text{ v } \sim Y]$

17. $[A \cdot (X \text{ v } Y)] \text{ v } \sim[(A \cdot X) \text{ v } (A \cdot Y)]$

★18. $[X \text{ v } (A \cdot Y)] \text{ v } \sim[(X \text{ v } A) \cdot (X \text{ v } Y)]$

19. $[X \cdot (A \text{ v } B)] \text{ v } \sim[(X \text{ v } A) \cdot (X \text{ v } B)]$

★20. $[X \text{ v } (A \cdot Y)] \text{ v } \sim[(X \text{ v } A) \text{ v } (X \text{ v } Y)]$

2.2   IMPLICATION

The compound statement 'If the train is late then we shall miss our connection' is a *conditional* (or a *hypothetical*, an *implication*, or an *implicative statement*). The component between the 'if' and the 'then' is called the *antecedent* (or the *implicans* or *protasis*), and the component which

★ Solutions to starred exercises will be found on pages 357–385.

follows the 'then' is the *consequent* (or the *implicate* or *apodosis*). A conditional does not assert either that its antecedent is true or that its consequent is true; it asserts only that *if* its antecedent is true then its consequent is true also, that is, that its antecedent *implies* its consequent. The key to the meaning of a conditional is the relation of *implication* asserted to hold between its antecedent and consequent, in that order.

If we examine a number of different conditionals we can see that there are different kinds of implications they may assert. In the conditional 'If all cats like liver and Dinah is a cat then Dinah likes liver', the consequent follows *logically* from its antecedent. On the other hand, in the conditional 'If the figure is a triangle then it has three sides', the consequent follows from the antecedent by the very *definition* of the word 'triangle'. But the truth of the conditional 'If gold is placed in *aqua regia* then the gold dissolves' is not a matter of either logic or definition. The connection asserted here is *causal*, and must be discovered empirically. These examples show that there are different kinds of implications which constitute different senses of the 'if-then' phrase. Having noted these differences, we now seek to find some identifiable common meaning, some partial meaning that is common to these admittedly different types of conditionals.

Our discussion of 'if-then' will parallel our previous discussion of the word 'or'. First, we pointed out two different senses of that word. Second, we noted that there was a common partial meaning: that *at least one disjunct is true* was seen to be involved in both the inclusive and the exclusive 'or'. Third, we introduced the special symbol 'v' to represent this common partial meaning (which was the whole meaning of 'or' in its inclusive sense). Fourth, we observed that since arguments like the Disjunctive Syllogism are valid on either interpretation of the word 'or', symbolizing *any* occurrence of the word 'or' by the wedge symbol preserves the validity of such arguments. And since we are interested in arguments from the point of view of determining their validity, this translation of the word 'or' into 'v', which may abstract from or ignore part of its meaning in some cases, is wholly adequate for our present purposes.

A common partial meaning of these different kinds of conditional statements emerges when we ask what circumstances would suffice to establish the *falsehood* of a conditional. Under what circumstances would we agree that the conditional 'If gold is placed in this solution then the gold dissolves' is false? Clearly the statement is false in case gold is actually placed in this solution and *does not dissolve*. Any conditional with a true antecedent and a false consequent must be false. Hence any conditional *if p then q* is known to be false in case the conjunction $p \cdot \sim q$ is known to be true, that is, in case its antecedent is true and its consequent false. For the conditional to be true, the indicated conjunction must be false, which means that the negation of that conjunction must be true. In other words, for any conditional *if p then q* to be true, $\sim(p \cdot \sim q)$, the negation of the conjunction of its antecedent with the negation of its consequent, must be true also. We may, then, regard the latter as a *part* of the meaning of the former.

We introduce the new symbol '$\supset$', called a *horseshoe*, to represent the partial meaning common to all conditional statements, defining '$p \supset q$' as an abbreviation for '$\sim(p \cdot \sim q)$'. The horseshoe is a truth-functional connective, whose exact significance is indicated by the following truth table:

p	q	$\sim q$	$p \cdot \sim q$	$\sim(p \cdot \sim q)$	$p \supset q$
T	T	F	F	T	T
T	F	T	T	F	F
F	T	F	F	T	T
F	F	T	F	T	T

Here the first two columns represent all possible truth values for the component statements p and q, and the third, fourth, and fifth represent successive stages in determining the truth value of the compound statement $\sim(p \cdot \sim q)$ in each case. The sixth column is identically the same as the fifth since the formulas which head them are defined to express the same proposition. The horseshoe symbol must not be thought of as representing *the* meaning of 'if-then', or *the* relation of implication, but rather a common partial factor of the various different kinds of implications signified by the 'if-then' phrase.

We can regard the horseshoe as symbolizing a special, extremely weak kind of implication, and it is expedient for us to do so, since convenient ways to read '$p \supset q$' are 'if p then q', 'p implies q', or 'p only if q'.

The weak implication symbolized by '⊃' is called *material implication*, and its special name indicates that it is a special notion, not to be confused with the other more usual kinds of implication. Some conditional statements in English do assert merely material implications, as for example 'If Communist China is a peace-loving nation then I'm a Dutchman'. It is clear that the implication asserted here is neither logical, definitional, nor causal. No 'real connection' is alleged to hold between what the antecedent asserts and what is asserted by the consequent. This sort of conditional is ordinarily intended as an emphatic or humorous method of denying the truth of its antecedent, for it always contains a notoriously or ridiculously false statement as consequent. Any such assertion about truth values is adequately symbolized using the truth-functional connective '⊃'.

Although most conditional statements assert more than a merely material implication between antecedent and consequent, we now propose to symbolize *any* occurrence of 'if-then' by the truth-functional connective '⊃'. It must be admitted that such symbolizing abstracts from or ignores part of the meaning of most conditional statements. But the proposal can be justified on the grounds that the validity of valid arguments involving conditionals is preserved when the conditionals are regarded as asserting material implications only, as will be established in the following sections.

EXERCISES

I. If A and B are true statements and X and Y are false statements, which of the following compound statements are true?

★1. $X \supset (X \supset Y)$
★2. $(X \supset X) \supset Y$
3. $(A \supset X) \supset Y$
4. $(X \supset A) \supset Y$
5. $A \supset (B \supset Y)$
6. $A \supset (X \supset B)$
7. $(X \supset A) \supset (B \supset Y)$
8. $(A \supset X) \supset (Y \supset B)$
9. $(A \supset B) \supset (\sim A \supset \sim B)$
10. $(X \supset Y) \supset (\sim X \supset \sim Y)$

11. $(X \supset A) \supset (\sim X \supset \sim A)$
12. $(X \supset \sim Y) \supset (\sim X \supset Y)$
★13. $[(A \cdot X) \supset Y] \supset (A \supset Y)$
14. $[(A \cdot B) \supset X] \supset [A \supset (B \supset X)]$
15. $[(X \cdot Y) \supset A] \supset [X \supset (Y \supset A)]$
16. $[(A \cdot X) \supset B] \supset [A \supset (B \supset X)]$
17. $[X \supset (A \supset Y)] \supset [(X \supset A) \supset Y]$
★18. $[X \supset (X \supset Y)] \supset [(X \supset X) \supset X]$
19. $[(A \supset B) \supset A] \supset A$
★20. $[(X \supset Y) \supset X] \supset X$

II. Symbolizing 'Amherst wins its first game' as *A*, 'Colgate wins its first game' as *C*, and 'Dartmouth wins its first game' as *D*, symbolize the following compound statements:

1. Either Amherst wins its first game and Colgate wins its first game or Dartmouth wins its first game.
2. Amherst wins its first game and either Colgate wins its first game or Dartmouth wins its first game.
3. If Amherst wins its first game then both Colgate and Dartmouth win their first games.
4. If Amherst wins its first game then either Colgate or Dartmouth wins its first game.
★5. If Amherst does not win its first game then it is not the case that either Colgate or Dartmouth wins its first game.
6. If it is not the case that both Amherst and Colgate win their first games then both Colgate and Dartmouth win their first games.
7. If Amherst wins its first game then not both Colgate and Dartmouth win their first games.
8. If Amherst does not win its first game then both Colgate and Dartmouth do not win their first games.
9. Either Amherst wins its first game and Colgate does not win its first game or if Colgate wins its first game then Dartmouth does not win its first game.
★10. If Amherst wins its first game then Colgate does not win its first game, but if Colgate does not win its first game then Dartmouth wins its first game.
11. If Amherst wins its first game then if Colgate does not win its first game then Dartmouth wins its first game.
12. Either Amherst and Colgate win their first games or it is not the case that if Colgate wins its first game then Dartmouth wins its first game.
13. Amherst wins its first game only if either Colgate or Dartmouth does not win its first game.
14. If Amherst wins its first game only if Colgate wins its first game, then Dartmouth does not win its first game.
★15. If Amherst and Colgate both do not win their first games, then Amherst and Colgate do not both win their first games.

2.3 ARGUMENT FORMS AND TRUTH TABLES

In this section we shall develop a purely mechanical method for testing the validity of arguments containing truth-functionally compound statements. That method is closely related to the familiar technique of *refutation by logical analogy* which was used in the first chapter to show the invalidity of the argument

If I am President then I am famous.
I am not President.
Therefore I am not famous.

That argument was shown to be invalid by constructing another argument of the same form:

If Rockefeller is President then he is famous.
Rockefeller is not President.
Therefore Rockefeller is not famous.

which is obviously invalid since its premises are true but its conclusion false. Any argument is proved invalid if another argument *of the same form* can be constructed with true premises and a false conclusion. This reflects the fact that validity and invalidity are purely *formal* characteristics of arguments: any two arguments having the same form are either both valid or both invalid, regardless of any differences in their subject matter. The notion of two arguments having *the same form* is one that deserves further examination.

It is convenient in discussing forms of arguments to use small letters from the middle part of the alphabet, '*p*', '*q*', '*r*', '*s*', . . . as *statement variables*, which are defined simply to be letters for which, or in place of which, statements may be substituted. Now we define an *argument form* to be any array of symbols which contains statement variables, such that when statements are substituted for the statement variables—the same statement replacing the same statement variable throughout—the result is an argument. For definiteness, we establish the convention that in any argument form, '*p*' shall be the first statement variable that occurs in it, '*q*' shall be the second, '*r*' the third, and so on.

Any argument which results from the substitution of statements for the statement variables of an argument form is said to *have* that form, or to be a *substitution instance* of that argument form. If we symbolize the simple statement 'The United Nations will be strengthened' as U, and the simple statement 'There will be a third world war' as W, then the Disjunctive Syllogism presented earlier can be symbolized as

(1) $U \vee W$

                                 $\sim U$

                                 $\therefore W$

It has the form

(2) $p \vee q$

                                 $\sim p$

                                 $\therefore q$

from which it results by replacing the statement variables p and q by the statements U and W, respectively. But that is not the only form of which it is a substitution instance. The same argument is obtained by replacing the statement variables p, q, and r in the argument form

(3) p

                                 q

                                 $\therefore r$

by the statements $U \vee W$, $\sim U$, and W, respectively. We define *the* form of a given argument as that argument form from which the argument results by replacing each distinct statement variable by a different *simple* statement. Thus *the* form of the argument (1) is the argument form (2). Although the argument form (3) is *a* form of the argument (1), it is not *the* form of it. The technique of refutation by logical analogy can now be described more precisely. If *the* form of a given argument can be shown to have any substitution instance with true premises and false conclusion, then the given argument is invalid.

The terms 'valid' and 'invalid' can be extended to apply to argument forms as well as arguments. An *invalid* argument form is one which has at least one substitution instance with true premises and a false conclusion. The technique of refutation by logical analogy presupposes that any argument of which *the* form is an invalid argument form is an invalid argument. Any argument form is *valid* which is not invalid; a *valid* argument form is one which has no substitution instance with true premisses and false conclusion. Any given argument can be proved valid if it can be shown that *the* form of the given argument is a valid argument form.

To determine the validity or invalidity of an argument form we must examine all possible substitution instances of it to see if any of them have true premisses and false conclusions. The arguments with which we are here concerned contain only simple statements and truth-functional compounds of them, and we are interested only in the truth values of their premisses and conclusions. We can obtain all possible substitution instances whose premisses and conclusions have different truth values, by considering all possible arrangements of truth values for the statements that can be substituted for the distinct statement variables in the argument form to be tested. These can be set forth most conveniently in the form of a truth table, with an initial or guide column for each distinct statement variable appearing in the argument form. Thus to prove the validity of the Disjunctive Syllogism form

$$p \lor q$$
$$\sim p$$
$$\therefore q$$

we construct the following truth table:

p	q	$p \lor q$	$\sim p$
T	T	T	F
T	F	T	F
F	T	T	T
F	F	F	T

Each row of this table represents a whole class of substitution instances. The **T**'s and **F**'s in the two initial columns represent the truth values of statements which can be substituted for the variables p and q in the argument form. These determine the truth values in the other columns, the third of which is headed by the first 'premiss' of the argument form and the fourth by the second 'premiss'. The second column's heading is the 'conclusion' of the argument form. An examination of this truth table reveals that whatever statements are substituted for the variables p and q, the resulting argument cannot have true premises and a false conclusion, for the third row represents the only possible case in which both premises are true, and there the conclusion is true also.

Since truth tables provide a purely mechanical or *effective* method of deciding the validity or invalidity of any argument of the general type here considered, we can now justify our proposal to symbolize all conditional statements by means of the truth-functional connective '⊃'. The justification for treating all implications as though they were mere material implications is that valid arguments containing conditional statements remain valid when those conditionals are interpreted as asserting material implications only. The three simplest and most intuitively valid forms of argument involving conditional statements are

Modus Ponens   If p then q
p
∴ q

Modus Tollens   If p then q
$\sim q$
∴ $\sim p$

and the

Hypothetical Syllogism   If p then q
If q then r
∴ If p then r

That they all remain valid when their conditionals are interpreted as asserting material implications is easily established by truth tables. The validity of *Modus Ponens* is shown by the same truth table that defines the horseshoe symbol:

p	q	$p \supset q$
T	T	T
T	F	F
F	T	T
F	F	T

Here the two premises are represented by the third and first columns, and the conclusion by the second. Only the first row represents substitution instances in which both premises are true, and in that row the conclusion is true also. The validity of *Modus Tollens* is shown by the truth table:

p	q	$p \supset q$	$\sim q$	$\sim p$
T	T	T	F	F
T	F	F	T	F
F	T	T	F	T
F	F	T	T	T

Here only the fourth row represents substitution instances in which both premises (the third and fourth columns) are true, and there the conclusion (the fifth column) is true also. Since the Hypothetical Syllogism form contains three distinct statement variables, the truth table for it must have three initial columns and will require eight rows for listing all possible substitution instances:

p	q	r	$p \supset q$	$q \supset r$	$p \supset r$
T	T	T	T	T	T
T	T	F	T	F	F
T	F	T	F	T	T
T	F	F	F	T	F
F	T	T	T	T	T
F	T	F	T	F	T
F	F	T	T	T	T
F	F	F	T	T	T

In constructing it, the three initial columns represent all possible arrangements of truth values for the statements substituted for the statement variables p, q, and r, the fourth column is filled in by reference to the first and second, the fifth by reference to the second and third, and the sixth by reference to the first and third. The premises are both true only in the first, fifth, seventh, and eighth rows, and in these rows the conclusion is true also. This suffices to demonstrate that the Hypothetical Syllogism remains valid when its conditionals are symbolized by means of the horseshoe symbol. Any doubts that remain about the claim that valid arguments containing conditionals remain valid when their conditionals are interpreted as asserting merely material implication can be allayed by the reader's providing, symbolizing, and testing his own examples by means of truth tables.

To test the validity of an argument form by a truth table requires one with a separate initial or guide column for each different statement variable, and a separate row for every possible assignment of truth values to the statement variables involved. Hence testing an argument form containing n distinct statement variables requires a truth table having 2^n rows. In constructing truth tables it is convenient to fix upon some uniform pattern for inscribing the **T**'s and **F**'s in their initial or guide columns. In this book we shall follow the practice of simply alternating **T**'s and **F**'s down the extreme right-hand initial column, alternating pairs of **T**'s with pairs of **F**'s down the column directly to its left, next alternating quadruples of **T**'s with quadruples of **F**'s, . . . , and finally filling in the top half of the extreme left-hand initial column with **T**'s and its bottom half with **F**'s.

There are two invalid argument forms that bear a superficial resemblance to the valid argument forms *Modus Ponens* and *Modus Tollens*. These are

$$p \supset q \qquad\qquad p \supset q$$
$$q \qquad \text{and} \qquad \sim p$$
$$\therefore p \qquad\qquad \therefore \sim q$$

and are known as the Fallacies of Affirming the Consequent and of Denying the Antecedent, respectively. The invalidity of both can be shown by a single truth table:

p	q	$p \supset q$	$\sim p$	$\sim q$
T	T	T	F	F
T	F	F	F	T
F	T	T	T	F
F	F	T	T	T

The two premisses in the Fallacy of Affirming the Consequent head the second and third columns, and are true in both the first and third rows. But the conclusion, which heads the first column, is false in the third row, which shows that the argument form does have a substitution instance with true premises and a false conclusion, and is therefore invalid. Columns three and four are headed by the two premises in the Fallacy of Denying the Antecedent, which are true in both the third and fourth rows. Its conclusion heads the fifth column, and is false in the third row, which shows that the second argument form is invalid also.

EXERCISES

I. Use truth tables to determine the validity or invalidity of each of the following argument forms:

★1. $p \cdot q$
∴ p

2. p
∴ $p \cdot q$

3. $p \vee q$
∴ p

4. p
∴ $p \vee q$

★5. p
∴ $p \supset q$

6. p
∴ $q \supset p$

7. $p \supset q$
∴ $\sim q \supset \sim p$

8. $p \supset q$
∴ $\sim p \supset \sim q$

9. $p \vee q$
p
∴ $\sim q$

★10. p
q
∴ $p \cdot q$

11. $p \supset q$
$q \supset p$
∴ $p \vee q$

12. $p \supset q$
$p \vee q$
∴ q

13. $p \supset (q \supset r)$
$p \supset q$
∴ $p \supset r$

14. $p \supset (q \supset r)$
$r \supset \sim p$
∴ $r \supset \sim q$

15. $(p \supset q) \cdot (p \supset r)$
p
∴ $q \vee r$

16. $p \supset (q \vee r)$
$p \supset \sim q$
∴ $p \vee r$

17. $(p \supset q) \cdot (r \supset s)$
$p \vee r$
∴ $q \vee s$

18. $(p \supset q) \cdot (r \supset s)$
$\sim q \vee \sim s$
∴ $\sim p \vee \sim r$

★19. $p \supset (q \vee r)$
$(r \cdot s) \supset t$
∴ $p \supset t$

★20. $p \supset (q \cdot r)$
$(r \vee s) \supset t$
∴ $p \supset t$

II. Use truth tables to determine the validity or invalidity of each of the following arguments:

★1. If Alice is elected class president then either Betty is elected vice-president or Carol is elected treasurer. Betty is elected vice-president. Therefore if Alice is elected class president then Carol is not elected treasurer.

2. If Alice is elected class president then either Betty is elected vice-president or Carol is elected treasurer. Carol is not elected treasurer. Therefore if Betty is not elected vice-president then Alice is not elected class president.

3. If Alice is elected class president, then Betty is elected vice-president and Carol is elected treasurer. Betty is not elected vice-president. Therefore Alice is not elected class president.

4. If Alice is elected class president then if Betty is elected vice-president then Carol is elected treasurer. Betty is not elected vice-president. Therefore either Alice is elected class president or Carol is elected treasurer.

★5. If the seed catalog is correct then if the seeds are planted in April then the flowers bloom in July. The flowers do not bloom in July. Therefore if the seeds are planted in April then the seed catalog is not correct.

6. If the seed catalog is correct then if the seeds are planted in April then the flowers bloom in July. The flowers bloom in July. Therefore if the seed catalog is correct then the seeds are planted in April.

7. If the seed catalog is correct then if the seeds are planted in April then the flowers bloom in July. The seeds are planted in April. Therefore if the flowers do not bloom in July then the seed catalog is not correct.

8. If the seed catalog is correct then if the seeds are planted in April then the flowers bloom in July. The flowers do not bloom in July. Therefore if the seeds are not planted in April then the seed catalog is not correct.

9. If Ed wins first prize then Fred wins second prize, and if Fred wins second prize then George is disappointed. Either Ed wins first prize or George is disappointed. Therefore Fred does not win second prize.

★10. If Ed wins first prize then either Fred wins second prize or George is disappointed. Fred does not win second prize. Therefore if George is disappointed then Ed does not win first prize.

11. If Ed wins first prize then Fred wins second prize, and if Fred wins second prize then George is disappointed. Either Fred does not win second prize or George is not disappointed. Therefore Ed does not win first prize.

12. If Ed wins first prize then Fred wins second prize, and if Fred wins second prize then George is disappointed. Either Ed does not win first prize or Fred does not win second prize. Therefore either Fred does not win second prize or George is not disappointed.

13. If the weather is warm and the sky is clear then we go swimming and we go boating. It is not the case that if the sky is clear then we go swimming. Therefore the weather is not warm.

14. If the weather is warm and the sky is clear then either we go swimming or we go boating. It is not the case that if the sky is clear then we go

swimming. Therefore if we do not go boating then the weather is not warm.

★15. If the weather is warm and the sky is clear then either we go swimming or we go boating. It is not the case that if we do not go swimming then the sky is not clear. Therefore either the weather is warm or we go boating.

2.4 TAUTOLOGIES, CONTRADICTIONS, AND CONTINGENCIES

The introduction of statement variables in the preceding section enabled us to define both argument forms in general and *the* form of a given argument. Now we define a *statement form* to be any sequence of symbols containing statement variables, such that when statements are substituted for the statement variables—the same statement replacing the same statement variable throughout—the result is a statement. Again for definiteness, we establish the convention that in any statement form 'p' shall be the first statement variable that occurs in it, 'q' shall be the second, 'r' the third, and so on. Any statement which results from substituting statements for the statement variables of a statement form is said to *have* that form, or to be a *substitution instance* of it. Just as we distinguished *the* form of a given argument, so we distinguish *the* form of a given statement as that statement form from which the given statement results by replacing each distinct statement variable by a different simple statement. For example, where A, B, and C are different simple statements, the compound statement $A \supset (B \lor C)$ is a substitution instance of the statement form $p \supset q$, and also of the statement form $p \supset (q \lor r)$, but only the latter is *the* form of the given statement.

Although the statements 'Balboa discovered the Pacific Ocean' (B) and 'Balboa discovered the Pacific Ocean or else he didn't' ($B \lor \sim B$) are both true, we discover their truth in quite different ways. The truth of B is a matter of history, and must be learned through empirical investigation. Moreover, events might possibly have been such as to make B false; there is nothing *necessary* about the truth of B. But the truth of the statement $B \lor \sim B$ *can* be known independently of empirical investigation, and no events could possibly have made it false, for it is a necessary truth. The statement $B \lor \sim B$ is a formal truth, a substitution instance of a statement form *all* substitution instances of which are true. A statement form that has only true substitution instances is said to be *tautologous*, or a *tautology*. *The* form of $B \text{ v} \sim B$ is $p \text{ v} \sim p$, and is proved a tautology by the following truth table:

p	$\sim p$	$p \text{ v} \sim p$
T	F	T
F	T	T

That there are only **T**'s in the column headed by the statement form in question shows that all of its substitution instances are true. Any statement that is a substitution instance of a tautologous statement form is formally true, and is itself said to be tautologous, or a tautology.

Similarly, although the statements 'Cortez discovered the Pacific' (C) and 'Cortez discovered the Pacific and Cortez did not discover the Pacific' ($C \cdot \sim C$) are both false, we discover their falsehood in quite different ways. The first simply *happens* to be false, and that must be learned empirically; whereas the second is necessarily false, and that can be known independently of empirical investigation. The statement $C \cdot \sim C$ is formally false, a substitution instance of a statement form *all* of whose substitution instances are false. One statement is said to contradict, or to be a contradiction of, another statement when it is logically impossible for them both to be true. In this sense, *contradiction* is a relation between statements. But there is another, related sense of that term. When it is logically impossible for a particular statement to be true, that statement itself is said to be self-contradictory, or a self-contradiction. Such statements are also said more simply to be contradictory, or contradictions, and we shall follow the latter usage here. A statement form that has only false substitution instances is said to be *contradictory*, or a *contradiction*, and the same terms are applied to its substitution instances. The statement form $p \cdot \sim p$ is proved a contradiction by the fact that in its truth table only **F**'s occur in the column which it heads.

Statements and statement forms which are neither tautologous nor contradictory are said to be *contingent*, or *contingencies*. For example, p, $\sim p$, $p \text{ v } q$, $p \cdot q$, and $p \supset q$ are contingent statement forms; and B, C, $\sim B$, $\sim C$, $B \cdot C$, $B \text{ v } C$ are contingent statements. The term is appropriate, since their truth values are not formally determined but are dependent or contingent upon what happens to be the case.

It is easily proved that $p \supset (q \supset p)$ and $\sim p \supset (p \supset q)$ are tautologies. When expressed in English as 'A true statement is implied by any statement whatever', and as 'A false statement implies any statement whatever', they seem rather strange. They have been called by some writers the *paradoxes of material implication*. But when it is kept in mind that the horseshoe symbol is a truth-functional connective which stands for *material* implication rather than either 'implication in general' or more usual kinds such as logical or causal, then the tautologous statement forms in question are not at all surprising. And when the misleading English formulations are corrected by inserting the word 'materially' before 'implied' and 'implies', then the air of paradox vanishes. Material implication is a special, technical notion, and the logician's motivation for introducing and using it is the tremendous extent to which it simplifies his task of discriminating valid from invalid arguments.

Two statements are said to be *materially equivalent* when they have the same truth value, and we symbolize the statement *that* they are materially equivalent by inserting the symbol '$\equiv$' between them. Being a truth-functional connective, the three bar symbol is defined by the following truth table:

p	q	$p \equiv q$
T	T	T
T	F	F
F	T	F
F	F	T

To say that two statements are materially equivalent is to say that they materially imply each other, as is easily verified by a truth table. Hence the three bar symbol may be read either 'is materially equivalent to' or 'if and only if'. A statement of the form $p \equiv q$ is called a *biconditional*. Two statements are said to be *logically equivalent* when the biconditional expressing their material equivalence is a tautology. The 'principle of Double Negation', expressed as $p \equiv \sim\sim p$ is proved to be tautologous by a truth table.

There are two logical equivalences which express important inter-relations of conjunctions, disjunctions, and negations. Since a conjunction asserts that both its conjuncts are true, its negation need only assert that at least one is false. Thus negating the conjunction $p \cdot q$ amounts to asserting the disjunction of the negations of p and q. This statement of equivalence is symbolized as $\sim(p \cdot q) \equiv (\sim p \vee \sim q)$, and proved to be a tautology by the following truth table:

p	q	$p \cdot q$	$\sim(p \cdot q)$	$\sim p$	$\sim q$	$\sim p \vee \sim q$	$\sim(p \cdot q) \equiv (\sim p \vee \sim q)$
T	T	T	F	F	F	F	T
T	F	F	T	F	T	T	T
F	T	F	T	T	F	T	T
F	F	F	T	T	T	T	T

Similarly, since a disjunction asserts merely that at least one disjunct is true, to negate it is to assert that both are false. Negating the disjunction $p \vee q$ amounts to asserting the conjunction of the negations of p and q. It is symbolized as $\sim(p \vee q) \equiv (\sim p \cdot \sim q)$, and is easily proved tautologous by a truth table. These two equivalences are known as De Morgan's Theorems, after the English mathematician-logician Augustus De Morgan (1806–1871), and can be stated compendiously

in English as: The negation of the $\begin{Bmatrix} \text{conjunction} \\ \text{disjunction} \end{Bmatrix}$ of two statements is

logically equivalent to the $\begin{Bmatrix} \text{disjunction} \\ \text{conjunction} \end{Bmatrix}$ of their negations.

Two statement forms are said to be logically equivalent if no matter what statements are substituted for their statement variables—the same statement replacing the same statement variable in both statement forms—the resulting pairs of statements are equivalent. Thus De Morgan's Theorem asserts that $\sim(p \vee q)$ and $\sim p \cdot \sim q$ are logically equivalent statement forms. Since $\sim(p \cdot \sim q)$ and $\sim p \vee q$ are logically equivalent, either can be taken as defining $p \supset q$; the second is the more usual choice.

To every argument corresponds a conditional statement whose antecedent is the conjunction of the argument's premises and whose consequent is the argument's conclusion. That corresponding conditional is a tautology if and only if the argument is valid. Thus to the valid argument form

$$p \lor q$$
$$\sim p$$
$$\therefore q$$

corresponds the tautologous statement form $[(p \lor q) \cdot \sim p] \supset q$; and to the invalid argument form

$$p \supset q$$
$$q$$
$$\therefore p$$

corresponds the nontautologous statement form $[(p \supset q) \cdot q] \supset p$. An argument form is valid if and only if its truth table has a **T** under its conclusion in every row in which there are **T**'s under all of its premises. Since an **F** can occur in the column headed by its corresponding conditional only where there are **T**'s under all of those premises and an **F** under the conclusion, it is clear that there can be only **T**'s under a conditional that corresponds to a valid argument form. If an argument is valid, the statement that the conjunction of its premises implies its conclusion is a tautology.

An alternative version of the truth table test of a statement form is the following, which corresponds to the preceding truth table.

~	(p	·	q)	≡	(~	p	v	~	q)
F	T	T	T	T	F	T	F	F	T
T	T	F	F	T	F	T	T	T	F
T	F	F	T	T	T	F	T	F	T
T	F	F	F	T	T	F	T	T	F
(1)	(2)	(3)	(4)	(5)	(6)	(7)	(8)	(9)	(10)

Here columns (2), (4), (7), (10) are the initial or guide columns. Column (3) is filled in by reference to columns (2) and (4), and column (1) by reference to column (3). Column (6) is filled in by reference to column (7), column (9) is filled in by reference to column (10), and then column (8) by reference to columns (6) and (9). Finally column (5) is filled in by reference to columns (1) and (8). That its main connective has only **T**'s under it in the truth table establishes that the statement form being tested is a tautology.

EXERCISES

I. Use truth tables to characterize the following statement forms as tautologous, contradictory, or contingent:

★1. $p \supset \sim p$

2. $(p \supset \sim p) \cdot (\sim p \supset p)$

3. $p \supset (p \supset p)$

4. $(p \supset p) \supset p$

★5. $p \supset (p \cdot p)$

6. $(p \cdot q) \supset p$

7. $(p \supset q) \supset [\sim(q \cdot r) \supset \sim(r \cdot p)]$

★8. $(\sim p \cdot q) \cdot (q \supset p)$

9. $[(p \supset q) \supset q] \supset q$

10. $[(p \supset q) \supset p] \supset p$

II. Use truth tables to decide which of the following are logical equivalences:

1. $(p \supset q) \equiv (\sim p \supset \sim q)$

2. $(p \supset q) \equiv (\sim q \supset \sim p)$

3. $[(p \cdot q) \supset r] \equiv [p \supset (q \supset r)]$

★4. $[p \supset (q \supset r)] \equiv [(p \supset q) \supset r]$

5. $[p \cdot (q \vee r)] \equiv [(p \cdot q) \vee (p \cdot r)]$

6. $[p \vee (q \cdot r)] \equiv [(p \vee q) \cdot r]$

7. $[p \vee (q \cdot r)] \equiv [(p \vee q) \cdot (p \vee r)]$

★8. $(p \equiv q) \equiv [(p \cdot q) \vee (\sim p \cdot \sim q)]$

9. $p \equiv [p \cdot (p \supset q)]$

10. $p \equiv [p \cdot (q \supset p)]$

3

THE
METHOD
OF
DEDUCTION

3.1 FORMAL PROOF OF VALIDITY

When we consider arguments containing more than two or three different simple statements as components, it becomes cumbersome and tedious to use truth tables to test their validity. A more convenient method of establishing the validity of some arguments is to *deduce* their conclusions from their premisses by a sequence of shorter, more elementary arguments already known to be valid. Consider, for example, the following argument, in which five different simple statements occur:

Either the Attorney General has imposed a strict censorship or if Black mailed the letter he wrote then Davis received a warning.

If our lines of communication have not broken down completely then if Davis received a warning then Emory was informed about the matter.

If the Attorney General has imposed a strict censorship then our lines of communication have broken down completely.

Our lines of communication have not broken down completely. Therefore if Black mailed the letter he wrote then Emory was informed about the matter.

It may be translated into our symbolism as

$$A \vee (B \supset D)$$
$$\sim C \supset (D \supset E)$$
$$A \supset C$$
$$\sim C$$
$$\therefore B \supset E$$

To establish the validity of this argument by means of a truth table would require a table with thirty-two rows. But we can prove the given argument valid by deducing its conclusion from its premisses by a sequence of just four arguments whose validity has already been remarked. From the third and fourth premisses, $A \supset C$ and $\sim C$, we validly infer $\sim A$ by *Modus Tollens*. From $\sim A$ and the first premiss, $A \vee (B \supset D)$, we validly infer $B \supset D$ by a Disjunctive Syllogism. From the second and fourth premisses, $\sim C \supset (D \supset E)$ and $\sim C$, we validly infer $D \supset E$ by *Modus Ponens*. And finally, from these last two conclusions (or subconclusions), $B \supset D$ and $D \supset E$, we validly infer $B \supset E$ by a Hypothetical Syllogism. That its conclusion can be deduced from its premisses using valid arguments exclusively *proves* the original argument to be valid. Here the elementary valid argument forms *Modus Ponens* (M.P.), *Modus Tollens* (M.T.), Disjunctive Syllogism (D.S.), and Hypothetical Syllogism (H.S.) are used as *Rules of Inference* by which conclusions are validly deduced from premisses.

A more formal and more concise way of writing out this proof of validity is to list the premisses and the statements deduced from them in one column, with the latter's "justifications" written beside them. In each case the "justification" for a statement specifies the preceding statements from which, and the Rule of Inference by which, the statement in question was deduced. It is convenient to put the conclusion to the right of the last premiss, separated from it by a slanting line which automatically marks all of the statements above it to be premisses. The formal proof of validity for the given argument can be written as

1. $A \vee (B \supset D)$
2. $\sim C \supset (D \supset E)$
3. $A \supset C$
4. $\sim C$ $/ \therefore B \supset E$
5. $\sim A$ 3, 4, M.T.
6. $B \supset D$ 1, 5, D.S.
7. $D \supset E$ 2, 4, M.P.
8. $B \supset E$ 6, 7, H.S.

A *formal proof of validity* for a given argument is defined to be a sequence of statements each of which is either a premiss of that argument or follows from preceding statements by an elementary valid argument, and such that the last statement in the sequence is the conclusion of the argument whose validity is being proved. This definition must be completed and made definite by specifying what is to count as an 'elementary valid argument'. We first define an *elementary valid argument* to be any argument that is a substitution instance of an elementary valid argument form, and then present a list of just nine argument forms that are sufficiently obvious to be regarded as elementary valid argument forms and accepted as Rules of Inference.

One matter to be emphasized is that *any* substitution instance of an elementary valid argument form is an elementary valid argument. Thus the argument

$$\sim C \supset (D \supset E)$$
$$\sim C$$
$$\therefore D \supset E$$

is an elementary valid argument because it is a substitution instance of the elementary valid argument form *Modus Ponens* (M.P.). It results from

$$p \supset q$$
$$p$$
$$\therefore q$$

by substituting $\sim C$ for p and $D \supset E$ for q, therefore it is of that form even though *Modus Ponens* is not *the* form of the given argument.

We begin our development of the method of deduction by presenting a list of just nine elementary valid argument forms that can be used in constructing formal proofs of validity:

RULES OF INFERENCE

1. *Modus Ponens* (M.P.)

    $p \supset q$

    p

    $\therefore q$

2. *Modus Tollens* (M.T.)

    $p \supset q$

    $\sim q$

    $\therefore \sim p$

3. Hypothetical Syllogism (H.S.)

    $p \supset q$

    $q \supset r$

    $\therefore p \supset r$

4. Disjunctive Syllogism (D.S.)

    $p \vee q$

    $\sim p$

    $\therefore q$

5. Constructive Dilemma (C.D.)

    $(p \supset q) \cdot (r \supset s)$

    $p \vee r$

    $\therefore q \vee s$

6. Destructive Dilemma (D.D.)

    $(p \supset q) \cdot (r \supset s)$

    $\sim q \vee \sim s$

    $\therefore \sim p \vee \sim r$

7. Simplification (Simp.)

    $p \cdot q$

    $\therefore p$

8. Conjunction (Conj.)

    p

    q

    $\therefore p \cdot q$

9. Addition (Add.)

    p

    $\therefore p \vee q$

These nine Rules of Inference are elementary valid argument forms whose validity is easily established by truth tables. They can be used to construct formal proofs of validity for a wide range of more complicated arguments. The names listed are for the most part standard, and the use of their abbreviations permits formal proofs to be set down with a minimum of writing.

EXERCISES

I. Each of the following is a formal proof of validity for the indicated argument. State the 'justification' for each line that is not a premiss:

★1. 1. $(A \cdot B) \supset [A \supset (D \cdot E)]$
    2. $(A \cdot B) \cdot C$ / ∴ $D \vee E$
    3. $A \cdot B$
    4. $A \supset (D \cdot E)$
    5. A
    6. $D \cdot E$
    7. D
    8. $D \vee E$

2. 1. $F \vee (G \vee H)$
    2. $(G \supset I) \cdot (H \supset J)$
    3. $(I \vee J) \supset (F \vee H)$
    4. $\sim F$ / ∴ H
    5. $G \vee H$
    6. $I \vee J$
    7. $F \vee H$
    8. H

3. 1. $K \supset L$
    2. $M \supset N$
    3. $(O \supset N) \cdot (P \supset L)$
    4. $(\sim N \vee \sim L) \cdot (\sim M \vee \sim O)$ / ∴ $(\sim O \vee \sim P) \cdot (\sim M \vee \sim K)$
    5. $(M \supset N) \cdot (K \supset L)$
    6. $\sim N \vee \sim L$
    7. $\sim M \vee \sim K$
    8. $\sim O \vee \sim P$
    9. $(\sim O \vee \sim P) \cdot (\sim M \vee \sim K)$

4. 1. $Q \supset (R \supset S)$
    2. $(R \supset S) \supset T$
    3. $(S \cdot U) \supset \sim V$
    4. $\sim V \supset (R \equiv \sim W)$
    5. $\sim T \vee \sim (R \equiv \sim W)$ / ∴ $\sim Q \vee \sim (S \cdot U)$
    6. $Q \supset T$
    7. $(S \cdot U) \supset (R \equiv \sim W)$
    8. $[Q \supset T] \cdot [(S \cdot U) \supset (R \equiv \sim W)]$
    9. $\sim Q \vee \sim (S \cdot U)$

★5. 1. $(\sim X \vee \sim Y) \supset [A \supset (P \cdot \sim Q)]$
    2. $(\sim X \cdot \sim R) \supset [(P \cdot \sim Q) \supset Z]$
    3. $(\sim X \cdot \sim R) \cdot (\sim Z \vee A)$ / ∴ $A \supset Z$

    4. $\sim X \cdot \sim R$
    5. $(P \cdot \sim Q) \supset Z$
    6. $\sim X$
    7. $\sim X \vee \sim Y$
    8. $A \supset (P \cdot \sim Q)$
    9. $A \supset Z$

6. 1. $A \supset B$
    2. $C \supset D$
    3. $\sim B \vee \sim D$
    4. $\sim \sim A$
    5. $(E \cdot F) \supset C$ $/ \therefore \sim(E \cdot F)$
    6. $(A \supset B) \cdot (C \supset D)$
    7. $\sim A \vee \sim C$
    8. $\sim C$
    9. $\sim(E \cdot F)$

7. 1. $(G \supset H) \supset (I \equiv J)$
    2. $K \vee \sim(L \supset M)$
    3. $(G \supset H) \vee \sim K$
    4. $N \supset (L \supset M)$
    5. $\sim(I \equiv J)$ $/ \therefore \sim N$
    6. $\sim(G \supset H)$
    7. $\sim K$
    8. $\sim(L \supset M)$
    9. $\sim N$

8. 1. $(O \supset \sim P) \cdot (\sim Q \supset R)$
    2. $(S \supset T) \cdot (\sim U \supset \sim V)$
    3. $(\sim P \supset S) \cdot (R \supset \sim U)$
    4. $(T \vee \sim V) \supset (W \cdot X)$
    5. $O \vee \sim Q$ $/ \therefore W \cdot X$
    6. $\sim P \vee R$
    7. $S \vee \sim U$
    8. $T \vee \sim V$
    9. $W \cdot X$

9. 1. $[(A \vee \sim B) \vee C] \supset [D \supset (E \equiv F)]$
    2. $(A \vee \sim B) \supset [(F \equiv G) \supset H]$
    3. $A \supset [(E \equiv F) \supset (F \equiv G)]$
    4. A $/ \therefore D \supset H$

 5. $A \vee \sim B$
 6. $(A \vee \sim B) \vee C$
 7. $D \supset (E \equiv F)$
 8. $(E \equiv F) \supset (F \equiv G)$
 9. $D \supset (F \equiv G)$
10. $(F \equiv G) \supset H$
11. $D \supset H$

★10.   1. $H \supset (I \supset J)$
 2. $K \supset (I \supset J)$
 3. $(\sim H \cdot \sim K) \supset (\sim L \vee \sim M)$
 4. $(\sim L \supset \sim N) \cdot (\sim M \supset \sim O)$
 5. $(P \supset N) \cdot (Q \supset O)$
 6. $\sim (I \supset J)$ $/ \therefore \sim P \vee \sim Q$
 7. $\sim H$
 8. $\sim K$
 9. $\sim H \cdot \sim K$
10. $\sim L \vee \sim M$
11. $\sim N \vee \sim O$
12. $\sim P \vee \sim Q$

II. Construct a formal proof of validity for each of the following arguments, using the abbreviations suggested:

★1. If either algebra is required or geometry is required then all students will study mathematics. Algebra is required and trigonometry is required. Therefore all students will study mathematics. (*A*: Algebra is required. *G*: Geometry is required. *S*: All students will study mathematics. *T*: Trigonometry is required.)

2. Either Smith attended the meeting or Smith was not invited to the meeting. If the directors wanted Smith at the meeting then Smith was invited to the meeting. Smith did not attend the meeting. If the directors did not want Smith at the meeting and Smith was not invited to the meeting then Smith is on his way out of the company. Therefore Smith is on his way out of the company. (*A*: Smith attended the meeting. *I*: Smith was invited to the meeting. *D*: The directors wanted Smith at the meeting. *W*: Smith is on his way out of the company.)

3. If a scarcity of commodities develops then prices rise. If there is a change of administration then fiscal controls will not be continued. If the threat of inflation persists then fiscal controls will be continued. If there is overproduction then prices do not rise. Either there is overproduction or there

is a change of administration. Therefore either a scarcity of commodities does not develop or the threat of inflation does not persist. (*S*: A scarcity of commodities develops. *P*: Prices rise. *C*: There is a change of administration. *F*: Fiscal controls will be continued. *I*: The threat of inflation persists. *O*: There is overproduction.)

4. If the investigation continues then new evidence is brought to light. If new evidence is brought to light then several leading citizens are implicated. If several leading citizens are implicated then the newspapers stop publicizing the case. If continuation of the investigation implies that the newspapers stop publicizing the case then the bringing to light of new evidence implies that the investigation continues. The investigation does not continue. Therefore new evidence is not brought to light. (*C*: The investigation continues. *N*: New evidence is brought to light. *I*: Several leading citizens are implicated. *S*: The newspapers stop publicizing the case.)

★5. If the king does not castle and the pawn advances then either the bishop is blocked or the rook is pinned. If the king does not castle then if the bishop is blocked then the game is a draw. Either the king castles or if the rook is pinned then the exchange is lost. The king does not castle and the pawn advances. Therefore either the game is a draw or the exchange is lost. (*K*: The king castles. *P*: The pawn advances. *B*: The bishop is blocked. *R*: The rook is pinned. *D*: The game is a draw. *E*: The exchange is lost.)

6. If Andrews is present then Brown is present, and if Brown is present then Cohen is not present. If Cohen is present then Davis is not present. If Brown is present then Emerson is present. If Davis is not present then Farley is present. Either Emerson is not present or Farley is not present. Therefore either Andrews is not present or Cohen is not present. (*A*: Andrews is present. *B*: Brown is present. *C*: Cohen is present. *D*: Davis is present. *E*: Emerson is present. *F*: Farley is present.)

7. If either George enrolls or Harry enrolls then Ira does not enroll. Either Ira enrolls or Harry enrolls. If either Harry enrolls or George does not enroll then Jim enrolls. George enrolls. Therefore either Jim enrolls or Harry does not enroll. (*G*: George enrolls. *H*: Harry enrolls. *I*: Ira enrolls. *J*: Jim enrolls.)

8. If Tom received the message then Tom took the plane, but if Tom did not take the plane then Tom missed the meeting. If Tom missed the meeting then Dave was elected to the board, but if Dave was elected to the board then Tom received the message. If either Tom did not miss the meeting

or Tom did not receive the message then either Tom did not take the plane or Dave was not elected to the board. Tom did not miss the meeting. Therefore either Tom did not receive the message or Tom did not miss the meeting. (*R*: Tom received the message. *P*: Tom took the plane. *M*: Tom missed the meeting. *D*: Dave was elected to the board.)

9. If Dick was recently vaccinated then he has a fever. Either Dick was recently vaccinated or if pocks begin to appear then Dick must be quarantined. Either Dick has measles or if a rash develops then there are complications. If Dick has measles then he has a fever. If Dick was not recently vaccinated and Dick does not have measles then either a rash develops or pocks begin to appear. Dick does not have a fever. Therefore either there are complications or Dick must be quarantined. (*V*: Dick was recently vaccinated. *F*: Dick has a fever. *P*: Pocks begin to appear. *Q*: Dick must be quarantined. *M*: Dick has measles. *R*: A rash develops. *C*: There are complications.)

★10. Either taxes are increased or if expenditures rise then the debt ceiling is raised. If taxes are increased then the cost of collecting taxes increases. If a rise in expenditures implies that the government borrows more money then if the debt ceiling is raised then interest rates increase. If taxes are not increased and the cost of collecting taxes does not increase then if the debt ceiling is raised then the government borrows more money. The cost of collecting taxes does not increase. Either interest rates do not increase or the government does not borrow more money. Therefore either the debt ceiling is not raised or expenditures do not rise. (*T*: Taxes are increased. *E*: Expenditures rise. *D*: The debt ceiling is raised. *C*: The cost of collecting taxes increases. *G*: The government borrows more money. *I*: Interest rates increase.)

There are many valid truth-functional arguments that cannot be proved valid using only the nine Rules of Inference given thus far. For example, a formal proof of validity for the obviously valid argument

$$A \lor B$$
$$\sim B \lor C$$
$$\therefore A \lor C$$

requires additional Rules of Inference.

Now the only compound statements that concern us here are truth-functionally compound statements. Hence if any part of a statement is replaced by an expression which is logically equivalent to that part, the truth value of the resulting statement is the same as that of the original statement. This is sometimes called the Rule of Replacement and sometimes the Principle of Extensionality.[1] We adopt the Rule of Replacement as an additional principle of inference. It permits us to infer from any statement the result of replacing all or part of that statement by any other statement logically equivalent to the part replaced. Thus using the Principle of Double Negation (D.N.), which asserts the logical equivalence of p and $\sim\sim p$, we can infer from $A \supset \sim\sim B$ any of the statements

$$A \supset B, \quad \sim\sim A \supset \sim\sim B, \quad A \supset \sim\sim\sim\sim B, \quad \text{or} \quad \sim\sim(A \supset \sim\sim B)$$

by the Rule of Replacement.

To make this new rule definite we list a number of logical equivalences with which it can be used. These equivalences constitute additional Rules of Inference that can be used in proving the validity of arguments. We number them consecutively after the first nine Rules already stated.

Rule of Replacement: Any of the following logically equivalent expressions can replace each other wherever they occur:

10. De Morgan's Theorems (De M.): $\quad \sim(p \cdot q) \equiv (\sim p \vee \sim q)$.
    $\quad \sim(p \vee q) \equiv (\sim p \cdot \sim q)$.

11. Commutation (Com.): $\quad (p \vee q) \equiv (q \vee p)$.
    $\quad (p \cdot q) \equiv (q \cdot p)$.

12. Association (Assoc.): $\quad [p \vee (q \vee r)] \equiv [(p \vee q) \vee r]$.
    $\quad [p \cdot (q \cdot r)] \equiv [(p \cdot q) \cdot r]$.

13. Distribution (Dist.): $\quad [p \cdot (q \vee r)] \equiv [(p \cdot q) \vee (p \cdot r)]$.
    $\quad [p \vee (q \cdot r)] \equiv [(p \vee q) \cdot (p \vee r)]$.

14. Double Negation (D.N.): $\quad p \equiv \sim\sim p$.

15. Transposition (Trans.): $\quad (p \supset q) \equiv (\sim q \supset \sim p)$.

16. Material Implication (Impl.): $\quad (p \supset q) \equiv (\sim p \vee q)$.

17. Material Equivalence (Equiv.): $\quad (p \equiv q) \equiv [(p \supset q) \cdot (q \supset p)]$.
    $\quad (p \equiv q) \equiv [(p \cdot q) \vee (\sim p \cdot \sim q)]$.

[1] It will be stated more formally, in an appropriate context, and demonstrated, in Chapter 7.

18. Exportation (Exp.): $[(p \cdot q) \supset r] \equiv [p \supset (q \supset r)]$.

19. Tautology (Taut.): $p \equiv (p \vee p)$.

                                      $p \equiv (p \cdot p)$.

A formal proof of validity for the argument given on page 41 can now be written:

1. $A \vee B$
2. $\sim B \vee C$ $/ \therefore A \vee C$
3. $\sim\sim A \vee B$ 1, D.N.
4. $\sim A \supset B$ 3, Impl.
5. $B \supset C$ 2, Impl.
6. $\sim A \supset C$ 4, 5, H.S.
7. $\sim\sim A \vee C$ 6, Impl.
8. $A \vee C$ 7, D.N.

Some argument forms, although very elementary and perfectly valid, are not included in our list of nineteen Rules of Inference. Although the argument

$$A \cdot B$$
$$\therefore B$$

is obviously valid, its form

$$p \cdot q$$
$$\therefore q$$

is not included in our list. Hence B does not follow from $A \cdot B$ by any single elementary valid argument form *as defined by our list*. It can be deduced, however, using *two* elementary valid arguments, and the formal proof of validity can be set down as

1. $A \cdot B$ $/ \therefore B$
2. $B \cdot A$ 1, Com.
3. B 2, Simp.

We could add the intuitively valid argument form

$$p \cdot q$$
$$\therefore q$$

to our list, of course, but if we began to expand our list in this way we might end up with a list that was too long and therefore unmanageable.

The list of Rules of Inference contains several redundancies, for example, *Modus Tollens* could be dropped from our list without any real weakening of the machinery, for any step deduced using it could be deduced using other Rules of the list. Thus in our first proof, on page 35, line 5, $\sim A$, which was deduced from lines 3 and 4, $A \supset C$ and $\sim C$, by *Modus Tollens*, could have been deduced without it, since $\sim C \supset \sim A$ follows from $A \supset C$ by Transposition, and $\sim A$ from $\sim C \supset \sim A$ and $\sim C$ by *Modus Ponens*. But *Modus Tollens* is so common and intuitive a principle of inference that it has been included anyway, and others have also been included for convenience despite their logical redundancy.

The test of whether or not a given sequence of statements is a formal proof is *effective*. That is, direct observation will suffice to decide whether or not every line beyond the premisses actually does follow from preceding lines by one of the given Rules of Inference. No 'thinking' is required: neither thinking about what the statements mean, nor using logical intuition to check the validity of any line's deduction. Even where the 'justification' of a statement is not written beside it, there is a finite, mechanical procedure for deciding whether or not the deduction is legitimate. Each line is preceded by only a finite number of other lines, and only a finite number of Rules of Inference have been adopted. Although time consuming, it can be verified by inspection whether the line in question follows from any single preceding line or any pair of preceding lines by any one of the Rules of Inference listed. For example, in the foregoing proof, line 2, $B \cdot A$, is preceded only by line 1, $A \cdot B$. Its legitimacy can be decided by observing that although it does not follow from $A \cdot B$ by *Modus Ponens*, nor by *Modus Tollens*, nor by a Hypothetical Syllogism, and so on through number 10, when we come to number 11 we can *see*, simply by observing the forms, that line 2 follows from line 1 by the principle of Commutation. Similarly, the legitimacy of any line can be decided by a finite number of observations, none of which involves anything more than comparing shapes or patterns. To preserve this property of effectiveness we lay down the rule that only one Rule of Inference should be applied at a time. The explanatory notation beside each statement is not, strictly speaking, part of the proof, but it is helpful and should always be included.

Although the test of whether or not a given sequence of statements is a formal proof is effective, *constructing* such a formal proof is *not* an effective procedure. In this respect the present method differs from the methods of the preceding chapter. The use of truth tables is *completely* mechanical: given any argument of the general sort with which we are now concerned, its validity can always be tested by following the simple rules presented in Chapter 2. But in constructing a formal proof of validity on the basis of the nineteen Rules of Inference listed, it is necessary to *think* or 'figure out' where to begin and how to proceed. Although we have no effective or purely mechanical method of procedure, it is usually much easier to construct a formal proof of validity than to write out a truth table with perhaps dozens or hundreds or even thousands of rows.

There is an important difference between the first nine and the last ten Rules of Inference. The first nine can be applied only to whole lines of a proof. Thus A can be inferred from $A \cdot B$ by Simplification only if $A \cdot B$ constitutes a whole line. But neither A nor $A \supset C$ follows from $(A \cdot B) \supset C$ by Simplification or by any other Rule of Inference. A does not follow because A can be false while $(A \cdot B) \supset C$ is true. $A \supset C$ does not follow because if A is true and B and C are both false, $(A \cdot B) \supset C$ is true whereas $A \supset C$ is false. On the other hand, any of the last ten Rules of Inference can be applied either to whole lines or to parts of lines. Not only can the statement $A \supset (B \supset C)$ be inferred from the whole line $(A \cdot B) \supset C$ by Exportation, but from the line $[(A \cdot B) \supset C]$ v D we can infer $[A \supset (B \supset C)]$ v D by Exportation. The Rule of Replacement authorizes specified logically equivalent expressions to replace each other wherever they occur, even where they do not constitute whole lines of a proof. But the first nine Rules of Inference can be used only with whole lines of a proof serving as premisses.

In the absence of mechanical rules for the construction of formal proofs of validity, two hints on procedure may be suggested. One is simply to begin with the premisses and deduce conclusions by the given Rules of Inference, for as more and more statements become available, the greater is the likelihood of being able to see a way of arriving at the conclusion of the argument to be proved valid. The other method is to work backward from the conclusion by looking for some statement or pair of statements from which it could be deduced by one of the given Rules of Inference, and then trying to deduce those intermediate statements from still others, and so on, until you come to some which are derivable from the original premisses. A judicious combination of these two methods is often the best way to proceed. Practice, of course, is the best method of acquiring facility in using the method of deduction.

EXERCISES

I. Each of the following is a formal proof of validity for the indicated argument. State the 'justification' for each line which is not a premiss:

★1.   1. $(A \vee B) \supset (C \cdot D)$
      2. $\sim C$ $/ \therefore \sim B$
      3. $\sim C \vee \sim D$
      4. $\sim (C \cdot D)$
      5. $\sim (A \vee B)$
      6. $\sim A \cdot \sim B$
      7. $\sim B \cdot \sim A$
      8. $\sim B$

2.   1. $(E \cdot F) \cdot G$
     2. $(F \equiv G) \supset (H \vee I)$ $/ \therefore I \vee H$
     3. $E \cdot (F \cdot G)$
     4. $(F \cdot G) \cdot E$
     5. $F \cdot G$
     6. $(F \cdot G) \vee (\sim F \cdot \sim G)$
     7. $F \equiv G$
     8. $H \vee I$
     9. $I \vee H$

3.   1. $(J \cdot K) \supset L$
     2. $(J \supset L) \supset M$
     3. $\sim K \vee N$ $/ \therefore K \supset (M \cdot N)$
     4. $(K \cdot J) \supset L$
     5. $K \supset (J \supset L)$
     6. $K \supset M$

    7. $\sim K \vee M$

    8. $(\sim K \vee M) \cdot (\sim K \vee N)$

    9. $\sim K \vee (M \cdot N)$

  10. $K \supset (M \cdot N)$

4. 1. $(O \supset \sim P) \cdot (P \supset Q)$

    2. $Q \supset O$

    3. $\sim R \supset P$ $/\therefore R$

    4. $\sim Q \vee O$

    5. $O \vee \sim Q$

    6. $(O \supset \sim P) \cdot (\sim Q \supset \sim P)$

    7. $\sim P \vee \sim P$

    8. $\sim P$

    9. $\sim\sim R$

  10. R

★5. 1. $S \supset (T \supset U)$

    2. $U \supset \sim U$

    3. $(V \supset S) \cdot (W \supset T)$ $/\therefore V \supset \sim W$

    4. $(S \cdot T) \supset U$

    5. $\sim U \vee \sim U$

    6. $\sim U$

    7. $\sim (S \cdot T)$

    8. $\sim S \vee \sim T$

    9. $\sim V \vee \sim W$

  10. $V \supset \sim W$

6. 1. $X \supset (Y \supset Z)$

    2. $X \supset (A \supset B)$

    3. $X \cdot (Y \vee A)$

    4. $\sim Z$ $/\therefore B$

    5. $(X \cdot Y) \supset Z$

    6. $(X \cdot A) \supset B$

    7. $(X \cdot Y) \vee (X \cdot A)$

    8. $[(X \cdot Y) \supset Z] \cdot [(X \cdot A) \supset B]$

    9. $Z \vee B$

  10. B

7. 1. $C \supset (D \supset \sim C)$

    2. $C \equiv D$ $/\therefore \sim C \cdot \sim D$

    3. $C \supset (\sim\sim C \supset \sim D)$

4. $C \supset (C \supset {\sim}D)$
5. $(C{\cdot}C) \supset {\sim}D$
6. $C \supset {\sim}D$
7. ${\sim}C \vee {\sim}D$
8. ${\sim}(C{\cdot}D)$
9. $(C{\cdot}D) \vee ({\sim}C{\cdot}{\sim}D)$
10. ${\sim}C{\cdot}{\sim}D$

8. 1. $E{\cdot}(F \vee G)$
2. $(E{\cdot}G) \supset {\sim}(H \vee I)$
3. $({\sim}H \vee {\sim}I) \supset {\sim}(E{\cdot}F)$ $/ \therefore H \equiv I$
4. $(E{\cdot}G) \supset ({\sim}H{\cdot}{\sim}I)$
5. ${\sim}(H{\cdot}I) \supset {\sim}(E{\cdot}F)$
6. $(E{\cdot}F) \supset (H{\cdot}I)$
7. $[(E{\cdot}F) \supset (H{\cdot}I)]{\cdot}[(E{\cdot}G) \supset ({\sim}H{\cdot}{\sim}I)]$
8. $(E{\cdot}F) \vee (E{\cdot}G)$
9. $(H{\cdot}I) \vee ({\sim}H{\cdot}{\sim}I)$
10. $H \equiv I$

9. 1. $J \vee ({\sim}K \vee J)$
2. $K \vee ({\sim}J \vee K)$ $/ \therefore (J{\cdot}K) \vee ({\sim}J{\cdot}{\sim}K)$
3. $({\sim}K \vee J) \vee J$
4. ${\sim}K \vee (J \vee J)$
5. ${\sim}K \vee J$
6. $K \supset J$
7. $({\sim}J \vee K) \vee K$
8. ${\sim}J \vee (K \vee K)$
9. ${\sim}J \vee K$
10. $J \supset K$
11. $(J \supset K){\cdot}(K \supset J)$
12. $J \equiv K$
13. $(J{\cdot}K) \vee ({\sim}J{\cdot}{\sim}K)$

★10. 1. $(L \vee M) \vee (N{\cdot}O)$
2. $({\sim}L{\cdot}O){\cdot}{\sim}({\sim}L{\cdot}M)$ $/ \therefore {\sim}L{\cdot}N$
3. ${\sim}L{\cdot}[O{\cdot}{\sim}({\sim}L{\cdot}M)]$
4. ${\sim}L$
5. $L \vee [M \vee (N{\cdot}O)]$
6. $M \vee (N{\cdot}O)$
7. $(M \vee N){\cdot}(M \vee O)$

8. $M \vee N$

9. $\sim L \cdot (M \vee N)$

10. $(\sim L \cdot M) \vee (\sim L \cdot N)$

11. $\sim (\sim L \cdot M) \cdot (\sim L \cdot O)$

12. $\sim (\sim L \cdot M)$

13. $\sim L \cdot N$

II. Construct a formal proof of validity for each of the following arguments, in each case using the suggested notation.

★1. If I study I make good grades. If I do not study I enjoy myself. Therefore either I make good grades or I enjoy myself. (S, G, E)

2. If the supply of silver remains constant and the use of silver increases then the price of silver rises. If an increase in the use of silver implies that the price of silver rises then there will be a windfall for speculators. The supply of silver remains constant. Therefore there will be a windfall for speculators. (S, U, P, W)

3. Either Adams is elected chairman or both Brown and Clark are elected to the board. If either Adams is elected chairman or Brown is elected to the board then Davis will lodge a protest. Therefore either Clark is elected to the board or Davis will lodge a protest. (A, B, C, D)

4. If he uses good bait then if the fish are biting then he catches the legal limit. He uses good bait but he does not catch the legal limit. Therefore the fish are not biting. (G, B, C)

★5. Either the governor and the lieutenant-governor will both run for reelection, or the primary race will be wide open and the party will be torn by dissension. The governor will not run for reelection. Therefore the party will be torn by dissension. (G, L, W, T)

6. If the Dodgers win the pennant then they will win the Series. Therefore if the Dodgers win the pennant then if they continue to hit then they will win the Series. (P, S, H)

7. If he attracts the farm vote then he will carry the rural areas, and if he attracts the labor vote then he will carry the urban centers. If he carries both the urban centers and the rural areas then he is certain to be elected. He is not certain to be elected. Therefore either he does not attract the farm vote or he does not attract the labor vote. (F, R, L, U, C)

8. Either Argentina does not join the alliance or Brazil boycotts it, but if Argentina joins the alliance then Chile boycotts it. If Brazil boycotts the alliance then if Chile boycotts it then Ecuador will boycott it. Therefore if Argentina joins the alliance then Ecuador will boycott it. (A, B, C, E)

9. If Argentina joins the alliance then both Brazil and Chile will boycott it. If either Brazil or Chile boycotts the alliance then the alliance will be ineffective. Therefore if Argentina joins the alliance then the alliance will be ineffective. (*A, B, C, I*)

★10. Steve took either the bus or the train. If he took the bus or drove his own car then he arrived late and missed the first session. He did not arrive late. Therefore he took the train. (*B, T, C, L, M*)

11. If you enroll in the course and study hard then you will pass, but if you enroll in the course and do not study hard then you will not pass. Therefore if you enroll in the course then either you study hard and pass or you do not study hard and do not pass. (*E, S, P*)

12. If Argentina joins the alliance then either Brazil or Chile will boycott it. If Brazil boycotts the alliance then Chile will boycott it also. Therefore if Argentina joins the alliance then Chile will boycott it. (*A, B, C*)

13. If either Argentina or Brazil joins the alliance then both Chile and Ecuador will boycott it. Therefore if Argentina joins the alliance then Chile will boycott it. (*A, B, C, E*)

14. If prices fall or wages rise then both retail sales and advertising activities increase. If retail sales increase then jobbers make more money, but jobbers do not make more money. Therefore prices do not fall. (*P, W, R, A, J*)

★15. If I work then I earn money, but if I am idle then I enjoy myself. Either I work or I am idle. However, if I work then I do not enjoy myself, while if I am idle then I do not earn money. Therefore I enjoy myself if and only if I do not earn money. (*W, M, I, E*)

16. If he enters the primary then if he campaigns vigorously then he wins the nomination. If he wins the nomination and receives the support of the party regulars then he will be elected. If he takes the party platform seriously then although he receives the support of the party regulars he will not be elected. Therefore if he enters the primary then if he campaigns vigorously then he does not take the party platform seriously. (*P, C, N, R, E, T*)

17. Either the tariff is lowered, or imports continue to decrease and our own industries prosper. If the tariff is lowered then our own industries prosper. Therefore our own industries prosper. (*T, I, O*)

18. Either he has his old car repaired or he buys a new car. If he has his old car repaired then he will owe a lot of money to the garage. If he owes a lot of money to the garage then he will not soon be out of debt. If he buys a new car then he must borrow money from the bank, and if he must borrow money from the bank then he will not soon be out of debt. Either

he will soon be out of debt or his creditors will force him into bankruptcy. Therefore his creditors will force him into bankruptcy. (R, N, G, S, B, C)

19. If he goes on a picnic then he wears sport clothes. If he wears sport clothes then he does not attend both the banquet and the dance. If he does not attend the banquet then he still has his ticket, but he does not still have his ticket. He does attend the dance. Therefore he does not go on a picnic. (P, S, B, D, T)

20. If he studies the sciences then he prepares to earn a good living, and if he studies the humanities then he prepares to live a good life. If he prepares to earn a good living or he prepares to live a good life then his college years are well spent. But his college years are not well spent. Therefore he does not study either the sciences or the humanities. (S, E, H, L, C)

21. If you plant tulips then your garden will bloom early, and if you plant asters then your garden will bloom late. So if you plant either tulips or asters then your garden will bloom either early or late. (T, E, A, L)

22. If you plant tulips then your garden will bloom early, and if you plant asters then your garden will bloom late. So if you plant both tulips and asters then your garden will bloom both early and late. (T, E, A, L)

23. If we go to Europe then we tour Scandinavia. If we go to Europe then if we tour Scandinavia then we visit Norway. If we tour Scandinavia then if we visit Norway then we will take a trip on a fiord. Therefore if we go to Europe then we will take a trip on a fiord. (E, S, N, F)

24. If Argentina joins the alliance then either Brazil or Chile boycotts it. If Ecuador joins the alliance then either Chile or Peru boycotts it. Chile does not boycott it. Therefore if neither Brazil nor Peru boycotts it then neither Argentina nor Ecuador joins the alliance. (A, B, C, E, P)

★25. If either Argentina or Brazil joins the alliance then if either Chile or Ecuador boycotts it then although Peru does not boycott it Venezuela boycotts it. If either Peru or Nicaragua does not boycott it then Uruguay will join the alliance. Therefore if Argentina joins the alliance then if Chile boycotts it then Uruguay will join the alliance. (A, B, C, E, P, V, N, U)

3.2 PROVING INVALIDITY

We can establish the invalidity of an argument by using a truth table to show that its form is invalid. The truth table proves invalidity if it contains at least one row in which truth values are assigned to the statement variables in such a way that the premisses are made true and the conclusion false. If we can devise such a truth value assignment without constructing the entire truth table, we shall have a shorter method of proving invalidity.

Consider the invalid argument

> If the Senator votes against this bill then he is opposed to more severe penalties against tax evaders.
>
> If the Senator is a tax evader himself then he is opposed to more severe penalties against tax evaders.
>
> Therefore if the Senator votes against this bill he is a tax evader himself.

which may be symbolized as

$$V \supset O$$
$$H \supset O$$
$$\therefore V \supset H$$

Instead of constructing a truth table, we can prove its invalidity by making an assignment of truth values to the component simple statements V, O, and H which will make the premises true and the conclusion false. The conclusion is made false by assigning **T** to V and **F** to H; and both premises are made true by assigning **T** to O. This method of proving invalidity is closely related to the truth table method. In effect, making the indicated truth value assignment amounts to describing one row of the relevant truth table—a row that suffices to establish the invalidity of the argument being tested. The relationship appears more clearly, perhaps, when the truth value assignments are written out horizontally, as

V	O	H	$V \supset O$	$H \supset O$	$V \supset H$
T	T	F	T	T	F

This new method of proving invalidity is shorter than writing out a complete truth table, and the amount of time and work saved is proportionally greater for more complicated arguments. In proving the invalidity of more extended arguments, a certain amount of trial and error may be needed to discover a truth value assignment which works. But even so, this method is quicker and easier than writing out the entire truth table. It is obvious that the present method will suffice to prove the invalidity of any argument which can be shown to be invalid by a truth table.

EXERCISES

Prove the invalidity of each of the following arguments by the method of assigning truth values:

★1. $A \supset B$
$C \supset D$
$B \vee C$
$\therefore A \vee D$

2. $E \supset (F \vee G)$
$G \supset (H \cdot I)$
$\sim H$
$\therefore E \supset I$

3. $J \supset (K \supset L)$
$K \supset (\sim L \supset M)$
$(L \vee M) \supset N$
$\therefore J \supset N$

4. $(O \vee P) \supset Q$
$Q \supset (P \vee R)$
$O \supset (\sim S \supset P)$
$(S \supset O) \supset \sim R$
$\therefore P \equiv Q$

★5. $T \equiv U$
$U \equiv (V \cdot W)$
$V \equiv (T \vee X)$
$T \vee X$
$\therefore T \cdot X$

6. $X \equiv (Y \supset Z)$
$Y \equiv (\sim X \cdot \sim Z)$
$Z \equiv (X \vee \sim Y)$
Y
$\therefore X \vee Z$

7. $(A \supset B) \cdot (C \supset D)$
$A \vee C$
$(B \vee D) \supset (E \cdot F)$
$E \supset (F \supset G)$
$G \supset (A \supset H)$
$\therefore H$

8. $I \vee (J \cdot K)$
$(I \vee J) \supset (L \equiv \sim M)$
$(L \supset \sim M) \supset (M \cdot \sim N)$
$(N \supset O) \cdot (O \supset M)$
$(J \supset K) \supset O$
$\therefore O$

9. $P \equiv (Q \equiv \sim R)$
$Q \supset (\sim R \vee \sim S)$
$[R \supset (Q \vee \sim T)] \cdot (P \supset Q)$
$[U \supset (S \cdot T)] \cdot (T \supset \sim V)$
$[(Q \cdot R) \supset \sim U] \cdot [U \supset (Q \vee R)]$
$(Q \vee V) \cdot \sim V$
$\therefore \sim U \cdot \sim V$

★10. $W \equiv (X \vee Y)$
$X \equiv (Z \supset Y)$
$Y \equiv (Z \equiv \sim A)$
$Z \equiv (A \supset B)$
$A \equiv (B \equiv Z)$
$B \vee \sim W$
$\therefore W \equiv B$

3.3 INCOMPLETENESS OF THE NINETEEN RULES[2]

The nineteen Rules of Inference presented thus far are *incomplete*, which is to say that there are truth functionally valid arguments whose validity cannot be proved using only those nineteen Rules. To discuss and establish this incompleteness it is useful to introduce the notion of a characteristic that is 'hereditary with respect to a set of rules of inference'. We offer this definition: a characteristic Φ is *hereditary with respect to a set of rules of inference* if and only if whenever Φ belongs to one or more statements it also belongs to every statement deduced from them by means of those Rules of Inference. For example, *truth* is a characteristic that is hereditary with respect to the nineteen Rules of Inference presented in the first section of the present chapter. As has already been remarked, any conclusion must be true if it can be deduced from true premises by means of our nineteen Rules of Inference. Indeed, we should not want to use any rules of inference with respect to which truth was *not* hereditary.

Now to prove that a set of rules of inference is incomplete we must find a characteristic Φ and a valid argument α such that

(1) Φ is hereditary with respect to the set of rules of inference; and
(2) Φ belongs to the premises of α but not to the conclusion of α.

The characteristic *truth* is hereditary with respect to any set of rules of inference in which we may be seriously interested, and therefore satisfies condition (1) above. But where α is a valid argument, it follows immediately from our definition of validity that *truth* can never satisfy condition (2) above. Hence to prove the incompleteness of our nineteen Rules we must find a characteristic other than *truth* which is hereditary with respect to our nineteen Rules, and can belong to the premises but not the conclusion of some valid argument α.

To obtain such a characteristic we introduce a three-element model in terms of which the symbols in our nineteen Rules can be interpreted. The three elements are the numbers **0**, **1**, and **2**, which play roles analogous to those of the truth values true (**T**) and false (**F**) introduced in Chapter 2. Every statement will have one of the three elements of the

---

[2] The following proof of incompleteness was communicated to me by my friend Professor Leo Simons of the University of Cincinnati.

model assigned to it, and it will be said to assume, take on, or have one of the three *values* **0**, **1**, or **2**. Just as in Chapter 2 the statement variables p, q, r, . . . , were allowed to range over the two truth values **T** and **F**, so here we allow the statement variables p, q, r, . . . to range over the three values **0**, **1**, and **2**.

The five symbols '$\sim$', '$\cdot$', 'v', '$\supset$', and '$\equiv$' that occur in our nineteen Rules can be redefined for (or in terms of) our three-element model by the following three-valued 'truth tables':

p	$\sim p$		p	q	$p \cdot q$	p v q	$p \supset q$	$p \equiv q$
0	2		0	0	0	0	0	0
1	1		0	1	1	0	1	1
2	0		0	2	2	0	2	2
			1	0	1	0	0	1
			1	1	1	1	1	1
			1	2	2	1	1	1
			2	0	2	0	0	2
			2	1	2	1	0	1
			2	2	2	2	0	0

Alternative (but equivalent) analytical definitions can be given as follows, where 'min(x, y)' denotes the minimum of the numbers x and y, and 'max(x, y)' denotes the maximum of the numbers x and y.

$$\sim p = 2 - p$$
$$p \cdot q = \max(p, q)$$
$$p \text{ v } q = \min(p, q)$$
$$p \supset q = \min(2 - p, q)$$
$$p \equiv q = \max(\min(2 - p, q), \min(2 - q, p))$$

The desired characteristic Φ that is hereditary with respect to our nineteen Rules of Inference is the property of having the value **0**. To prove that it is hereditary with respect to the nineteen Rules it will suffice to show that it is hereditary with respect to each of the nineteen Rules. This can be shown for each rule by means of a three-valued 'truth table'. For example, that having the value **0** is hereditary with respect to *Modus Ponens*, can be seen by examining the truth table (on page 55) that defines the value of '$p \supset q$' as a function of the values of 'p' and of 'q'. The two premises 'p' and '$p \supset q$' have the value **0** only in the first row, and there the conclusion '*q*' has the value 0 also. Examining the same truth table shows that having the value 0 is hereditary also for Simplification, Conjunction, and Addition. Filling in additional columns for '~*p*' and '~*q*' will show that having the value 0 is hereditary with respect to *Modus Tollens* and Disjunctive Syllogism also. That it is hereditary with respect to Hypothetical Syllogism can be shown by the following table:

p	*q*	*r*	*p* ⊃ *q*	*q* ⊃ *r*	*p* ⊃ *r*
0	0	0	0	0	0
0	0	1	0	1	1
0	0	2	0	2	2
0	1	0	1	0	0
0	1	1	1	1	1
0	1	2	1	1	2
0	2	0	2	0	0
0	2	1	2	0	1
0	2	2	2	0	2
1	0	0	0	0	0
1	0	1	0	1	1
1	0	2	0	2	1
1	1	0	1	0	0
1	1	1	1	1	1
1	1	2	1	1	1
1	2	0	1	0	0
1	2	1	1	0	1
1	2	2	1	0	1
2	0	0	0	0	0
2	0	1	0	1	0
2	0	2	0	2	0
2	1	0	0	0	0
2	1	1	0	1	0
2	1	2	0	1	0
2	2	0	0	0	0
2	2	1	0	0	0
2	2	2	0	0	0

Only in the first, tenth, nineteenth, twenty-second, twenty-fifth, twenty-sixth, and twenty-seventh rows do the two premisses '$p \supset q$' and '$q \supset r$' have the value 0, and in each of them the conclusion '$p \supset r$' has the value 0 also. Even larger tables would be needed to show that having the value 0 is hereditary with respect to Constructive Dilemma and Destructive Dilemma, but they are easily constructed.

When we construct three-valued 'truth tables' to verify that having the value 0 is hereditary with respect to replacement of statements by their logical equivalents, we notice that although the biconditionals themselves need not have the value 0, the expressions flanking the equivalence sign necessarily have the same value. For example, in the table appropriate to the first of De Morgan's Theorems,

p	q	$\sim p$	$\sim q$	$p \cdot q$	$\sim(p \cdot q)$	$\sim p \vee \sim q$	$\sim(p \cdot q) \equiv (\sim p \vee \sim q)$
0	0	2	2	0	2	2	0
0	1	2	1	1	1	1	1
0	2	2	0	2	0	0	0
1	0	1	2	1	1	1	1
1	1	1	1	1	1	1	1
1	2	1	0	2	0	0	0
2	0	0	2	2	0	0	0
2	1	0	1	2	0	0	0
2	2	0	0	2	0	0	0

the equivalent expressions '$\sim(p \cdot q)$' and '$\sim p \vee \sim q$' have the same value in every row even though the statement of their equivalence fails to have the value 0 in rows two, four, and five. It should be obvious, however, that having the value 0 is hereditary with respect to the replacement of all or part of any statement by any other statement equivalent to the part replaced.

Alternative proofs that having the value 0 is hereditary with respect to the nineteen Rules make use of our analytical definitions of the logical symbols.[3] For example, that having the value 0 is hereditary with respect to Constructive Dilemma can be shown by the following argument. By assumption, '$(p \supset q) \cdot (r \supset s)$' and '$p \vee r$' both have the value 0. Hence both '$p \supset q$' and '$r \supset s$' have the value 0, so either

[3] This was pointed out to me by my friend and former student Mrs. W. L. Barbee.

$p = 2$ or $q = 0$ and either $r = 2$ or $s = 0$. Since '$p \vee r$' has the value **0**, either $p = 0$ or $r = 0$. If $p = 0$ then $p \neq 2$ whence $q = 0$, and if $r = 0$ then $r \neq 2$ whence $s = 0$, therefore either $q = 0$ or $s = 0$ whence '$q \vee s$' has the value **0**, which was to be shown.

Having shown that the characteristic of having the value 0 is hereditary with respect to the nineteen Rules, to prove the incompleteness of those Rules we need only exhibit a valid argument whose premisses have the value 0 but whose conclusion does not have the value 0. Such an argument is

$$A \supset B$$
$$\therefore A \supset (A \cdot B)$$

whose validity is easily established by a truth table. In case 'A' has the value **1** and 'B' has the value **0**, the premiss '$A \supset B$' has the value **0** but the conclusion '$A \supset (A \cdot B)$' has the value **1**. Therefore the nineteen Rules of Inference presented thus far are incomplete.

3.4   THE RULE OF CONDITIONAL PROOF

In this section we introduce a new rule to use in the method of deduction: the rule of Conditional Proof. For the present, this rule will be applied only to arguments whose conclusions are conditional statements. The new rule can best be explained and justified by reference to the principle of Exportation and the correspondence, noted in Chapter 2, between valid argument forms and tautologies.

To every argument there corresponds a conditional statement whose antecedent is the conjunction of the argument's premisses and whose consequent is the argument's conclusion. As has been remarked, an argument is valid if and only if its corresponding conditional is a tautology. If an argument has a conditional statement for its conclusion, which we may symbolize as $A \supset C$, then if we symbolize the conjunction of its premisses as P, the argument is valid if and only if the conditional

(1) $$P \supset (A \supset C)$$

is a tautology. If we can deduce the conclusion $A \supset C$ from the premisses in P by a sequence of elementary valid arguments, we thereby prove the argument to be valid and the associated conditional (1) to be a tautology. By the principle of Exportation, (1) is logically equivalent to

(2) $(P \cdot A) \supset C$

But (2) is the conditional associated with a somewhat different argument. This second argument has as its premises all of the premises of the first argument *plus* an additional premiss which is the antecedent of the conclusion of the first argument. And the conclusion of the second argument is the consequent of the conclusion of the first argument. Now if we deduce the conclusion of the second argument, C, from the premises in $P \cdot A$ by a sequence of elementary valid arguments, we thereby prove that its associated conditional statement (2) is a tautology. But since (1) and (2) are logically equivalent, this fact proves that (1) is a tautology also, from which it follows that the original argument, with one less premiss and the conditional conclusion $A \supset C$, is valid also. Now the rule of Conditional Proof permits us to infer the validity of any argument

$$P$$
$$\therefore \ A \supset C$$

from a formal proof of validity for the argument

$$P$$
$$A$$
$$\therefore \ C$$

Given any argument whose conclusion is a conditional statement, a proof of its validity using the rule of Conditional Proof, that is, a conditional proof of its validity, is constructed by assuming the antecedent of its conclusion as an additional premiss and then deducing the consequent of its conclusion by a sequence of elementary valid arguments. Thus a conditional proof of validity for the argument

$$(A \vee B) \supset (C \cdot D)$$
$$(D \vee E) \supset F$$
$$\therefore \ A \supset F$$

may be written as

1. $(A \lor B) \supset (C \cdot D)$
2. $(D \lor E) \supset F$　／∴ $A \supset F$
3. A　　　　　　／∴ F　　(C.P.)
4. $A \lor B$　　　　　3, Add.
5. $C \cdot D$　　　　　1, 4, M.P.
6. $D \cdot C$　　　　　5, Com.
7. D　　　　　　6, Simp.
8. $D \lor E$　　　　　7, Add.
9. F　　　　　　2, 8, M.P.

Here the second slant line and three dot 'therefore' symbol, as well as the parenthesized 'C.P.', indicate that the rule of Conditional Proof is being used.

Since the rule of Conditional Proof can be used in dealing with any valid argument having a conditional statement as conclusion, it can be applied more than once in the course of the same deduction. Thus a conditional proof of validity for

$$A \supset (B \supset C)$$
$$B \supset (C \supset D)$$
$$\therefore A \supset (B \supset D)$$

will be a proof of validity for

$$A \supset (B \supset C)$$
$$B \supset (C \supset D)$$
$$A$$
$$\therefore B \supset D$$

and since the latter itself has a conditional conclusion, it can be given a conditional proof by proving the validity of

$$A \supset (B \supset C)$$
$$B \supset (C \supset D)$$
$$A$$
$$B$$
$$\therefore D$$

Each use of the conditional method should be signalled by an additional slant line and 'therefore' sign, in addition to the notation '(C.P.)'. The suggested proof would be written:

1. $A \supset (B \supset C)$
2. $B \supset (C \supset D)$ $/ \therefore A \supset (B \supset D)$
3. A $/ \therefore B \supset D$ (C.P.)
4. B $/ \therefore D$ (C.P.)
5. $B \supset C$ 1, 3, M.P.
6. C 5, 4, M.P.
7. $C \supset D$ 2, 4, M.P.
8. D 7, 6, M.P.

The rule of Conditional Proof is a genuine addition to the proof apparatus presented in Section 3.1. Not only does it permit the construction of *shorter* proofs of validity for arguments which could be proved valid by appealing to the original list of nineteen Rules of Inference alone, but it permits us to establish the validity of valid arguments whose validity could *not* be proved by reference to the original list alone. For example, it was shown in Section 3.3 that the obviously valid argument

$$A \supset B$$
$$\therefore A \supset (A \cdot B)$$

cannot be proved valid using only the original list of nineteen Rules of Inference. But it is easily proved valid by using, in addition, the rule of Conditional Proof. Its conditional proof of validity is

1. $A \supset B$ $/ \therefore A \supset (A \cdot B)$
2. A $/ \therefore A \cdot B$ (C.P.)
3. B 1, 2, M.P.
4. $A \cdot B$ 2, 3, Conj.

EXERCISES

Give conditional proofs of validity for Exercises 21, 22, ★23, 24, and ★25 on page 51.

3.5   THE RULE OF INDIRECT PROOF

The method of *indirect proof*, often called the method of proof by *reductio ad absurdum*, is familiar to all who have studied elementary geometry. In deriving his theorems, Euclid often begins by assuming the opposite of what he wants to prove. If that assumption leads to a contradiction, or 'reduces to an absurdity', then that assumption must be false, and so its negation—the theorem to be proved—must be true.

An indirect proof of validity for a given argument is constructed by assuming, as an additional premiss, the negation of its conclusion, and then deriving an explicit contradiction from the augmented set of premisses. Thus an indirect proof of validity for the argument

$$A \supset (B \cdot C)$$
$$(B \vee D) \supset E$$
$$D \vee A$$
$$\therefore E$$

may be set down as follows:

1. $A \supset (B \cdot C)$
2. $(B \vee D) \supset E$
3. $D \vee A$ $/\therefore E$
4. $\sim E$ I.P. (Indirect Proof)
5. $\sim (B \vee D)$ 2, 4, M.T.
6. $\sim B \cdot \sim D$ 5, De M.
7. $\sim D \cdot \sim B$ 6, Com.
8. $\sim D$ 7, Simp.
9. A 3, 8, D.S.
10. $B \cdot C$ 1, 9, M.P.
11. B 10, Simp.
12. $\sim B$ 6, Simp.
13. $B \cdot \sim B$ 11, 12, Conj.

Here line 13 is an explicit contradiction, so the demonstration is complete, for the validity of the original argument follows by the rule of Indirect Proof.

It is easy to show that from a contradiction *any* conclusion can validly be deduced. In other words, any argument of the form

$$p$$
$$\sim p$$
$$\therefore q$$

is valid, no matter what statements are substituted for the variables *p* and *q*. Thus from lines 11 and 12 in the preceding proof, the conclusion *E* can be derived in just two more lines. Such a continuation would proceed:

14. $B \vee E$ 11, Add.
15. E 14, 12, D.S.

Hence it is possible to regard an indirect proof of the validity of a given argument not as the deduction of its validity *from the fact that* a contradiction was obtained, but rather as deducing that argument's conclusion *from the contradiction itself*. Thus instead of viewing a *reductio ad absurdum* proof as proceeding *only up to* the contradiction, we can regard it as *going on through* the contradiction to the conclusion of the original argument. If we symbolize the premises of an argument as *P* and its conclusion as *C*, then an indirect proof of the validity of

$$P$$
$$\therefore C$$

will be provided by a formal proof of validity for the argument

$$P$$
$$\sim C$$
$$\therefore C$$

What connection is there between the two arguments

$$P \qquad\qquad P$$
$$\therefore C \quad \text{and} \quad \sim C$$
$$\therefore C$$

which makes proving the second valid suffice to establish the validity of the first? A formal proof of validity for the latter constitutes a conditional proof of validity for a third argument

$$P$$
$$\therefore \sim C \supset C$$

But the conclusion of this third argument is logically equivalent to the conclusion of the first. By the definition of material implication, $\sim C \supset C$ is logically equivalent to $\sim\sim C \vee C$, which is logically equivalent to $C \vee C$ by the principle of Double Negation. And $C \vee C$ and C are logically equivalent by the principle of Tautology. Since the first and third arguments have identical premisses and logically equivalent conclusions, any proof of validity for one is a proof of validity for the other also. A proof of validity for the second argument is both a conditional proof of the third and an indirect proof of the first. Thus we see that there is an intimate relationship between the conditional and the indirect methods of proof, that is, between the rule of Conditional Proof and the rule of Indirect Proof.

Adding the rule of Indirect Proof serves to strengthen our proof apparatus still further. Any argument whose conclusion is a tautology can be shown to be valid, regardless of what its premisses may be, by the method of truth tables. But if the tautologous conclusion of an argument is not a conditional statement, and the premisses are consistent with each other and quite irrelevant to that conclusion, then the argument cannot be proved valid by the method of deduction without use being made of the rule of Indirect Proof. Although the argument

$$A$$
$$\therefore B \vee (B \supset C)$$

cannot be proved valid by the means set forth in the preceding sections, its validity is easily established using the rule of Indirect Proof. One proof of its validity is this:

1. A $/ \therefore B \vee (B \supset C)$
2. $\sim[B \vee (B \supset C)]$ I.P.
3. $\sim[B \vee (\sim B \vee C)]$ 2, Impl.
4. $\sim[(B \vee \sim B) \vee C]$ 3, Assoc.
5. $\sim(B \vee \sim B) \cdot \sim C$ 4, De M.
6. $\sim(B \vee \sim B)$ 5, Simp.
7. $\sim B \cdot \sim\sim B$ 6, De M.

Having augmented our original list of nineteen Rules of Inference by the rules of Conditional and Indirect Proof, our exposition of the method of deduction is now complete. Any argument whose validity can be established by the use of truth tables can be proved valid by the method of deduction as set forth in Sections 3.1, 3.4, and 3.5. This will not be proved, however, until the end of Chapter 7.

EXERCISES

For each of the following arguments construct both a formal proof of validity and an indirect proof, and compare their lengths:

1. $A \lor (B \cdot C)$
   $A \supset C$
   $\therefore C$

2. $(D \lor E) \supset (F \supset G)$
   $(\sim G \lor H) \supset (D \cdot F)$
   $\therefore G$

★3. $(H \supset I) \cdot (J \supset K)$
   $(I \lor K) \supset L$
   $\sim L$
   $\therefore \sim (H \lor J)$

4. $(M \lor N) \supset (O \cdot P)$
   $(O \lor Q) \supset (\sim R \cdot S)$
   $(R \lor T) \supset (M \cdot U)$
   $\therefore \sim R$

★5. $(V \supset \sim W) \cdot (X \supset Y)$
   $(\sim W \supset Z) \cdot (Y \supset \sim A)$
   $(Z \supset \sim B) \cdot (\sim A \supset C)$
   $V \cdot X$
   $\therefore \sim B \cdot C$

3.6 PROOFS OF TAUTOLOGIES

The conditional and indirect methods of proof can be used not only to establish the validity of arguments, but also to prove that certain statements and statement forms are tautologies. Any conditional statement corresponds, in a sense, to an argument whose single premiss is the antecedent of the conditional, and whose conclusion is the conditional's consequent. The conditional is a tautology if and only if that argument is valid. Hence a conditional is proved tautologous by deducing its consequent from its antecedent by a sequence of elementary valid arguments. Thus the statement $(A \cdot B) \supset A$ is proved tautologous by the same sequence of lines which proves the validity of the argument

$$A \cdot B$$
$$\therefore A$$

It has already been noted that the conditional method can be used repeatedly in a single proof. Thus the conditional statement

$$(Q \supset R) \supset [(P \supset Q) \supset (P \supset R)]$$

is proved tautologous by the following:

1. $Q \supset R$ / $\therefore$ $(P \supset Q) \supset (P \supset R)$ (C.P.)
2. $P \supset Q$ / $\therefore$ $P \supset R$ (C.P.)
3. $P \supset R$ 2, 1, H.S.

For some more complicated conditional statements, this method of proving them tautologous is shorter and easier than constructing truth tables.

There are many tautologies that are not conditional in form, and to these the preceding method cannot be applied. But any tautology can be established as tautologous by the indirect method. As applied to an *argument*, the indirect method of proving validity proceeds by adding the negation of its conclusion to the argument's premisses and then deducing a contradiction by a sequence of elementary valid arguments. As applied to a *statement*, the indirect method of proving it tautologous proceeds by taking its negation as premiss and then deducing a contradiction by a sequence of elementary valid arguments. Thus the statement $B \vee \sim B$ is proved to be a tautology by the following:

1. $\sim(B \vee \sim B)$ / $\therefore$ $B \vee \sim B$ (I.P.)
2. $\sim B \cdot \sim \sim B$ 1, De M.

To say that a statement is a tautology is to assert that its truth is unconditional, so it can be established without appealing to any other statements as premisses. Another, perhaps not too misleading, way of saying the same thing is to assert the validity of the 'argument' which has the statement in question as 'conclusion', but has no premisses at all. If the 'conclusion' *is* a tautology, then the method of deduction permits us to prove that the 'argument' is valid even though it has no premisses—using either the rule of Conditional Proof or the rule of Indirect Proof. Any tautology can be established by the method of deduction, although this will not be proved until the end of Chapter 7.

EXERCISES

I. Use the method of conditional proof to verify that the following are tautologies:

★1. $P \supset (Q \supset P)$
 2. $[P \supset (Q \supset R)] \supset [(P \supset Q) \supset (P \supset R)]$
 3. $[P \supset (Q \supset R)] \supset [Q \supset (P \supset R)]$
 4. $(P \supset Q) \supset (\sim Q \supset \sim P)$
★5. $\sim\sim P \supset P$
 6. $P \supset \sim\sim P$
 7. $(A \supset B) \supset [(B \supset C) \supset (A \supset C)]$
 8. $[(A \supset B) \cdot (A \supset C)] \supset [A \supset (B \vee C)]$
 9. $[(A \supset B) \cdot (A \supset C)] \supset [A \supset (B \cdot C)]$
★10. $(A \supset B) \supset [A \supset (A \cdot B)]$
 11. $(A \supset B) \supset [(\sim A \supset B) \supset B]$
 12. $(A \supset B) \supset [(A \cdot C) \supset (B \cdot C)]$
 13. $[(A \supset B) \supset B] \supset (A \vee B)$
 14. $(B \supset C) \supset [(A \vee B) \supset (C \vee A)]$
★15. $[A \supset (B \cdot C)] \supset \{[B \supset (D \cdot E)] \supset (A \supset D)\}$
 16. $[(A \vee B) \supset C] \supset \{[(C \vee D) \supset E] \supset (A \supset E)\}$
 17. $[(A \supset B) \supset A] \supset A$
 18. $P \supset (P \cdot P)$
 19. $(P \cdot Q) \supset P$
★20. $(P \supset Q) \supset [\sim(Q \cdot R) \supset \sim(R \cdot P)]$

II. Use the method of indirect proof to verify that the following are tautologies:

★1. $(A \supset B) \vee (A \supset \sim B)$
 2. $(A \supset B) \vee (\sim A \supset B)$
 3. $(A \supset B) \vee (B \supset A)$

4. $(A \supset B) \lor (B \supset C)$

*5. $(A \supset B) \lor (\sim A \supset C)$

6. $A \lor (A \supset B)$

7. $P \equiv \sim\sim P$

8. $A \equiv [A \cdot (A \lor B)]$

9. $A \equiv [A \lor (A \cdot B)]$

*10. $\sim[(A \supset \sim A) \cdot (\sim A \supset A)]$

3.7 SHORTER TRUTH TABLE TECHNIQUE—*REDUCTIO AD ABSURDUM* METHOD

There is still another method of testing the validity of arguments, and of classifying statements as tautologous, contradictory, or contingent. In the preceding section it was pointed out that an argument is invalid if and only if it is possible to assign truth values to its component simple statements in such a way as to make all its premisses true and its conclusion false. It is impossible to make such truth value assignments in the case of a valid argument. Hence to prove the validity of an argument it suffices to prove that no such truth values can be assigned. We do so by showing that its premisses can be made true and its conclusion false only by assigning truth values *inconsistently*, so that some component statement is assigned both a **T** and an **F**. In other words, if the truth value **T** is assigned to each premiss of a valid argument and the truth value **F** is assigned to its conclusion, this will necessitate assigning *both* **T** and **F** to some component statement, which, is, of course, a contradiction.

Thus to prove the validity of the argument

$$(A \lor B) \supset (C \cdot D)$$
$$(D \lor E) \supset F$$
$$\therefore A \supset F$$

we assign **T** to each premiss and **F** to the conclusion. Assigning **F** to the conclusion requires that **T** be assigned to A and **F** be assigned to F. Since **T** is assigned to A, the antecedent of the first premiss is true, and since the premiss has been assigned **T**, its consequent must be true also, so **T** must be assigned to both C and D. Since **T** is assigned to D, the antecedent of the second premiss is true, and since the premiss has been assigned **T**, its consequent must be true also, so **T** must be assigned to *F*. But we have already been forced to assign **F** to *F* to make the conclusion false. Hence the argument is invalid only if the statement *F* is both true and false, which is impossible. This method of proving the validity of an argument is a version of the *reductio ad absurdum* technique, which uses truth value assignments rather than Rules of Inference.

It is easy to extend the use of this method to the classification of statements (and statement forms). Thus to certify that Peirce's Law $[(p \supset q) \supset p] \supset p$ is a tautology, we assign it the truth value **F**, which requires us to assign **T** to its antecedent $[(p \supset q) \supset p]$ and **F** to its consequent *p*. For the conditional $[(p \supset q) \supset p]$ to be true while *its* consequent *p* is false, its antecedent $(p \supset q)$ must be assigned the truth value **F** also. But for the conditional $p \supset q$ to be false, its antecedent *p* must be assigned **T** and its consequent *q* assigned **F**. However, we were previously forced to assign **F** to *p* so assuming Peirce's Law false leads to a contradiction, which proves it a tautology.

If it *is* possible to assign truth values consistently to its components on the assumption that it is false, then the expression in question is not a tautology, but must be either contradictory or contingent. In such a case we attempt to assign truth values to make it true. If this attempt leads to a contradiction the expression cannot possibly be true and must be a contradiction. But if truth values can be assigned to make it true and (other) truth values assigned to make it false, then it is neither a tautology nor a contradiction, but is contingent.

The *reductio ad absurdum* method of assigning truth values is by far the quickest and easiest method of testing arguments and classifying statements. It is, however, more readily applied in some cases than in others. If **F** is assigned to a disjunction, **F** must be assigned to both disjuncts, and where **T** is assigned to a conjunction, **T** must be assigned to both conjuncts. Here the sequence of assignments is forced. But where **T** is assigned to a disjunction or **F** to a conjunction, that assignment by itself does not determine *which* disjunct is true or *which* conjunct is false. Here we should have to experiment and make various 'trial assignments', which will tend to diminish the advantage of the method for such cases. Despite these complications, however, in the vast majority of cases the *reductio ad absurdum* method is superior to any other method known.

EXERCISES

1. Use the *reductio ad absurdum* method of assigning truth values to decide the validity or invaliditv of the arguments and argument forms in Exercises I and II on pages 25–27.
2. Use the *reductio ad absurdum* method of assigning truth values to establish that the statements in Exercises I and II on pages 67–68 are tautologies.
3. Use the *reductio ad absurdum* method of assigning truth values to classify the statement forms in Exercise I on page 32 as tautologous, contradictory, or contingent.

4

PROPOSITIONAL
FUNCTIONS
AND
QUANTIFIERS

4.1 SINGULAR PROPOSITIONS AND GENERAL PROPOSITIONS

The logical techniques developed thus far apply only to arguments whose validity depends upon the way in which simple statements are truth-functionally combined into compound statements. Those techniques cannot be applied to such arguments as the following:

All humans are mortal.
Socrates is human.
Therefore Socrates is mortal.

The validity of such an argument depends upon the inner logical structure of the noncompound statements it contains. To appraise such arguments we must develop methods for analyzing noncompound statements and symbolizing their inner structures.

The second premiss of the preceding argument is a *singular proposition;*[1]

---

[1] In the following chapters we shall follow tradition in using the term 'proposition' as synonymous with 'statement'. It should be observed that this usage deviates from that presented in Chapter 1.

it asserts that the individual Socrates has the property of being human. We call 'Socrates' the *subject* term and 'human' the *predicate* term. Any (affirmative) singular proposition asserts that the individual referred to by its subject term has the property designated by its predicate term. We regard as individuals not only persons, but any *things*, such as animals, cities, nations, planets, or stars, of which properties can significantly be predicated. Properties can be designated not only by adjectives, but by nouns or even verbs: thus 'Helen is a gossip' and 'Helen gossips' have the same meaning, which can also be expressed as 'Helen is gossipy'.

In symbolizing singular propositions we use the small letters '*a*' through '*w*' to denote individuals, ordinarily using the first letter of an individual's name to denote that individual. Because these symbols denote individuals we call them 'individual constants'. To designate properties we use capital letters, being guided by the same principle in their selection. Thus in the context of the preceding argument we denote Socrates by the small letter '*s*' and symbolize the properties *human* and *mortal* by the capital letters '*H*' and '*M*'. To express a singular proposition in our symbolism we write the symbol for its predicate term to the left of the symbol for its subject term. Thus we symbolize 'Socrates is human' as '*Hs*' and 'Socrates is mortal' as '*Ms*'.[2]

Examining the symbolic formulations of singular propositions having the same predicate term, we observe them to have a common pattern. The symbolic formulations of the singular propositions 'Aristotle is human', 'Boston is human', 'California is human', 'Descartes is human', . . . , which are '*Ha*', '*Hb*', '*Hc*', '*Hd*', . . . , each consists of the property symbol '*H*' followed by an individual constant. We use the expression '*Hx*' to symbolize the pattern common to all singular propositions asserting individuals to have the property *human*. The small letter '*x*'—called an 'individual variable'—is a mere *place marker* that serves to indicate where an individual constant can be written to produce a singular proposition. The singular propositions '*Ha*', '*Hb*', '*Hc*', '*Hd*', . . . are either true or false; but '*Hx*' is neither

---

[2] Some logicians enclose the individual constant in parentheses, symbolizing 'Socrates is human' as '*H(s)*', but we shall not follow that practice here.

true nor false, not being a proposition. Such expressions as 'Hx' are called 'propositional functions'. These are defined to be expressions which contain individual variables and become propositions when their individual variables are replaced by individual constants.[3] Any singular proposition can be regarded as a *substitution instance* of the propositional function from which it results by the substitution of an individual constant for the individual variable in the propositional function. The process of obtaining a proposition from a propositional function by substituting a constant for a variable is called 'instantiation'. The negative singular propositions 'Aristotle is not human' and 'Boston is not human', symbolized as '$\sim Ha$' and '$\sim Hb$', result by *instantiation* from the propositional function '$\sim Hx$', of which they are substitution instances. Thus we see that symbols other than property symbols and individual variables can occur in propositional functions.

General propositions such as 'Everything is mortal' and 'Something is mortal' differ from singular propositions in not containing the names of any individuals. However, they also can be regarded as resulting from propositional functions, not by instantiation, but by the process called 'generalization' or 'quantification'. The first example, 'Everything is mortal', can alternatively be expressed as

Given any thing in the universe, it is mortal.

Here the relative pronoun 'it' refers back to the indefinite word 'thing' which precedes it in the statement. We can use the individual variable 'x' in place of the pronoun 'it' and its indefinite antecedent 'thing' to paraphrase the first general proposition as

Given any x in the universe, x is mortal.

Then we can use the notation already introduced to rewrite it as

Given any x in the universe, Mx.

The phrase 'Given any x in the universe' is called a 'universal quantifier', and is symbolized as '(x)'. Using this new symbol we can com-

---

[3] Some writers have defined 'propositional functions' to be the *meanings* of such expressions; but here we define them to be the expressions themselves.

pletely symbolize our first general proposition as

$$(x)Mx$$

We can similarly paraphrase the second general proposition, 'Something is mortal', successively as

There exists at least one thing which is mortal.
There exists at least one thing such that it is mortal.
There exists at least one x such that x is mortal.

and as

There exists at least one x such that Mx.

The phrase 'There exists at least one x such that' is called an 'existential quantifier' and is symbolized as '$(\exists x)$'. Using the new symbol we can completely symbolize our second general proposition as

$$(\exists x)Mx$$

A general proposition is formed from a propositional function by placing either a universal or an existential quantifier before it. It is obvious that the universal quantification of a propositional function is true if and only if all of its substitution instances are true, and that the existential quantification of a propositional function is true if and only if it has at least one true substitution instance. If we grant that there is at least one individual in the universe then every propositional function has at least one substitution instance (true or false). Under this assumption, if the universal quantification of a propositional function is true, then its existential quantification must be true also.

A further relationship between universal and existential quantification can be shown by considering two additional general propositions, 'Something is not mortal' and 'Nothing is mortal', which are the respective negations of the first two general propositions considered. 'Something is not mortal' is symbolized as '$(\exists x)\sim Mx$' and 'Nothing is mortal' is symbolized as '$(x)\sim Mx$'. These show that the negation of the universal (existential) quantification of a propositional function is logically equivalent to the existential (universal) quantification of the new propositional function which results from placing a negation symbol in front of the first propositional function. Where we use the Greek letter *phi* to represent any property symbol whatever, the general connections between universal and existential quantification can be described in terms of the following square array:

Assuming the existence of at least one individual: we can say that the two top propositions are *contraries*, i.e., they might both be false but cannot both be true; the two bottom propositions are *subcontraries*, i.e., they can both be true but cannot both be false; propositions which are at opposite ends of the diagonals are *contradictories*, of which one must be true and the other false; and finally, on each side, the truth of the lower proposition is implied by the truth of the proposition which is directly above it.

Traditional logic emphasized four types of subject-predicate propositions illustrated by the following:

All humans are mortal.
No humans are mortal.
Some humans are mortal.
Some humans are not mortal.

These were classified as 'universal affirmative', 'universal negative', 'particular affirmative', and 'particular negative', respectively, and their types abbreviated as '*A*', '*E*', '*I*', '*O*', again respectively. (The letter names have been presumed to come from the Latin '*AffIrmo*' and '*nEgO*', meaning *I affirm* and *I deny*.) These four special forms of subject-predicate propositions are easily symbolized by means of propositional functions and quantifiers.[4] The first of them, the *A* proposition, can successively be paraphrased as

---

[4] An alternative method of symbolizing them is presented in Appendix B.

Given any thing in the universe, if it is human then it is mortal.
Given any x in the universe, if x is human then x is mortal.
Given any x in the universe, x is human $\supset$ x is mortal.

and finally symbolized as

$$(x)[Hx \supset Mx]$$

Our symbolic formulation of the **A** proposition is the universal quantification of the complex propositional function '$Hx \supset Mx$', which has as its substitution instances not singular propositions but conditionals whose antecedents and consequents are singular propositions having the same subject terms. Among the substitution instances of the propositional function '$Hx \supset Mx$' are the conditionals '$Ha \supset Ma$', '$Hb \supset Mb$', '$Hc \supset Mc$', and so on. In symbolizing an **A** proposition the square brackets serve as punctuation marks to indicate that the universal quantifier '(x)' *applies to* or *has within its scope* the whole of the complex propositional function '$Hx \supset Mx$'. The notion of the *scope of a quantifier* is very important, for differences in scope correspond to differences in meaning. The expression '$(x)[Hx \supset Mx]$' is a proposition which asserts that all substitution instances of the propositional function '$Hx \supset Mx$' are true. On the other hand, the expression '$(x)Hx \supset Mx$' is a propositional function whose substitution instances are '$(x)Hx \supset Ma$', '$(x)Hx \supset Mb$', '$(x)Hx \supset Mc$', etc.

The **E** proposition 'No humans are mortals' may similarly be paraphrased successively as

Given anything in the universe, if it is human then it is not mortal.
Given any x in the universe, if x is human then x is not mortal.
Given any x in the universe, x is human $\supset$ x is not mortal.

and then symbolized as

$$(x)[Hx \supset \sim Mx]$$

Similarly, the **I** proposition 'Some humans are mortals', may be paraphrased as

There exists at least one thing which is human and mortal.
There exists at least one thing such that it is human and it is mortal.
There exists at least one x such that x is human and x is mortal.
There exists at least one x such that x is human$\cdot x$ is mortal.

and completely symbolized as

$$(\exists x)[Hx \cdot Mx]$$

Finally, the **O** proposition 'Some humans are not mortal', becomes

> There exists at least one thing which is human but not mortal.
> There exists at least one thing such that it is human and it is not mortal.
> There exists at least one x such that x is human and x is not mortal.

and is completely symbolized as

$$(\exists x)[Hx \cdot {\sim} Mx]$$

Where the Greek letters *phi* and *psi* are used to represent any property symbols whatever, the four general subject-predicate propositions of traditional logic may be represented in a square array as

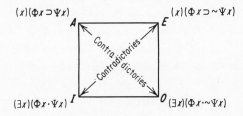

Of these, the **A** and the **O** are contradictories, and the **E** and the **I** are contradictories also. But none of the other relationships discussed in connection with the square array on page 75 hold for the traditional **A**, **E**, **I**, and **O** propositions, even where we assume that there exists at least one individual in the universe. Where 'Φx' is a propositional function that has no true substitution instances, then regardless of what property is symbolized by 'Ψ', the propositional functions '$\Phi x \supset \Psi x$' and '$\Phi x \supset {\sim}\Psi x$' have only true substitution instances, for all their substitution instances are conditional statements with false antecedents. In such cases the **A** and **E** propositions that are the universal quantifications of these complex propositional functions are true, so **A** and **E** propositions are not contraries. Again, where 'Φx' is a propositional function that has no true substitution instances, then regardless of what

'Ψx' might be, the propositional functions '$\Phi x \cdot \Psi x$' and '$\Phi x \cdot \sim \Psi x$' have only false substitution instances, for their substitution instances are conjunctions whose first conjuncts are false. In such cases the I and O propositions that are the existential quantifications of these complex propositional functions are false, so I and O propositions are not sub-contraries. In all such cases, then, since the A and E propositions are true and the I and O propositions are false, the truth of a universal does *not* imply the truth of the corresponding particular; no implication relation holds between them.

If we make the assumption that there exists at least one individual in the universe, then '$(x)[\Phi x \supset \Psi x]$' does imply '$(\exists x)[\Phi x \supset \Psi x]$'. But the latter is *not* an I proposition. An I proposition of the form 'Some Φ's are Ψ's' is symbolized as '$(\exists x)[\Phi x \cdot \Psi x]$', which asserts that there is at least one thing having both the property Φ and the property Ψ. But the proposition '$(\exists x)[\Phi x \supset \Psi x]$' asserts only that there is at least one object which either has the property Ψ or does not have the property Φ, which is a very different and much weaker assertion.

The four traditional subject-predicate forms A, E, I, and O are not the only forms of general propositions. There are others that involve the quantification of more complicated propositional functions. Thus the general proposition 'All members are either parents or teachers', which does *not* mean the same as 'All members are parents or all members are teachers', is symbolized as '$(x)[Mx \supset (Px \lor Tx)]$'. And the general proposition 'Some Senators are either disloyal or mis-guided', is symbolized as '$(\exists x)[Sx \cdot (Dx \lor Mx)]$'. It should be observed that such a statement as 'Apples and bananas are nourishing' can be symbolized either as the conjunction of two A propositions, '$\{(x)[Ax \supset Nx]\} \cdot \{(x)[Bx \supset Nx]\}$', or as a single noncompound general proposi-tion, '$(x)[(Ax \lor Bx) \supset Nx]$'. But it should *not* be symbolized as '$(x)[(Ax \cdot Bx) \supset Nx]$', for to say that apples and bananas are nourish-ing is to say that anything is nourishing which is *either* an apple *or* a banana, *not* to say that anything is nourishing which is *both* an apple and a banana (whatever that might be). It must be emphasized that there are no mechanical rules for translating statements from English into our logical notation. In every case one must *understand the meaning* of the English sentence, and then *re-express* that meaning in terms of propositional functions and quantifiers.

EXERCISES

Symbolize each of the following statements using propositional functions and quantifiers, in each case using the suggested notation:

1. Snakes are reptiles. (*Sx*: *x* is a snake. *Rx*: *x* is a reptile.)
2. Snakes are not all poisonous. (*Sx*: *x* is a snake. *Px*: *x* is poisonous.)
3. Children are present. (*Cx*: *x* is a child. *Px*: *x* is present.)
4. Executives all have secretaries. (*Ex*: *x* is an executive. *Sx*: *x* has a secretary.)
★5. Only executives have secretaries. (*Ex*: *x* is an executive. *Sx*: *x* has a secretary.)
6. Only property owners may vote in special municipal elections. (*Px*: *x* is a property owner. *Vx*: *x* may vote in special municipal elections.)
7. Employees may use only the service elevator. (*Ux*: *x* is an elevator that employees may use. *Sx*: *x* is a service elevator.)
8. Only employees may use the service elevator. (*Ex*: *x* is an employee. *Ux*: *x* may use the service elevator.)
9. All that glitters is not gold. (*Gx*: *x* glitters. *Ax*: *x* is gold.)
★10. None but the brave deserve the fair. (*Bx*: *x* is brave. *Dx*: *x* deserves the fair.)
11. Not every visitor stayed for dinner. (*Vx*: *x* is a visitor. *Sx*: *x* stayed for dinner.)
12. Not any visitor stayed for dinner. (*Vx*: *x* is a visitor. *Sx*: *x* stayed for dinner.)
13. Nothing in the house escaped destruction. (*Hx*: *x* was in the house. *Ex*: *x* escaped destruction.)
14. Some students are both intelligent and hard workers. (*Sx*: *x* is a student. *Ix*: *x* is intelligent. *Hx*: *x* is a hard worker.)
★15. No coat is waterproof unless it has been specially treated. (*Cx*: *x* is a coat. *Wx*: *x* is waterproof. *Sx*: *x* has been specially treated.)
16. Some medicines are dangerous only if taken in excessive amounts. (*Mx*: *x* is a medicine. *Dx*: *x* is dangerous. *Ex*: *x* is taken in excessive amounts.)
17. All fruits and vegetables are wholesome and nourishing. (*Fx*: *x* is a fruit. *Vx*: *x* is a vegetable. *Wx*: *x* is wholesome. *Nx*: *x* is nourishing.)
18. Everything enjoyable is either immoral, illegal, or fattening. (*Ex*: *x* is enjoyable. *Mx*: *x* is moral. *Lx*: *x* is legal. *Fx*: *x* is fattening.)
19. A professor is a good lecturer if and only if he is both well informed and entertaining. (*Px*: *x* is a professor. *Gx*: *x* is a good lecturer. *Wx*: *x* is well informed. *Ex*: *x* is entertaining.)
★20. Only policemen and firemen are both indispensable and underpaid. (*Px*: *x* is a policeman. *Fx*: *x* is a fireman. *Ix*: *x* is indispensable. *Ux*: *x* is underpaid.)

21. Not every actor is talented who is famous. (*Ax: x* is an actor. *Tx: x* is talented. *Fx: x* is famous.)

22. Any girl is attractive if she is neat and well groomed. (*Gx: x* is a girl. *Ax: x* is attractive. *Nx: x* is neat. *Wx: x* is well groomed.)

23. It is not true that every watch will keep good time if and only if it is wound regularly and not abused. (*Wx: x* is a watch. *Kx: x* keeps good time. *Rx: x* is wound regularly. *Ax: x* is abused.)

24. Not every person who talks a great deal has a great deal to say. (*Px: x* is a person. *Tx: x* talks a great deal. *Hx: x* has a great deal to say.)

★25. No automobile that is over ten years old will be repaired if it is severely damaged. (*Ax: x* is an automobile. *Ox: x* is over ten years old. *Rx: x* will be repaired. *Dx: x* is severely damaged.)

In symbolizing the following, use the abbreviations: *Hx: x* is a horse. *Gx: x* is gentle. *Tx: x* has been well trained.

26. Some horses are gentle and have been well trained.

27. Some horses are gentle only if they have been well trained.

28. Some horses are gentle if they have been well trained.

★29. Any horse is gentle that has been well trained.

★30. Any horse that is gentle has been well trained.

31. No horse is gentle unless it has been well trained.

32. Any horse is gentle if it has been well trained.

33. Any horse has been well trained if it is gentle.

34. Any horse is gentle if and only if it has been well trained.

35. Gentle horses have all been well trained.

4.2   PROVING VALIDITY: PRELIMINARY QUANTIFICATION RULES

To construct formal proofs of validity for arguments symbolized by means of quantifiers and propositional functions we must augment our list of Rules of Inference. We shall add four rules governing quantification, offering an oversimplified preliminary statement of them in this section, and giving a more adequate formulation in Section 4.5.

1. Universal Instantiation (Preliminary Version). Because the universal quantification of a propositional function is true if and only if all substitution instances of that propositional function are true, we can add to our list of Rules of Inference the principle that any substitution instance of a propositional function can validly be inferred from its universal quantification. We can express this rule symbolically as

$$\frac{(x)\Phi x}{\therefore \ \Phi\nu} \text{ (where } \nu \text{ is any individual symbol)}$$

Since this rule permits substitution instances to be inferred from universal quantifications, we refer to it as the 'principle of Universal Instantiation', and abbreviate it as '**UI**'.[5] The addition of **UI** permits us to give a formal proof of validity for the argument: 'All humans are mortal; Socrates is human; therefore Socrates is mortal'.

1. $(x)[Hx \supset Mx]$
2. Hs $/\therefore Ms$
3. $Hs \supset Ms$ 1, **UI**
4. Ms 3, 2, M.P.

2. Universal Generalization (Preliminary Version). We can explain our next rule by analogy with fairly standard mathematical practice. A geometer may begin a proof by saying, 'Let ABC be any arbitrarily selected triangle'. Then he may go on to prove that the triangle ABC has some specified property, and concludes that *all* triangles have that property. Now what justifies his final conclusion? Why does it follow from triangle ABC's having a specified property that *all* triangles do? The answer is that if no assumption other than its triangularity is made about ABC, then the expression 'ABC' can be taken as denoting any triangle you please. And if the argument has established that *any* triangle must have the property in question, then it follows that *all* triangles do. We now introduce a notation analogous to that of the geometer in his reference to 'any arbitrarily selected triangle'. The hitherto unused small letter 'y' will be used to denote *any arbitrarily selected individual*. In this usage the expression 'Φy' is a substitution instance of the propositional function 'Φx', and it asserts that *any arbitrarily selected individual* has the property Φ. Clearly 'Φy' follows validly from '$(x)\Phi x$' by **UI**, since what is true of all individuals

---

[5] This rule and the three which follow are variants of rules for 'natural deduction' which were devised independently by Gerhard Gentzen and Stanislaw Jaśkowski in 1934.

is true of any arbitrarily selected individual. The inference is equally valid in the other direction, since what is true of *any arbitrarily selected individual* must be true of *all* individuals. We augment our list of Rules of Inference further by adding the principle that the universal quantification of a propositional function can validly be inferred from its substitution instance with respect to the symbol '*y*'. Since this rule permits the inference of general propositions that are universal quantifications, we refer to it as the 'principle of Universal Generalization', and abbreviate it as '**UG**'. Our symbolic expression for this second quantification rule is

$$\frac{\Phi y}{\therefore \ (x)\Phi x} \text{ (where '}y\text{' denotes any arbitrarily selected individual)}$$

We can use the new notation and the additional rule **UG** to construct a formal proof of validity for the argument: 'No mortals are perfect; all humans are mortal; therefore no humans are perfect'.

1. $(x)[Mx \supset \sim Px]$
2. $(x)[Hx \supset Mx]$ $/\therefore \ (x)[Hx \supset \sim Px]$
3. $Hy \supset My$ 2, **UI**
4. $My \supset \sim Py$ 1, **UI**
5. $Hy \supset \sim Py$ 3, 4, H.S.
6. $(x)[Hx \supset \sim Px]$ 5, **UG**

3. Existential Generalization (Preliminary Version). Because the existential quantification of a propositional function is true if and only if that propositional function has at least one true substitution instance, we can add to our list of Rules of Inference the principle that the existential quantification of a propositional function can validly be inferred from any substitution instance of that propositional function. This rule permits the inference of general propositions which are existentially quantified, so we call it the 'principle of Existential Generalization' and abbreviate it as '**EG**'. Its symbolic formulation is

$$\frac{\Phi \nu}{\therefore \ (\exists x)\Phi x} \text{ (where } \nu \text{ is any individual symbol)}$$

4. Existential Instantiation (Preliminary Version). One further quantification rule is required. The existential quantification of a propositional function asserts that there exists at least one individual the substitution of whose name for the variable '*x*' in that propositional function will yield a true substitution instance of it. Of course we may not know anything else about that individual. But we can take any individual constant, say '*w*', which has had no prior occurrence in that context and use it to denote the individual, or one of the individuals, whose existence has been asserted by the existential quantification. Knowing that there is such an individual, and having agreed to denote it by '*w*', we can infer from the existential quantification of a propositional function the substitution instance of that propositional function with respect to the individual symbol '*w*'. We add as our final quantification rule the principle that from the existential quantification of a propositional function we may validly infer the truth of its substitution instance with respect to an individual constant which has no prior occurrence in that context. The new rule may be written as

$$\frac{(\exists x)\Phi x}{\therefore \Phi \nu}$$ (where ν is an individual constant having no prior occurrence

    in the context)

It is referred to as the 'principle of Existential Instantiation' and abbreviated as '**EI**'.

We make use of the last two quantification rules in constructing a formal proof of validity for the argument: 'All dogs are carnivorous; some animals are dogs; therefore some animals are carnivorous'.

1. $(x)[Dx \supset Cx]$
2. $(\exists x)[Ax \cdot Dx]$ $/ \therefore (\exists x)[Ax \cdot Cx]$
3. $Aw \cdot Dw$ 2, **EI**
4. $Dw \supset Cw$ 1, **UI**
5. $Dw \cdot Aw$ 3, Com.
6. Dw 5, Simp.
7. Cw 4, 6, M.P.
8. Aw 3, Simp.
9. $Aw \cdot Cw$ 8, 7, Conj.
10. $(\exists x)[Ax \cdot Cx]$ 9, **EG**

We can show the need for the indicated restriction on the use of **EI** by considering the obviously invalid argument: 'Some cats are animals; some dogs are animals; therefore some cats are dogs'. If we ignored the restriction on **EI** that the substitution instance inferred by it can contain only an individual constant which had no prior occurrence in the context, we might be led to construct the following 'proof':

1. $(\exists x)[Cx \cdot Ax]$
2. $(\exists x)[Dx \cdot Ax]$ / $\therefore$ $(\exists x)[Cx \cdot Dx]$
3. $Cw \cdot Aw$ 1, **EI**
4. $Dw \cdot Aw$ 2, **EI** (wrong)
5. Cw 3, Simp.
6. Dw 4, Simp.
7. $Cw \cdot Dw$ 5, 6, Conj.
8. $(\exists x)[Cx \cdot Dx]$ 7, **EG**

The mistake here occurs at line 4. The second premiss assures us that there is at least one thing that is both a dog and an animal. But we are not free to use the symbol 'w' to denote that thing because 'w' has already been used to denote one of the things asserted by the first premiss to be both a cat and an animal. To avoid errors of this sort we must obey the indicated restriction in using **EI**. It should be clear that whenever we use both **EI** and **UI** in a proof to instantiate with respect to the same individual constant, we must use **EI** first.

5. Strengthened Rule of Conditional Proof.   In the preceding chapter the method of Conditional Proof was applied only to arguments whose conclusions were conditional in form. But now we must consider arguments whose conclusions are noncompound general propositions. To deal with them we shall strengthen our rule of Conditional Proof and thereby give it wider applicability.

To formulate our strengthened rule of Conditional Proof it is useful to adopt a new method of writing out proofs that make use of the Conditional Method. As explained in the preceding chapter, we used the method of Conditional Proof to establish the validity of an argument having a conditional as conclusion by adding the antecedent of that conditional to the argument's premisses as an assumption, and then deducing the conditional's consequent. The old notation involved the use of an additional slant line and an extra *therefore* sign, as in proving the validity of the argument

$$A \supset B$$
$$\therefore A \supset (A \cdot B)$$

by the following four line proof (as explained in Section 3.4):

1. $A \supset B$ / $\therefore$ $A \supset (A \cdot B)$
2. A / $\therefore$ $A \cdot B$ (C.P.)
3. B 1, 2, M.P.
4. $A \cdot B$ 2, 3, Conj.

A Conditional Proof of validity for that same argument is set down in our new notation as the following sequence of five lines:

1. $A \supset B$ / $\therefore$ $A \supset (A \cdot B)$
2. A assumption
3. B 1, 2, M.P.
4. $A \cdot B$ 2, 3, Conj.
5. $A \supset (A \cdot B)$ 2–4, C.P.

Here the fifth line is inferred not from any one or two of the preceding lines but from the *sequence* of lines 2, 3, 4, which constitutes a valid deduction of line 4 from lines 1 and 2. In line 5 we infer the validity of the argument

$$A \supset B$$
$$\therefore A \supset (A \cdot B)$$

from the demonstrated validity of the argument

$$A \supset B$$
$$A$$
$$\therefore A \cdot B$$

That inference is 'justified' by noting the sequence of lines to which appeal is made, and using the letters 'C.P.' to show that the principle of Conditional Proof is being used.

In the second of the preceding proofs, line 2, the assumption, has lines 3 and 4 dependent upon it. Line 5, however, is *not* dependent upon line 2, but only upon line 1. Line 5 is therefore *outside* or *beyond the scope* of the assumption made as line 2. When an assumption is made in a Conditional Proof of validity, its 'scope' is always *limited*, never extending all the way to the last line of the demonstration.

A notation is now introduced which is very helpful in keeping track of assumptions and their *scopes*. A bent arrow is used for this purpose, with its head pointing at the assumption from the left, its shaft bent down to run along all lines within the scope of the assumption, and then bent inward to mark the end of the scope of that assumption. The scope of the assumption in the preceding proof is indicated thus:

$$1.\ A \supset B \quad /\therefore\ A \supset (A \cdot B)$$
$$2.\ A \qquad\qquad \text{assumption}$$
$$3.\ B \qquad\qquad 1, 2, \text{M.P.}$$
$$4.\ A \cdot B \qquad\quad\ 2, 3, \text{Conj.}$$
$$5.\ A \supset (A \cdot B) \quad 2\text{–}4, \text{C.P.}$$

It should be observed that only a line inferred by the principle of Conditional Proof ends the scope of an assumption, and that every use of the rule of Conditional Proof serves to end the scope of an assumption. When the scope of an assumption has been ended, the assumption is said to have been *discharged*, and no subsequent line can be justified by reference to it or to any line lying between it and the line inferred by the rule of Conditional Proof that discharges it. Only lines lying between an assumption of limited scope and the line that discharges it can be justified by reference to that assumption. After one assumption of limited scope has been discharged, another such assumption may be made and then discharged. Or a second assumption of limited scope may be written within the scope of a first, but when it is, it must be discharged before the first is discharged. Scopes of different assumptions may follow each other with no overlap, or one scope may be contained entirely within another. But two scopes may not partially overlap: that is strictly forbidden.

If the scope of an assumption does *not* extend all the way to the end of a proof, then the final line of the proof does not *depend* on that assumption, but has been proved to follow from the original premisses alone. Hence we need not restrict ourselves to using as assumptions only the antecedents of conditional conclusions. *Any* proposition can be taken as an assumption of limited scope, for the final line that is the conclusion will always be beyond its scope and independent of it.

A more complex demonstration that involves making *two* assumptions is the following (incidentally, when our bent arrow notation is used, the word 'assumption' need not be written, since each assumption is sufficiently identified as such by the arrowhead on its left):

```
  1. (A v B) ⊃ [(C v D) ⊃ E]   /∴ A ⊃ [(C·D) ⊃ E]
→2. A
  3. A v B                      2, Add.
  4. (C v D) ⊃ E                1, 3, M.P.
→5. C·D
  6. C                          5, Simp.
  7. C v D                      6, Add.
  8. E                          4, 7, M.P.
  9. (C·D) ⊃ E                  5–8, C.P.
 10. A ⊃ [(C·D) ⊃ E]            2–9, C.P.
```

In this proof, lines 2 through 9 lie within the scope of the first assumption, while lines 5, 6, 7, and 8 lie within the scope of the second assumption. From these examples it is clear that the scope of an assumption α in a proof consists of all lines α through φ where the line following φ is of the form $\alpha \supset \varphi$ and is inferred by C.P. from that sequence of lines. In the preceding proof, the second assumption lies within the scope of the first because it lies between the first assumption and line 10 which is inferred by C.P. from the sequence of lines 2 through 9.

When we use this new method of writing out a Conditional Proof of validity the scope of every original premiss extends all the way to the end of the proof. The original premisses may be supplemented by additional assumptions provided that the latter's scopes are limited and do not extend to the end of the proof. Each line of a formal proof of validity must be either a premiss, or an assumption of limited scope, or must follow validly from one or two preceding lines by a Rule of Inference, or must follow from a *sequence* of preceding lines by the principle of Conditional Proof.

It should be remarked that the strengthened principle of Conditional Proof includes the method of Indirect Proof as a special case. Since any assumption of limited scope may be made in a Conditional Proof of validity, we can take as our assumption the negation of the argument's conclusion. Once a contradiction is obtained, we can *continue on through* the contradiction to obtain the desired conclusion by Addition and the Disjunctive Syllogism.[6] Once that is done, we can use the rule of Conditional Proof to end the scope of that assumption and obtain a conditional whose consequent is the argument's conclusion and whose antecedent is the negation of that conclusion. And from such a conditional the argument's conclusion will follow by Implication, Double Negation, and Tautology.

Any assumption of limited scope may be made in a Conditional Proof of validity, and in particular we are free to make an assumption of the form 'Φy'. Thus the argument 'All freshmen and sophomores are invited and will be welcome; therefore all freshmen are invited' is proved valid by the following Conditional Proof:

1. $(x)[(Fx \lor Sx) \supset (Ix \cdot Wx)]$ $/ \therefore (x)[Fx \supset Ix]$
2. Fy
3. $(Fy \lor Sy) \supset (Iy \cdot Wy)$ 1, **UI**
4. $Fy \lor Sy$ 2, Add.
5. $Iy \cdot Wy$ 3, 4, M.P.
6. Iy 5, Simp.
7. $Fy \supset Iy$ 2–6, C.P.
8. $(x)[Fx \supset Ix]$ 7, **UG**

More than one assumption of limited scope can be made in proving the validity of arguments involving quantifiers, as in the following Conditional Proof:

[6] As explained on page 63.

1. $(x)[(Ax \lor Bx) \supset (Cx \cdot Dx)]$
2. $(x)\{(Cx \lor Ex) \supset [(Fx \lor Gx) \supset Hx\}$ $/ \therefore (x)[Ax \supset (Fx \supset Hx)]$
3. $(Ay \lor By) \supset (Cy \cdot Dy)$ 1, **UI**
4. $(Cy \lor Ey) \supset [(Fy \lor Gy) \supset Hy]$ 2, **UI**
5. Ay
6. $Ay \lor By$ 5, Add.
7. $Cy \cdot Dy$ 3, 6, M.P.
8. Cy 7, Simp.
9. $Cy \lor Ey$ 8, Add.
10. $(Fy \lor Gy) \supset Hy$ 4, 9, M.P.
11. Fy
12. $Fy \lor Gy$ 11, Add.
13. Hy 10, 12, M.P.
14. $Fy \supset Hy$ 11–13, C.P.
15. $Ay \supset (Fy \supset Hy)$ 5–14, C.P.
16. $(x)[Ax \supset (Fx \supset Hx)]$ 15, **UG**

EXERCISES

Construct formal proofs of validity for the following arguments, using the rule of Conditional Proof wherever you wish:

★1. All athletes are brawny. Charles is not brawny. Therefore Charles is not an athlete. (Ax, Bx, c)

2. No contractors are dependable. Some contractors are engineers. Therefore some engineers are not dependable. (Cx, Dx, Ex)

3. All fiddlers are gay. Some hunters are not gay. Therefore some hunters are not fiddlers. (Fx, Gx, Hx)

4. No judges are idiots. Kanter is an idiot. Therefore Kanter is not a judge. (Jx, Ix, k)

★5. All liars are mendacious. Some liars are newspapermen. Therefore some newspapermen are mendacious. (Lx, Mx, Nx)

6. No osteopaths are pediatricians. Some quacks are pediatricians. Therefore some quacks are not osteopaths. (Ox, Px, Qx)

7. Only salesmen are retailers. Not all retailers are travelers. Therefore some salesmen are not travelers. (Sx, Rx, Tx)

8. There are no uniforms that are not washable. There are no washable velvets. Therefore there are no velvet uniforms. (Ux, Wx, Vx)

9. Only authoritarians are bureaucrats. Authoritarians are all churlish. Therefore any bureaucrat is churlish. (*Ax, Bx, Cx*)

★10. Dates are edible. Only food is edible. Food is good. Therefore all dates are good. (*Dx, Ex, Fx, Gx*)

11. All dancers are graceful. Mary is a student. Mary is a dancer. Therefore some students are graceful. (*Dx, Gx, Sx, m*)

12. Tigers are fierce and dangerous. Some tigers are beautiful. Therefore some dangerous things are beautiful. (*Tx, Fx, Dx, Bx*)

13. Bananas and grapes are fruits. Fruits and vegetables are nourishing. Therefore bananas are nourishing. (*Bx, Gx, Fx, Vx, Nx*)

14. A communist is either a fool or a knave. Fools are naive. Not all communists are naive. Therefore some communists are knaves. (*Cx, Fx, Kx, Nx*)

★15. All butlers and valets are both obsequious and dignified. Therefore all butlers are dignified. (*Bx, Vx, Ox, Dx*)

16. All houses built of brick are warm and cozy. All houses in Englewood are built of brick. Therefore all houses in Englewood are warm. (*Hx, Bx, Wx, Cx, Ex*)

17. All professors are learned. All learned professors are savants. Therefore all professors are learned savants. (*Px, Lx, Sx*)

18. All diplomats are statesmen. Some diplomats are eloquent. All eloquent statesmen are orators. Therefore some diplomats are orators. (*Dx, Sx, Ex, Ox*)

19. Doctors and lawyers are college graduates. Any altruist is an idealist. Some lawyers are not idealists. Some doctors are altruists. Therefore some college graduates are idealists. (*Dx, Lx, Cx, Ax, Ix*)

★20. Bees and wasps sting if they are either angry or frightened. Therefore any bee stings if it is angry. (*Bx, Wx, Sx, Ax, Fx*)

21. Any author is successful if and only if he is well read. All authors are intellectuals. Some authors are successful but not well read. Therefore all intellectuals are authors. (*Ax, Sx, Wx, Ix*)

22. Every passenger is either in first class or in tourist class. Each passenger is in tourist class if and only if he is not wealthy. Some passengers are wealthy. Not all passengers are wealthy. Therefore some passengers are in tourist class. (*Px, Fx, Tx, Wx*)

23. All members are both officers and gentlemen. All officers are fighters. Only a pacifist is either a gentleman or not a fighter. No pacifists are gentlemen if they are fighters. Some members are fighters if and only if they are officers. Therefore not all members are fighters. (*Mx, Ox, Gx, Fx, Px*)

24. Wolfhounds and terriers are hunting dogs. Hunting dogs and lap dogs are domesticated animals. Domesticated animals are gentle and useful. Some wolfhounds are neither gentle nor small. Therefore some terriers are small but not gentle. (*Wx, Tx, Hx, Lx, Dx, Gx, Ux, Sx*)

★25. No man who is a candidate will be defeated if he is a good campaigner. Any man who runs for office is a candidate. Any candidate who is not defeated will be elected. Every man who is elected is a good campaigner. Therefore any man who runs for office will be elected if and only if he is a good campaigner. (*Mx, Cx, Dx, Gx, Rx, Ex*)

4.3 PROVING INVALIDITY

In the preceding chapter we proved the invalidity of invalid arguments containing truth-functional compound statements by assigning truth values to their component simple statements in such a way as to make their premisses true and their conclusions false. We can use a very similar method to prove the invalidity of invalid arguments involving quantifiers. The method of proving invalidity about to be described is closely connected with our basic assumption that the universe is non-empty, that is, that there exists at least one individual in the universe.

The assumption that the universe is nonempty could be satisfied in infinitely many different ways: if there is exactly one individual, or if there are exactly two individuals, or if there are exactly three individuals, or etc. For any such case there is a strict logical equivalence between noncompound general propositions and truth-functional compounds of singular propositions. If there is exactly one individual in the universe, say a, then

$$[(x)\Phi x] \equiv \Phi a \quad \text{and} \quad [(\exists x)\Phi x] \equiv \Phi a$$

If there are exactly two individuals in the universe, say a and b, then

$$[(x)\Phi x] \equiv [\Phi a \cdot \Phi b] \quad \text{and} \quad [(\exists x)\Phi x] \equiv [\Phi a \vee \Phi b]$$

And for any number k, if there are exactly k individuals in the universe, say $a, b, c, \ldots, k$, then

$$[(x)\Phi x] \equiv [\Phi a \cdot \Phi b \cdot \Phi c \cdot \ldots \cdot \Phi k]$$

and

$$[(\exists x)\Phi x] \equiv [\Phi a \vee \Phi b \vee \Phi c \vee \ldots \vee \Phi k]$$

For any possible nonempty universe containing some finite number of individuals, every general proposition is logically equivalent to some truth-functional compound of singular propositions. Hence for any such universe every argument involving quantifiers is logically equivalent to some argument containing only singular propositions and truth-functional compounds of them.

It should be clear that an argument involving quantifiers is valid only if for every possible nonempty universe it is logically equivalent to a truth-functional argument which is valid. Hence we can prove the invalidity of a given argument by showing that there is a possible non-empty universe for which the given argument is logically equivalent to an *invalid* truth-functional argument. We can accomplish this purpose by translating the given argument involving quantifiers into a logically equivalent argument involving only singular propositions and truth-functional compounds of them, and then using the method of assigning truth values to prove the latter invalid. For example, given the argument

> All whales are heavy.
> All elephants are heavy.
> Therefore all whales are elephants.

we first symbolize it as

$$(x)[Wx \supset Hx]$$
$$(x)[Ex \supset Hx]$$
$$\therefore (x)[Wx \supset Ex]$$

In the case of a universe containing exactly one individual, say a, the given argument is logically equivalent to

$$Wa \supset Ha$$
$$Ea \supset Ha$$
$$\therefore Wa \supset Ea$$

and the latter is proved invalid by assigning the truth value **T** to 'Wa' and 'Ha' and **F** to 'Ea'. Hence the given argument is *invalid*.

It must be emphasized that in proving the invalidity of arguments involving quantifiers *no use is made of our quantification rules*. For a possible universe containing just the one individual a we do not *infer* the statement '$Wa \supset Ha$' from the statement '$(x)[Wx \supset Hx]$' by **UI**; those two statements are logically equivalent for such a possible universe because '$Wa \supset Ha$' is the *only* substitution instance of the propositional function '$Wx \supset Hx$'.

It *can* happen that an invalid argument involving quantifiers is logically equivalent, for a universe containing exactly one individual, to a valid truth-functional argument, although it will be logically equivalent, for any universe containing more than one individual, to an invalid truth-functional argument. For example, consider the argument

> All whales are heavy.
> Some elephants are heavy.
> Therefore all whales are elephants.

which is symbolized as

$$(x)[Wx \supset Hx]$$
$$(\exists x)[Ex \cdot Hx]$$
$$\therefore (x)[Wx \supset Ex]$$

For a possible universe containing just the one individual a this argument is logically equivalent to

$$Wa \supset Ha$$
$$Ea \cdot Ha$$
$$\therefore Wa \supset Ea$$

which is a valid argument. But for a possible universe containing just the two individuals a and b the given argument is logically equivalent to

$$(Wa \supset Ha) \cdot (Wb \supset Hb)$$
$$(Ea \cdot Ha) \text{ v } (Eb \cdot Hb)$$
$$\therefore (Wa \supset Ea) \cdot (Wb \supset Hb)$$

which is proved invalid by assigning the truth value **T** to 'Wa', 'Wb', 'Ha', 'Hb', 'Eb', and the truth value **F** to 'Ea'. Hence the original argument is invalid, because there is a possible nonempty universe for which it is logically equivalent to an invalid truth-functional argument.

Another illustration is

Some dogs are pointers.
Some dogs are spaniels.
Therefore some pointers are spaniels.

which we symbolize as

$$(\exists x)[Dx \cdot Px]$$
$$(\exists x)[Dx \cdot Sx]$$
$$\therefore \ (\exists x)[Px \cdot Sx]$$

For a possible universe containing just the one individual a it is logically equivalent to

$$Da \cdot Pa$$
$$Da \cdot Sa$$
$$\therefore \ Pa \cdot Sa$$

which is valid. But for a possible universe containing just the two individuals a and b it is equivalent to

$$(Da \cdot Pa) \text{ v } (Db \cdot Pb)$$
$$(Da \cdot Sa) \text{ v } (Db \cdot Sb)$$
$$\therefore \ (Pa \cdot Sa) \text{ v } (Pb \cdot Sb)$$

which is proved invalid by assigning the truth value **T** to 'Da', 'Db', 'Pa', 'Sb', and the truth value **F** to 'Pb' and 'Sa'. Here, too, the original argument is invalid, because there is a nonempty universe for which it is logically equivalent to an invalid truth-functional argument.

An invalid argument involving quantifiers may be valid for any possible nonempty universe containing fewer than k individuals, even though it must be invalid for every possible nonempty universe containing k or more individuals. Hence in using this method to prove the invalidity of an argument involving quantifiers it may be necessary to consider larger and larger possible nonempty universes. The question naturally arises: how large a possible nonempty universe must we consider in trying to prove the invalidity of an argument of this type? A theoretically satisfactory answer to this question has been found. If an argument contains n different predicate symbols then if it is valid for a possible nonempty universe containing 2^n individuals then it is valid for every possible nonempty universe, or universally valid.[7] Although theoretically satisfactory, this solution is not of much practical help. If we were to go straight to the theoretically crucial case for deciding the validity or invalidity of any of the arguments already considered in this section we should have to consider possible nonempty universes containing eight individuals. And for some exercises in the following set the theoretically crucial case would be a possible nonempty universe containing $2^8 = 256$ individuals. In fact, however, none of the following exercises requires consideration of a possible nonempty universe containing more than four individuals to prove their invalidity.

EXERCISES

I. Prove that each of the following arguments is invalid:

1. All astronauts are brave. Jim is brave. Therefore Jim is an astronaut.
2. No cowboys are dudes. Bill is not a dude. Therefore Bill is a cowboy.
★3. All evergreens are fragrant. Some gum trees are not fragrant. Therefore some evergreens are not gum trees.
4. All heathens are idolaters. No heathen is joyful. Therefore no idolater is joyful.
5. No kittens are large. Some mammals are large. Therefore no kittens are mammals.
6. All novelists are observant. Some poets are not observant. Therefore no novelists are poets.
★7. All statesmen are intelligent. Some politicians are intelligent. Not all politicians are intelligent. Therefore no statesmen are politicians.
★8. All statesmen are intelligent. Some politicians are intelligent. Not all politicans are intelligent. Therefore all statesmen are politicians.
9. All statesmen are politicians. Some statesmen are intelligent. Some politicians are not statesmen. Therefore some politicians are not intelligent.
10. Horses and cows are mammals. Some animals are mammals. Some animals are not mammals. Therefore all horses are animals.

II. Prove the validity or prove the invalidity of each of the following arguments:

---

[7] See Paul Bernays and Moses Schönfinkel, 'Zum Entscheidungsproblem der mathematischen Logik,' *Mathematische Annalen*, vol. 99 (1928), and Wilhelm Ackermann, *Solvable Cases of The Decision Problem*, Amsterdam, 1954, Chapter IV.

1. All aviators are brave. Jones is brave. Therefore Jones is an aviator.

2. All collegians are debonair. Smith is a collegian. Therefore Smith is debonair.

3. No educators are fools. All gamblers are fools. Therefore no educators are gamblers.

4. No historians are illiterates. All illiterates are underprivileged. Therefore no historians are underprivileged.

5. Only citizens are voters. Not all residents are citizens. Therefore some residents are not voters.

6. Only citizens are voters. Not all citizens are residents. Therefore some voters are not residents.

★7. Automobiles and wagons are vehicles. Some automobiles are Fords. Some automobiles are trucks. All trucks are vehicles. Therefore some Fords are trucks.

★8. Automobiles and wagons are vehicles. Some automobiles are Fords. Some automobiles are trucks. All vehicles are trucks. Therefore some Fords are trucks.

9. Automobiles and wagons are vehicles. Some automobiles are Fords. Some automobiles are trucks. Some wagons are not vehicles. Therefore some Fords are trucks.

10. All tenors are either overweight or effeminate. No overweight tenor is effeminate. Some tenors are effeminate. Therefore some tenors are overweight.

11. All tenors are either overweight or effeminate. No overweight tenor is effeminate. Some tenors are effeminate. Therefore some tenors are not overweight.

★12. No applicant will be either hired or considered who is either untrained or inexperienced. Some applicants are inexperienced beginners. All applicants who are women will be disappointed if they are not hired. Every applicant is a woman. Some women will be hired. Therefore some applicants will be disappointed.

★13. No candidate is either elected or appointed who is either a liberal or a radical. Some candidates are wealthy liberals. All candidates who are politicians are disappointed if they are not elected. Every candidate is a politician. Some politicians are elected. Therefore some candidates are not disappointed.

14. Abbots and bishops are churchmen. No churchmen are either dowdy or elegant. Some bishops are elegant and fastidious. Some abbots are not fastidious. Therefore some abbots are dowdy.

15. Abbots and bishops are churchmen. No churchmen are both dowdy and elegant. Some bishops are elegant and fastidious. Some abbots are not fastidious. Therefore some abbots are not dowdy.

4.4 MULTIPLY GENERAL PROPOSITIONS

Thus far we have limited our attention to general propositions containing only a single quantifier. A general proposition that contains exactly one quantifier is said to be *singly* general. We turn next to *multiply* general propositions, which contain two or more quantifiers. In our use of the term, any compound statement whose components are general propositions is to be counted as a multiply general proposition. For example, the conditional 'If all dogs are carnivorous then some animals are carnivorous', symbolized as '$(x)[Dx \supset Cx] \supset (\exists x)[Ax \cdot Cx]$', is a multiply general proposition. Other multiply general propositions are more complex and require a more complicated notation. To develop the new notation we must turn again to the notion of a propositional function.

All propositional functions considered up to now have had as substitution instances either singular propositions or truth-functional compounds of singular propositions having the same subject terms. If we consider a compound statement whose components are singular propositions having *different* subject terms, such as '$Fa \cdot Gb$', we can regard it as a substitution instance either of the propositional function '$Fx \cdot Gb$' or of the propositional function '$Fa \cdot Gx$'. Some propositional functions, we see, may contain singular propositions as parts. And if we consider a compound statement of which one component is a general proposition and the other component is a singular proposition, such as 'If all dogs are carnivorous then Rover is carnivorous', symbolized as '$(x)[Dx \supset Cx] \supset Cr$', we can regard it as a substitution instance of the propositional function '$(x)[Dx \supset Cx] \supset Cx$'. Thus we see that some propositional functions may contain general propositions as parts.

At this point two new technical terms may properly be introduced. An occurrence of the variable 'x' which does not occur within, or lie within the scope of, a universal or existential quantifier[8] '(x)' or '$(\exists x)$'

---

[8] As explained on page 76.

will be called a *free occurrence* of that variable. On the other hand, an occurrence of the variable '*x*' which is either part of a quantifier or lies within the scope of a quantifier '(*x*)' or '(∃*x*)' will be called a *bound occurrence* of that variable.[9] Thus in the expression '(*x*)[*Dx* ⊃ *Cx*] ⊃ *Cx*' the first occurrence of the variable '*x*' is *part of a quantifier* and is therefore considered to be *bound*. The second and third occurrences are bound occurrences also. But the fourth occurrence is a free occurrence. Thus we see that propositional functions may contain both free and bound occurrences of variables. On the other hand, all occurrences of variables in propositions must be bound, since every proposition must be either true or false. A propositional function must contain at least one free occurrence of a variable, but no proposition can contain any free occurrences of any variable.

The proposition '*Fa·Gb*' can also be regarded as a substitution instance of '*Fx·Gy*', where the latter is a propositional function containing *two different variables*. Up to now we have explicitly admitted only one individual variable, the letter '*x*'. However, in our previous *use* of the letter '*y*' to denote *any arbitrarily selected* individual, we were in effect using it as a variable without admitting the fact. And in introducing a letter by **EI** to denote *some particular* individual having a specified property, without really knowing *which* individual it denoted, we were in effect using that letter as a variable also. We now proceed to acknowledge explicitly what was implicit in our former usage. Some propositional functions may contain two or more different individual variables. It will be convenient to have a larger supply of individual variables available, so we readjust our notational conventions to include the letters '*u*', '*v*', '*w*', '*x*', '*y*', and '*z*' as individual variables. Propositional functions now include such expressions as '*Fu*', '*Fu* v *Gw*', '(*Fx·Gy*) ⊃ *Hz*', '*Fx* v (*Gy·Hx*)', and the like.

In replacing variables by constants to obtain a proposition from a propositional function, the same constant must replace every free occurrence of the same variable. Thus among the substitution instances of the propositional function '*Fx* v (*Gy·Hx*)' are

---

[9] An alternative, less common nomenclature refers to free variables as 'real' variables, and to bound variables as 'apparent' variables.

Fa v $(Gb \cdot Ha)$, Fa v $(Gc \cdot Ha)$, Fa v $(Gd \cdot Ha)$, . . .
Fb v $(Ga \cdot Hb)$, Fb v $(Gc \cdot Hb)$, Fb v $(Gd \cdot Hb)$, . . .
Fc v $(Ga \cdot Hc)$, Fc v $(Gb \cdot Hc)$, Fc v $(Gd \cdot Hc)$, . . .

. . . .

but *not* such propositions as 'Fa v $(Gb \cdot Hc)$'. On the other hand, the *same* constant can replace free occurrences of *different* variables, provided, of course, that if it replaces any free occurrence of a variable it must replace all free occurrences of that variable. Thus additional substitution instances of the propositional function 'Fx v $(Gy \cdot Hx)$' are 'Fa v $(Ga \cdot Ha)$', 'Fb v $(Gb \cdot Hb)$', 'Fc v $(Gc \cdot Hc)$', . . .

Having admitted the letters 'u', 'v'. 'w', 'y', and 'z' as individual variables in addition to 'x', we now adjust our notation for universal and existential quantification to conform to our expanded stock of variables. The proposition 'All F's are G's' may be alternatively symbolized as '$(u)[Fu \supset Gu]$', '$(v)[Fv \supset Gv]$', '$(w)[Fw \supset Gw]$', '$(x)[Fx \supset Gx]$', '$(y)[Fy \supset Gy]$', or '$(z)[Fz \supset Gz]$'. Similarly the proposition 'There are some H's' may be alternatively symbolized as '$(\exists u)Hu$', '$(\exists v)Hv$', '$(\exists w)Hw$', '$(\exists x)Hx$', '$(\exists y)Hy$', or '$(\exists z)Hz$'. The difference between '$(x)Fx$' and '$(y)Fy$' (as between '$(\exists x)Gx$' and '$(\exists y)Gy$') is purely notational, and either may be written in place of the other wherever it occurs. Of course where a propositional function contains free occurrences of two or more different variables, such as '$Fx \cdot Gy$', the two propositional functions that result from quantifying it differently as

$$(x)[Fx \cdot Gy] \quad \text{and} \quad (y)[Fx \cdot Gy]$$

are very different indeed, and their difference is more than merely notational. The substitution instances of the first are

$$(x)[Fx \cdot Ga], \ (x)[Fx \cdot Gb], \ (x)[Fx \cdot Gc], \ . . .$$

while the substitution instances of the second are

$$(y)[Fa \cdot Gy], \ (y)[Fb \cdot Gy], \ (y)[Fc \cdot Gy], \ . . .$$

If every individual has the property F and some but not all individuals have the property G, then some substitution instances of the first will be true propositions, while all substitution instances of the second will be false, a considerable difference indeed! This example should serve to indicate the need for speaking not of "*the* universal (or existential) quantification of a propositional function" but rather of "the universal (or existential) quantification of a propositional function *with respect to the variable 'x'*" or "the universal (or existential) quantification of a propositional function *with respect to the variable 'y'*" and so on.

It should be clear that since '$(x)[Fx \supset Gx]$' and '$(y)[Fy \supset Gy]$' are alternative translations of the proposition 'Everything which is an F is also a G', the universal quantification of '$Fx \supset Gx$' with respect to 'x' has the same meaning and is logically equivalent to the universal quantification with respect to 'y' of the propositional function which results from replacing all free occurrences of 'x' in '$Fx \supset Gx$' by 'y'— for the result of that replacement is '$Fy \supset Gy$'. In the early stages of our work it will be desirable to have at most one quantification with respect to a given variable in a single proposition. This is not strictly *necessary*, but it is helpful in preventing confusion. Thus the first multiply general proposition considered, 'If all dogs are carnivorous then some animals are carnivorous', is more conveniently symbolized as '$(x)[Dx \supset Cx] \supset (\exists y)[Ay \cdot Cy]$' than as '$(x)[Dx \supset Cx] \supset (\exists x)[Ax \cdot Cx]$', although neither is *incorrect*.

It has been remarked that no proposition can contain a free occurrence of any variable. Hence in symbolizing any proposition we must take care that every occurrence of every variable used lies within the scope of a quantifier with respect to that variable. Some examples will help to make the matter clear. The proposition

> If something is wrong with the house then everyone in the house complains.

is properly symbolized as a conditional whose antecedent and consequent contain different quantifiers:

> $(\exists x)[x$ is wrong with the house$] \supset (y)[(y$ is a person in the house$) \supset (y$ complains$)]$

Here the scope of the initial quantifier does not extend past the main implication sign. But if we turn now to another proposition which bears a superficial resemblance to the first:

> If something is wrong then it should be rectified.

it would be *incorrect* to symbolize it as

$(\exists x)[x$ is wrong$] \supset (x$ should be rectified$)$

For since the scope of the initial quantifier ends at the implication sign, the occurrence of 'x' in the consequent *cannot* refer back to the initial quantifier because it does not lie within its scope. We have here a free occurrence of a variable, which means that the proposed symbolization is not a proposition and therefore not an adequate translation of the given statement. The error is not to be corrected by *simply* extending the scope of the initial quantifier through rebracketing, for the symbolic expression

$(\exists x)[(x$ is wrong$) \supset (x$ should be rectified$)]$

although a proposition, does not have the same meaning as the original proposition in English. Instead, it says merely that there is at least one thing which should be rectified if it is wrong, but the sense of the English sentence is clearly that *anything* which is wrong should be rectified. Hence a correct symbolization is neither of the preceding, but rather

$(x)[(x$ is wrong$) \supset (x$ should be rectified$)]$

The situation is more complicated, but no different in principle, when one quantifier occurs *within the scope of another quantifier*. Here the same warning against dangling or unquantified variables must be sounded. The proposition

If something is missing then if nobody calls the police someone will be unhappy.

is properly symbolized as

$(\exists x)[x$ is missing$] \supset \{(y)[(y$ is a person$) \supset \sim(y$ calls the police$)]$
$\supset (\exists z)[(z$ is a person$)\cdot(z$ will be unhappy$)]\}$

But the following proposition, which is superficially analogous to the preceding:

If something is missing then if nobody calls the police it will not be recovered.

is *not* to be symbolized as

$(\exists x)[x$ is missing$] \supset \{(y)[(y$ is a person$) \supset \sim(y$ calls the police$)]$
$\supset \sim(x$ will be recovered$)\}$

for the last occurrence of the variable '*x*' is outside the scope of the initial quantifier, being left dangling. It cannot be corrected simply by rebracketing, as

$(\exists x)\{(x$ is missing$) \supset \{(y)[(y$ is a person$) \supset \sim(y$ calls the police$)]$
$\supset \sim(x$ will be recovered$)\}\}$

for this expression fails equally to preserve the sense of the English sentence, in the same way as in the previous example. That sense is expressed by the formula

$(x)\{(x$ is missing$) \supset \{(y)[(y$ is a person$) \supset \sim(y$ calls the police$)]$
$\supset \sim(x$ will be recovered$)\}\}$

which is therefore a correct symbolization of the given proposition.

EXERCISES

Symbolize each of the following propositions, in each case using the suggested notation, and making the symbolic formula parallel the English as closely as possible:

1. If anything is damaged someone will be blamed. (*Dx*: *x* is damaged. *Px*: *x* is a person. *Bx*: *x* will be blamed.)

2. If anything is damaged the tenant will be charged for it. (*Dx*: *x* is damaged. *Cx*: *x* will be charged to the tenant.)

3. If nothing is damaged nobody will be blamed. (*Dx*: *x* is damaged. *Px*: *x* is a person. *Bx*: *x* will be blamed.)

4. If something is damaged but nobody is blamed the tenant will not be charged for it. (*Dx*: *x* is damaged. *Px*: *x* is a person. *Bx*: *x* is blamed. *Cx*: *x* will be charged to the tenant.)

5. If any bananas are yellow they are ripe. (*Bx*: *x* is a banana. *Yx*: *x* is yellow. *Rx*: *x* is ripe.)

6. If any bananas are yellow then some bananas are ripe. (*Bx*: *x* is a banana. *Yx*: *x* is yellow. *Rx*: *x* is ripe.)

★7. If any bananas are yellow, then if all yellow bananas are ripe, they are ripe. (*Bx*: *x* is a banana. *Yx*: *x* is yellow. *Rx*: *x* is ripe.)

8. If all ripe bananas are yellow some yellow things are ripe. (*Rx*: *x* is ripe. *Bx*: *x* is a banana. *Yx*: *x* is yellow.)

★9. If all officers present are either captains or majors then either some captains are present or some majors are present. (Ox: x is an officer. Px: x is present. Cx: x is a captain. Mx: x is a major.)

10. If any officer is present then either no majors are present or he is a major. (Ox: x is an officer. Px: x is present. Mx: x is a major.)

11. If some officers are present then if all officers present are captains then some captains are present. (Ox: x is an officer. Px: x is present. Cx: x is a captain.)

12. If some officers are present then if all officers present are captains then they are captains. (Ox: x is an officer. Px: x is present. Cx: x is a captain.)

13. If all survivors are fortunate and only women were survivors then if there are any survivors then some women are fortunate. (Sx: x is a survivor. Fx: x is fortunate. Wx: x is a woman.)

★14. If any survivors are women then if all women are fortunate they are fortunate. (Sx: x is a survivor. Wx: x is a woman. Fx: x is fortunate.)

15. If there are any survivors and only women are survivors then they are women. (Sx: x is a survivor. Wx: x is a woman.)

16. If every position has a future and no employees are lazy then some employees will be successful. (Px: x is a position. Fx: x has a future. Ex: x is an employee. Lx: x is lazy. Sx: x will be successful.)

17. If any employees are lazy then if some positions have no future then they will not be successful. (Ex: x is an employee. Lx: x is lazy. Px: x is a position. Fx: x has a future. Sx: x will be successful.)

★18. If any employees are lazy and some positions have no future then some employees will not be successful. (Ex: x is an employee. Lx: x is lazy. Px: x is a position. Fx: x has a future. Sx: x will be successful.)

19. If any husband is unsuccessful then if all wives are ambitious then some wives will be disappointed. (Hx: x is a husband. Sx: x is successful. Wx: x is a wife. Ax: x is ambitious. Dx: x will be disappointed.)

20. If any husband is unsuccessful then if some wives are ambitious he will be unhappy. (Hx: x is a husband. Sx: x is successful. Wx: x is a wife. Ax: x is ambitious. Ux: x will be unhappy.)

4.5   QUANTIFICATION RULES

1. Inferences Involving Propositional Functions.   In constructing a formal proof of validity for a given argument, the premises with which we begin and the conclusion with which we end are all propositions. But wherever the rules of Existential Instantiation or Universal

Generalization are used some of the intermediate lines must contain free variables, and will therefore be propositional functions rather than propositions. Each line of a formal proof of validity must be either a premiss, or an assumption of limited scope, or follow validly from preceding lines by an elementary valid argument form accepted as a Rule of Inference, or follow from a sequence of preceding steps by the (strengthened) principle of Conditional Proof. Three questions naturally arise at this point: In what sense can a propositional function be said to follow *validly* from other propositional functions? In what sense can a propositional function be said to follow *validly* from propositions? And in what sense can a proposition be said to follow *validly* from propositional functions?

To answer these questions it is useful to introduce a revised, more general sense of the word 'valid'. Propositional functions contain free variables, and are therefore neither true nor false. But a propositional function is made into a proposition by having all its free variables replaced by constants, and the resulting substitution instance is either true or false. One propositional function can be said to follow *validly* as conclusion from one or more other propositional functions as premisses when every replacement of free occurrences of variables by constants (the same constants replacing the same variables in both premisses and conclusion, of course) results in a valid argument. For example, the propositional function 'Gx' follows validly from the propositional functions '$Fx \supset Gx$' and 'Fx', because every replacement of 'x' by a constant results in an argument of the form *Modus Ponens*. We may say of such an inference that it is valid by the principle of *Modus Ponens* despite the fact that propositional functions rather than propositions are involved. It should be clear that any inference is valid which proceeds by way of any of the nineteen Rules of Inference on our original list, regardless of whether the premisses and conclusion are propositions or propositional functions. In passing we may note that this is so even where the conclusion contains more free variables than the premisses, as when by the principle of Addition we validly infer the propositional function of two variables '$Fx \lor Gy$' from the propositional function of one variable 'Fx'.

The original list of nineteen Rules of Inference also permits the inference of propositional functions from propositions, as when by the principle of Addition we infer the propositional function '*Fa* v *Gx*' from the proposition '*Fa*'. That such inferences as these are valid, in the new sense explained, is obvious. Moreover, propositions can validly be inferred from propositional functions by our Rules of Inference, as when by the principle of Simplification we infer the proposition '*Fa*' from the propositional function '*Fa·Gx*'. Hence the letters '*p*', '*q*', '*r*', '*s*' in our nineteen Rules of Inference now range over, or represent, *either* propositions *or* propositional functions.

We can now adopt a more general definition of formal proof of validity, which parallels our earlier definition exactly except that lines of a proof can be either propositions or propositional functions. If each line after the initial premises follows validly from preceding lines, in the generalized sense of 'valid' explained, then the last line validly follows from the initial premises. And if our initial premises and conclusion are propositions rather than propositional functions, then the conclusion validly follows from the initial premises in the original sense of 'valid' which applies to arguments whose premises and conclusions are all statements or propositions. This can be seen by the following considerations. As we go from our original premises to propositional functions, if we go validly, then if the premises are true, all substitution instances of the inferred propositional functions must be true also. And as we go from previously inferred propositional functions to other propositional functions, if we go validly, then all substitution instances of the latter must be true also. Finally, when we go from validly inferred propositional functions to the final conclusion which is a proposition, then if we go validly, since all substitution instances of the former are true, the final conclusion must be true also.

The preceding remarks require some modification to take account of assumptions of limited scope that contain free variables, but the modifications are best introduced as alterations in the quantification rules themselves. The preliminary versions of our quantification rules must be replaced in any case, for as stated they apply only to propositions, not to propositional functions. The two rules for generalizing, **UG** and **EG**, must now permit the quantification (or binding) of free variables, while the instantiation rules **UI** and **EI** must now permit the freeing of bound variables, to permit the introduction of propositional functions rather than (pretended) substitution instances of them.

In our earlier discussion of propositional functions (of the single variable 'x') we introduced the Greek letters *phi* and *psi*, and let 'Φx' and 'Ψx' denote any propositional function of 'x', such as 'Fx', 'Gx', '$Fx \cdot Hx$', '$(Fx \lor Gx) \supset Hx$', . . . no matter how complicated such functions might be. It will be useful to continue to use these Greek letters, but now letting 'Φx' denote any propositional function which contains at least one free occurrence of the variable 'x', even including those propositional functions which contain free occurrences of other variables. Thus 'Φx' may denote any of the following:

$$Fx, \ Fx \lor Gx, \ Ga \supset Hx, \ Fw \cdot Fx, \ (\exists z)[Gz \equiv Hx], \ . \ . \ .$$

Similarly, 'Φy' may denote any of the propositional functions

$$Fy, \ Fy \lor Gy, \ Ga \supset Hy, \ Fw \cdot Fy, \ (\exists z)[Gz \equiv Hy], \ . \ . \ .$$

To be able to refer to *any* propositional function in *either* of the preceding groups it will be convenient to introduce the Greek letters *mu* and *nu* ('μ' and 'ν') to denote individual symbols. Thus '$\Phi \mu$' may denote any of the preceding propositional functions of either 'x' or 'y', according as 'μ' is taken as denoting 'x' or 'y'. Similarly, according as 'μ' is taken as denoting 'x' or 'y', '$(\mu)\Phi \mu$' will denote the universal quantification with respect to 'x' or 'y' of any of the preceding propositional functions of 'x' or 'y', and '$(\exists \mu)\Phi \mu$' will denote the existential quantification.

It is convenient to allow '$\Phi \mu$' also to denote either a proposition or a propositional function containing *no* free occurrence of the variable denoted by 'μ'. In such a case $(\mu)\Phi \mu$ and $(\exists \mu)\Phi \mu$ will be called 'vacuous' quantifications, and will be equivalent to each other and to $\Phi \mu$ itself. This somewhat unnatural notion is included only for the sake of the completeness described and proved for the axiomatic development of Quantification Theory presented in Chapter 9. We shall make no use of it until then.

The Greek letters *phi* and *psi* may also be used in conjunction with an individual constant to denote either propositions or propositional functions containing that constant. Thus 'Φa' may denote any of the expressions

$$Fa, \ Fa \text{ v } Ga, \ Ga \supset Ha, \ Fw{\cdot}Fa, \ (\exists z)[Gz \equiv Ha], \ \ldots$$

and 'Φb' may denote any of the expressions

$$Fb, \ Fb \text{ v } Gb, \ Ga \supset Hb, \ Fw{\cdot}Fb, \ (\exists z)[Gz \equiv Hb], \ \ldots$$

By the convention already introduced, '$\Phi \nu$' may denote any expression of the two preceding groups according as 'ν' is taken as denoting 'a' or 'b'. This notation will be useful in reformulating our quantification rules.

2. Universal Instantiation. The presentation of our quantification rules will be accompanied by examples of valid arguments which they must permit, and also by examples of invalid arguments to be avoided by restrictions placed on those rules. The following inferences are clearly valid:

$$\frac{(x)Fx}{\therefore Fa}, \ \frac{(y)[Fy \text{ v } Gb]}{\therefore Fa \text{ v } Gb}, \ \frac{(z)[Fz \supset Gb]}{\therefore Fb \supset Gb}, \ \frac{(x)[Fx \equiv Gy]}{\therefore Fc \equiv Gy}, \ \frac{(x)\{Fx{\cdot}(\exists x)[Gx{\cdot}Hy]\}}{\therefore Fb{\cdot}(\exists x)[Gx{\cdot}Hy]}$$

They may be described generally as being of the form

$$\frac{(\mu)\Phi\mu}{\therefore \Phi\nu}$$

where μ is an individual variable, ν is an individual constant, and $\Phi\nu$ results from $\Phi\mu$ by replacing all free occurrences of μ in $\Phi\mu$ by ν. Of course there can be no free occurrence of μ in $(\mu)\Phi\mu$, but there may be any number of free occurrences of μ in $\Phi\mu$. On the other hand, not every occurrence of μ in $\Phi\mu$ need be free: for example, where 'μ' denotes 'x' and '$\Phi\mu$' denotes '$Fx \supset (\exists x)[Gx \text{ v } Hy]$', only the first occurrence of μ in $\Phi\mu$ is free, since the second is part of the existential quantifier $(\exists\mu)$ and the third is within the scope of that quantifier.

Also valid are such inferences as

$$\frac{(x)Fx}{\therefore Fy}, \ \frac{(x)Fx}{\therefore Fx}, \ \frac{(y)[Fy \text{ v } Gb]}{\therefore Fx \text{ v } Gb}, \ \frac{(z)[Fz \supset Gx]}{\therefore Fx \supset Gx}, \ \frac{(x)\{Fx{\cdot}(\exists x)[Gx{\cdot}Hy]\}}{\therefore Fz{\cdot}(\exists x)[Gx{\cdot}Hy]}, \ \ldots$$

which are also of the form

$$\frac{(\mu)\Phi\mu}{\therefore \ \Phi\nu}$$

except that here *both* μ and ν are individual variables. Here the premiss $(\mu)\Phi\mu$ may be a proposition but the conclusion $\Phi\nu$ must be a propositional function.

Just as we count valid the inference

$$\frac{(z)[Fz \lor Gb]}{\therefore \ Fb \lor Gb}$$

where the instantiating constant 'b' occurs in the premiss as well as in the conclusion, so we wish to count as valid such inferences as

$$\frac{(x)[Fx \lor Gy]}{\therefore \ Fy \lor Gy}, \ \frac{(y)[Fx \supset Gy]}{\therefore \ Fx \supset Gx}, \ \frac{(z)[Fx \supset (Gy{\cdot}Hz)]}{\therefore \ Fx \supset (Gy{\cdot}Hy)}, \ \ldots$$

in which the instantiating *variable* occurs free in the premiss as well as in the conclusion. In general, when $\Phi\nu$ is inferred from $(\mu)\Phi\mu$ validly, ν must occur free in $\Phi\nu$ at every place where μ occurs free in $\Phi\mu$, but there *may* be more free occurrences of ν in $\Phi\nu$ than there are free occurrences of μ in $\Phi\mu$. There will be more whenever ν occurs free in $\Phi\mu$.

All the preceding inferences must be legitimized by our principle of Universal Instantiation. It will be convenient to establish, for the present chapter, two definite conventions governing the expressions '$\Phi\mu$' and '$\Phi\nu$', so that each may be used in the same sense in the statements of all four quantification rules. The first convention is that *mu* ('μ') denotes individual variables exclusively, whereas *nu* ('ν') denotes both individual variables and individual constants. The second convention is this:

The expression '$\Phi\mu$' denotes any proposition or propositional function. The expression '$\Phi\nu$' denotes the result of replacing every free occurrence of μ in $\Phi\mu$ by ν, provided that if ν is a variable it must occur free in $\Phi\nu$ at all places that μ occurs free in $\Phi\mu$. (If $\Phi\mu$ contains no free occurrence of μ then $\Phi\nu$ and $\Phi\mu$ are identical. ν and μ may of course be the same variable: if they are, in this case too $\Phi\nu$ and $\Phi\mu$ are identical.)

This general convention helps to prevent unwanted (that is, invalid) inferences from being allowed by our four quantification rules. How it contributes to this end will be explained following the formulations of each of the four rules.

Our first Quantification Rule, Universal Instantiation, is stated as

$$\textbf{UI:} \ \frac{(\mu)\Phi\mu}{\therefore \ \Phi\nu}$$

The general convention governing $\Phi\mu$ and $\Phi\nu$ serves to prevent such an erroneous inference as

$$\frac{(x)[(\exists y)(Fx \equiv \sim Fy)]}{\therefore \ (\exists y)(Fy \equiv \sim Fy)}$$

from being allowed by **UI**, because ν ('y') does not occur free in $\Phi\nu$ ('$(\exists y)(Fy \equiv \sim Fy)$') at all places that μ ('x') occurs free in $\Phi\mu$ ('$(\exists y)(Fx \equiv \sim Fy)$'). Hence '$(\exists y)(Fy \equiv \sim Fy)$' is not a legitimate $\Phi\nu$ for use in applying **UI** where $(\mu)\Phi\mu$ is '$(x)[(\exists y)(Fx \equiv \sim Fy)]$'. It should be obvious that the inference is invalid: it fails for a universe containing some things that are F and some things that are not F, which would make the premiss true, whereas the conclusion is false for any possible universe, being self-contradictory.

3. Existential Generalization.   Turning now to Existential Generalization, we observe that all the following are valid inferences:

$$\frac{Fa}{\therefore \ (\exists x)Fx}, \ \frac{Fa}{\therefore \ (\exists y)Fy}, \ \frac{Fa \lor Gb}{\therefore \ (\exists x)(Fx \lor Gb)}, \ \frac{Fa \supset Gb}{\therefore \ (\exists y)(Fa \supset Gy)}, \ \ldots$$

They may be described generally as being of the form

$$\frac{\Phi\nu}{\therefore \ (\exists\mu)\Phi\mu}$$

Here both premisses and conclusions are propositions. Also valid are such inferences involving propositional functions as

$$\frac{Fx}{\therefore \ (\exists y)Fy}, \ \frac{Fa \lor Gy}{\therefore \ (\exists x)(Fa \lor Gx)}, \ \frac{Fx \supset Gy}{\therefore \ (\exists y)(Fx \supset Gy)}, \ \frac{Fx \cdot Gx}{\therefore \ (\exists y)(Fy \cdot Gx)}, \ \ldots$$

which are of the same pattern as the preceding except that here ν is a variable instead of a constant.

Our second Quantification Rule, Existential Generalization, is stated as

$$\textbf{EG:} \quad \frac{\Phi\nu}{\therefore \ (\exists\mu)\Phi\mu}$$

The general convention governing $\Phi\mu$ and $\Phi\nu$ serves to prevent such an erroneous inference as

$$\frac{Fx \equiv \sim Fy}{\therefore \ (\exists x)(Fx \equiv \sim Fx)}$$

from being allowed by **EG**, because ν ('y') does not occur free in $\Phi\nu$ ('$Fx \equiv \sim Fy$') at all places that μ ('x') occurs free in $\Phi\mu$ ('$Fx \equiv \sim Fx$'). Hence '$Fx \equiv \sim Fy$' is not a legitimate $\Phi\nu$ from which '$(\exists x)(Fx \equiv \sim Fx)$' can be obtained as $(\exists\mu)\Phi\mu$ by **EG**. It should be obvious that the inference is invalid: for though the conclusion is false, being self-contradictory, the premiss could be obtained from '$(\exists x)(\exists y)(Fx \equiv \sim Fy)$', which would be true for any universe containing some things that are F and some things that are not F.

Having both **UI** and **EG** available, we may illustrate their use in proving the validity of the argument

All men are mortal.
_____
Therefore if Socrates is a man then some men are mortal.

by the following conditional proof:

1. $(x)(Hx \supset Mx)$ $\quad / \therefore \ Hs \supset (\exists x)(Hx \cdot Mx)$
2. Hs
3. $Hs \supset Ms$ $\qquad\qquad$ 1, **UI**
4. Ms $\qquad\qquad\qquad$ 3, 2, M.P.
5. $Hs \cdot Ms$ $\qquad\qquad$ 2, 4, Conj.
6. $(\exists x)(Hx \cdot Mx)$ $\qquad$ 5, **EG**
7. $Hs \supset (\exists x)(Hx \cdot Mx)$ $\quad$ 2–6, C.P.

A simple pattern of deduction suffices to establish the validity of any argument of the form

$$\frac{(\mu)\Phi\mu}{\therefore \ (\exists\mu)\Phi\mu}$$

Here the pattern of proof is

1. $(\mu)\Phi\mu$ $/\therefore$ $(\exists\mu)\Phi\mu$
2. $\Phi\nu$ 1, **UI**
3. $(\exists\mu)\Phi\mu$ 2, **EG**

4. Existential Instantiation. Before discussing our new formulation of Existential Instantiation it will be useful to establish the logical truth of equivalences of the form

(E) $(\nu)[\Phi\nu \supset p] \equiv [(\exists\mu)\Phi\mu \supset p]$

where ν occurs free in $\Phi\nu$ at all *and only* those places that μ occurs free in $\Phi\mu$, and where p contains no free occurrence of the variable ν. In case p is true both sides of the equivalence must be true: for if p is true then $\Phi\nu \supset p$ is true for every value of ν, whence $(\nu)[\Phi\nu \supset p]$ is true; and the truth of $(\exists\mu)\Phi\mu \supset p$ also follows immediately from the truth of p. In case p is false and $(\nu)[\Phi\nu \supset p]$ is true, every substitution instance of $\Phi\nu \supset p$ is true and so every substitution instance of $\Phi\nu$ must be false, whence $(\exists\mu)\Phi\mu$ must be false and so $(\exists\mu)\Phi\mu \supset p$ is true. In case p is false and $(\exists\mu)\Phi\mu \supset p$ is true, $(\exists\mu)\Phi\mu$ must be false and so every substitution instance of $\Phi\nu$ must be false, whence every substitution instance of $\Phi\nu \supset p$ must be true, and so $(\nu)[\Phi\nu \supset p]$ is true also. This argument establishes the truth of every equivalence of the form (E), for if p is true both sides are true, and if p is false each side implies the other.

Turning now to Existential Instantiation, we want to permit going from $(\exists x)Fx$ to Fx or Fy only under very stringent restrictions. Not only must the instantiating variable not have any prior free occurrence (as discussed on pages 83–84), but we must not permit $(x)Fx$ to be inferred from $(\exists x)Fx$ by way of Existential Instantiation and Universal Generalization. There are many ways of imposing such restrictions.[10] One is to formulate the rule of Existential Instantiation in such a way that the

---

[10] As reported earlier, the new phrasing of **EI** is similar to, and the new phrasing of **UG** is the same as, rephrasings of Gentzen's rules suggested by Professor Hugues Leblanc. I am indebted to Professor Leblanc for permission to borrow his new formulations, which he plans to substitute in the second edition of his *Techniques of Deductive Inference*, Englewood Cliffs, N.J.: Prentice-Hall, 1966, for the rules now employed there.

formula or line *finally* inferred by its means contains no free variables introduced by it. The feasibility of this procedure can be seen by the following considerations.

Here, as in earlier sections, we are concerned to construct proofs of validity only for arguments whose premisses and conclusions are propositions, not propositional functions containing free variables. Hence we never end a proof with a propositional function containing a free variable. So in any proof of validity in which the rule of Existential Instantiation involves going from $(\exists\mu)\Phi\mu$ to $\Phi\nu$, the propositional function $\Phi\nu$ serves only to permit the subsequent inference of a formula not containing any free occurrence of the variable ν.

Suppose we already have $(\exists\mu)\Phi\mu$ as a line in a proof, and know that in the presence of other lines already obtained, if we also had $\Phi\nu$ we should be able to derive a desired formula p containing no free occurrence of the variable ν. We can proceed by writing down $\Phi\nu$ as an assumption of limited scope. Then after p has been derived we can close the scope of the assumption and infer the formula $\Phi\nu \supset p$ by the strengthened Rule of Conditional Proof. From this line (subject to reasonable restrictions) the formula $(\nu)[\Phi\nu \supset p]$ can be inferred by Universal Generalization. And from the latter formula, by equivalence (E), we can infer $(\exists\mu)\Phi\mu \supset p$. Now from this formula and the earlier line $(\exists\mu)\Phi\mu$ we can obtain p by *Modus Ponens*. This whole process can be represented schematically as

i. $\quad(\exists\mu)\Phi\mu$

$\quad\quad\quad\cdot$

$\quad\quad\quad\cdot$

$\quad\quad\quad\cdot$

j. $\quad\Phi\nu$

$\quad\quad\quad\cdot$

$\quad\quad\quad\cdot$

$\quad\quad\quad\cdot$

k. $\quad p$

k+1. $\Phi\nu \supset p$ $\quad\quad$ j−k, C.P.

k+2. $(\nu)[\Phi\nu \supset p]$ $\quad$ k+1, **UG**

k+3. $(\exists\mu)\Phi\mu \supset p$ $\quad$ k+2, Equivalence (E)

k+4. p $\quad\quad\quad\quad\quad$ k+3, i, M.P.

The preceding discussion can be regarded as providing an informal justification for the rule of Existential Instantiation, which we now state as

$$\textbf{EI: } (\exists\mu)\Phi\mu$$

.
.
.

$\to \Phi\nu$
.
.
.
p

$\therefore p$

provided that ν is a variable that does not occur free either in p or in any line preceding $\Phi\nu$.

Before discussing the restrictions in the statement of **EI** it may be helpful to present a proof of validity which makes use of the new rule:

1. $(x)(Fx \supset Gx)$
2. $(\exists y)Fy$ /$\therefore$ $(\exists z)Gz$
3. Fu
4. $Fu \supset Gu$ 1, **UI**
5. Gu 4, 3, M.P.
6. $(\exists z)Gz$ 5, **EG**
7. $(\exists z)Gz$ 2, 3–6, **EI**

There can be, though there need not be, other lines intervening between the premiss $(\exists\mu)\Phi\mu$ (line 2 above) and the propositional function $\Phi\nu$ (line 3 above) marked as an assumption of limited scope. When the desired formula p (line 6 above) is reached, the next line is simply p again, and the justification written next to it is the number of the line consisting of $(\exists\mu)\Phi\mu$, the hyphenated numbers of the line consisting of $\Phi\nu$ and the first line consisting of p, and the notation **EI**.

The general convention governing $\Phi\mu$ and $\Phi\nu$ serves to prevent such an erroneous "proof" as

1. $(\exists x)(Fx{\cdot}Gx)$ /$\therefore$ $(x)Fx$
2. $Fx{\cdot}Gy$ (wrong as part of **EI**)
3. Fx 2, Simp.
4. Fx 1, 2–3, **EI** (wrong)
5. $(x)Fx$ 4, **UG**

from being allowed by **EI**, because ν ('y') does not occur free in $\Phi\nu$ ('$Fx \cdot Gy$') at all places that μ ('x') occurs free in $\Phi\mu$ ('$Fx \cdot Gx$'). Hence '$Fx \cdot Gy$' is not a legitimate $\Phi\nu$ for use in applying **EI** where $(\exists\mu)\Phi\mu$ is '$(\exists x)(Fx \cdot Gx)$'. It should be obvious that the argument is invalid: that something is both an F and a G clearly does not entail that everything is an F.

The restriction that ν does not occur free in p is essentially involved in the equivalence (E) discussed in introducing the present version of **EI**. Because a p that was allowed to contain a free occurrence of ν could be $\Phi\nu$ itself, the first restriction prevents subsequent use of Universal Generalization to derive $(\mu)\Phi\mu$ as conclusion from $(\exists\mu)\Phi\mu$ as premiss.

The restriction that ν does not occur free in any line preceding $\Phi\nu$ serves to prevent such an erroneous "proof" as

1. $(x)(\exists y)(Fx \equiv {\sim}Fy)$ / $\therefore$ $(\exists x)(Fx \equiv {\sim}Fx)$
2. $(\exists y)(Fx \equiv {\sim}Fy)$ 1, **UI**
3. $Fx \equiv {\sim}Fx$ (wrong as part of **EI**)
4. $(\exists x)(Fx \equiv {\sim}Fx)$ 3, **EG**
5. $(\exists x)(Fx \equiv {\sim}Fx)$ 2, 3–4, **EI** (wrong)

from being allowed by **EI**, because ν ('x') does occur free in line 2 which precedes $\Phi\nu$ ('$Fx \equiv {\sim}Fx$') in line 3. Hence '$Fx \equiv {\sim}Fx$' is not a legitimate $\Phi\nu$ for use in applying **EI** where $(\exists\mu)\Phi\mu$ is '$(\exists y)(Fx \equiv {\sim}Fy)$'. It should be obvious that the argument is invalid: it fails for a universe containing some things that are F and some things that are not F, which would make the premiss true, whereas the conclusion is false for any possible universe, being self-contradictory.

5. Universal Generalization. The complicated and highly restricted formulation of **EI** just given permits a somewhat less restricted formulation of the rule of Universal Generalization, which we now state as

$$\text{UG: } \frac{\Phi\nu}{\therefore (\mu)\Phi\mu}$$

provided that ν is a variable that does not occur free either in $(\mu)\Phi\mu$ or in any assumption within whose scope $\Phi\nu$ lies.

The general convention governing $\Phi\mu$ and $\Phi\nu$ serves to prevent such an erroneous "proof" as

1. $(\exists x)(y)(Fx \supset \sim Fy)$ $/\therefore$ $(x)(Fx \supset \sim Fx)$
2. $(y)(Fx \supset \sim Fy)$
3. $Fx \supset \sim Fy$ **2, UI**
4. $(x)(Fx \supset \sim Fx)$ **3, UG** (wrong)
5. $(x)(Fx \supset \sim Fx)$ **1, 2–4, EI**

from being allowed by **UG**, because ν ('y') does not occur free in $\Phi\nu$ ('$Fx \supset \sim Fy$') at all places that μ ('x') occurs free in $\Phi\mu$ ('$Fx \supset \sim Fx$'). Hence '$Fx \supset \sim Fy$' is not a legitimate $\Phi\nu$ from which '$(x)(Fx \supset \sim Fx)$' can be obtained as $(\mu)\Phi\mu$ by **UG**. It should be obvious that the argument is invalid, for its premiss is true if there is at least one thing that is not an F, whereas its conclusion states that there are no F's at all.

The restriction that ν does not occur free in $(\mu)\Phi\mu$ serves to prevent such an erroneous "proof" as

1. $(x)(Fx \equiv Fx)$ $/\therefore$ $(x)(y)(Fx \equiv Fy)$
2. $Fx \equiv Fx$ **1, UI**
3. $(y)(Fx \equiv Fy)$ **2, UG** (wrong)
4. $(x)(y)(Fx \equiv Fy)$ **3, UG**

from being allowed by **UG**, because ν ('x') does occur free in $(\mu)\Phi\mu$ ('$(y)(Fx \equiv Fy)$'). Hence '$Fx \equiv Fx$' is not a legitimate $\Phi\nu$ from which '$(y)(Fx \equiv Fy)$' can be derived as $(\mu)\Phi\mu$ by **UG**. It should be obvious that the argument is invalid, for its premiss states only that any thing is an F if and only if it is an F, whereas its conclusion states that of any things x and y, x is an F if and only if y is an F also.

The restriction that ν does not occur free in any assumption within whose scope $\Phi\nu$ lies serves to prevent such an erroneous "proof" as

1. $(\exists x)Fx$ $/\therefore$ $(x)Fx$
2. Fy
3. $(x)Fx$ **2, UG** (wrong)
4. $(x)Fx$ **1, 2–3, EI**

from being allowed by **UG**, because ν ('y') occurs free in the assumption
'Fy' within whose scope the premiss $\Phi\nu$ ('Fy') lies. Hence in this case
'Fy' is not a legitimate $\Phi\nu$ from which '$(x)Fx$' can be derived as $(\mu)\Phi\mu$
by **UG**. The argument is of course obviously invalid.

EXERCISES

Identify and explain all of the mistakes in the following erroneous "proofs":

1. 1. Fx
   2. $(y)Fy$ 1, **UG**
   3. $Fx \supset (y)Fy$ 1–2, C.P.
   4. $(x)[Fx \supset (y)Fy]$ 3, **UG**

2. 1. $(\exists x)(Fx \cdot Gx)$ / $\therefore$ $(\exists x)Fx$
   2. $Fx \cdot Gx$
   3. Fx 2, Simp.
   4. Fx 1, 2–3, **EI**
   5. $(\exists x)Fx$ 4, **EG**

★3. 1. $(x)(\exists y)(Fx \equiv Gy)$ / $\therefore$ $(\exists y)(x)(Fx \equiv Gy)$
   2. $(\exists y)(Fx \equiv Gy)$ 1, **UI**
   3. $Fx \equiv Gy$
   4. $(x)(Fx \equiv Gy)$ 3, **UG**
   5. $(\exists y)(x)(Fx \equiv Gy)$ 4, **EG**
   6. $(\exists y)(x)(Fx \equiv Gy)$ 2, 3–5, **EI**

4. 1. $(x)(\exists y)(Fx \supset Gy)$ / $\therefore$ $(\exists y)(x)(Fx \supset Gy)$
   2. $(\exists y)(Fx \supset Gy)$ 1, **UI**
   3. $Fx \supset Gx$
   4. $(x)(Fx \supset Gx)$ 3, **UG**
   5. $(\exists y)(x)(Fx \supset Gy)$ 4, **EG**
   6. $(\exists y)(x)(Fx \supset Gy)$ 2, 3–5, **EI**

5. 1. $(y)(\exists x)(Fx \lor Gy)$ / ∴ $(\exists x)(y)(Fx \lor Gy)$
    2. $(\exists x)(Fx \lor Gy)$ 1, **UI**
    →3. $Fx \lor Gx$
    4. $(y)(Fx \lor Gy)$ 3, **UG**
    5. $(\exists x)(y)(Fx \lor Gy)$ 4, **EG**
    6. $(\exists x)(y)(Fx \lor Gy)$ 2, 3–5, **EI**

★6. 1. $(\exists x)(y)[(Fx \cdot Gx) \supset Hy]$ / ∴ $(\exists x)[(Fx \cdot Gx) \supset Hx]$
    →2. $(y)[(Fz \cdot Gz) \supset Hy]$
    3. $(Fz \cdot Gz) \supset Hy$ 2, **UI**
    4. $(\exists x)[(Fx \cdot Gz) \supset Hy]$ 3, **EG**
    5. $(y)(\exists x)[(Fx \cdot Gy) \supset Hy]$ 4, **UG**
    6. $(y)(\exists x)[(Fx \cdot Gy) \supset Hy]$ 1, 2–5, **EI**
    7. $(\exists x)[(Fx \cdot Gx) \supset Hx]$ 6, **UI**

7. 1. $(\exists x)Fx$
    2. $(\exists x)Gx$ / ∴ $(\exists x)(Fx \cdot Gx)$
    →3. Fy
    →4. Gy
    5. $Fy \cdot Gy$ 3, 4, Conj.
    6. $(\exists x)(Fx \cdot Gx)$ 5, **EG**
    7. $(\exists x)(Fx \cdot Gx)$ 2, 4–6, **EI**
    8. $(\exists x)(Fx \cdot Gx)$ 1, 3–7, **EI**

8. 1. $(\exists x)(\exists y)[(Fx \lor Gy) \cdot Hy]$ / ∴ $(x)(y)(Fy \lor Gx)$
    →2. $(\exists y)[(Fx \lor Gy) \cdot Hy]$
    →3. $(Fx \lor Gx) \cdot Hx$
    4. $Fx \lor Gx$ 3, Simp.
    5. $Fx \lor Gx$ 2, 3–4, **EI**
    6. $Fx \lor Gx$ 1, 2–5, **EI**
    7. $(y)(Fy \lor Gx)$ 6, **UG**
    8. $(x)(y)(Fy \lor Gx)$ 7, **UG**

★9. 1. $(\exists x)(Fx \cdot Gx)$
    2. $(\exists x)(\sim Fx \cdot Gx)$ $/ \therefore (\exists x)(Fx \cdot \sim Fx)$
    3. $Fx \cdot Gy$
    4. Fx 3, Simp.

    5. Fx 1, 3–4, **EI**
    6. $\sim Fx \cdot Gx$
    7. $\sim Fx$ 6, Simp.

    8. $\sim Fx$ 2, 6–7, **EI**
    9. $Fx \cdot \sim Fx$ 5, 8, Conj.
   10. $(\exists x)(Fx \cdot \sim Fx)$ 9, **EG**

10. 1. $(x)[(Fx \supset Gx) \cdot \sim Ga]$ $/ \therefore (x)\sim Fx$
    2. $(x)[(Fx \supset Gx) \cdot \sim Gy]$
    3. $(Fz \supset Gz) \cdot \sim Gy$ 2, **UI**
    4. $(y)[(Fy \supset Gy) \cdot \sim Gy]$ 3, **UG**
    5. $(Fu \supset Gu) \cdot \sim Gu$ 4, **UI**
    6. $Fu \supset Gu$ 5, Simp.
    7. $\sim Gu \cdot (Fu \supset Gu)$ 5, Com.
    8. $\sim Gu$ 7, Simp.
    9. $\sim Fu$ 6, 8, M.T.
   10. $(x)\sim Fx$ 9, **UG**
   11. $(x)[(Fx \supset Gx) \cdot \sim Gy] \supset (x)\sim Fx$ 2–10, C.P.
   12. $(w)\{(x)[(Fx \supset Gx) \cdot \sim Gw] \supset (x)\sim Fx\}$ 11, **UG**
   13. $(x)[(Fx \supset Gx) \cdot \sim Ga] \supset (x)\sim Fx$ 12, **UI**
   14. $(x)\sim Fx$ 13, 1, M.P.

6. Shorter Proofs of Validity. At this stage of our work it is desirable to cut down the length of our formal proofs of validity by permitting short cuts to be taken in the application of the original list of Rules of Inference. We can combine any use of the principle of Double Negation with any other step, which will permit us to go directly from '$\sim A \supset B$' to '$A \vee B$', or vice versa, without having to write down the intermediate step '$\sim \sim A \vee B$'. We can short cut tedious uses of the principle of Commutation by permitting not only '$A \therefore A \vee B$' by the principle of Addition, but also such inferences as '$A \therefore B \vee A$'. Also we permit such inferences as '$A \vee B, \sim B \therefore A$' by the principle of the Disjunctive Syllogism as well as '$A \vee B$, $\sim A \therefore B$'. Since the definition of Material Implication and the principle of Distribution can always be used to obtain '$A \supset (B \cdot C)$' from '$(A \supset B) \cdot (A \supset C)$', and vice versa, our demonstrations can be shortened by permitting Distribution to be applied directly to conditionals having conjunctions as their consequents. This is tantamount to adding the form '$[p \supset (q \cdot r)] \equiv [(p \supset q) \cdot (p \supset r)]$' to our list as an alternative version of the principle of Distribution. By repeated application of the principles of Association and Commutation we can rearrange the terms of any conjunction or disjunction in any way we please. Hence we can shorten our demonstrations by omitting parentheses, brackets, etc., from conjunctions of any three or more propositions. Thus such propositions as '$A \cdot \{B \cdot [C \cdot (D \cdot E)]\}$', '$(A \cdot B) \cdot [C \cdot (D \cdot E)]$', '$(A \cdot B) \cdot [(C \cdot D) \cdot E]$', '$[(A \cdot B) \cdot C] \cdot (D \cdot E)$', '$[A \cdot (B \cdot C)] \cdot (D \cdot E)$', '$\{[(A \cdot B) \cdot C] \cdot D\} \cdot E$', '$A \cdot [(B \cdot C) \cdot (D \cdot E)]$', . . . will all be written indifferently as '$A \cdot B \cdot C \cdot D \cdot E$', and *any* permutation will be justified simply by the principle of Commutation. Moreover, if it is desired to infer the conjunction of *some* of the indicated conjuncts, in any order, this can be done in one step and justified by the principle of Simplification. Thus from '$A \cdot B \cdot C \cdot D \cdot E$' we can infer '$E \cdot B \cdot D$' in a single step. Also the principle of Conjunction can be applied to any number of lines to produce a new line that is the conjunction of all of them. Finally we shall permit the telescoping of the rules of Material Implication, De Morgan, and Double Negation to obtain '$\sim(A \supset B)$' from '$A \cdot \sim B$' and vice versa, which amounts to adding the form '$\sim(p \supset q) \equiv (p \cdot \sim q)$' to our list as an alternative version of Material Implication.

In proving the validity of some arguments all four of our quantification rules must be used. Consider the following moderately complex argument:

If all drugs are contaminated then all negligent technicians are scoundrels. If there are any drugs which are contaminated then all drugs are contaminated and unsafe. All germicides are drugs. Only the negligent are absent-minded. Therefore if any technician is absent-minded then if some germicides are contaminated then he is a scoundrel.

Using fairly obvious abbreviations, it may be symbolized and proved valid as follows:

1. $(x)[Dx \supset Cx] \supset (y)[(Ny \cdot Ty) \supset Sy]$
2. $(\exists x)[Dx \cdot Cx] \supset (y)[Dy \supset (Cy \cdot Uy)]$
3. $(x)[Gx \supset Dx]$
4. $(x)[Ax \supset Nx]$ $/\therefore (x)\{(Tx \cdot Ax) \supset \{(\exists y)[Gy \cdot Cy] \supset Sx\}\}$
5. $Tu \cdot Au$
6. $(\exists y)[Gy \cdot Cy]$
7. $Gw \cdot Cw$
8. $Gw \supset Dw$ 3, **UI**
9. Gw 7, Simp.
10. Dw 8, 9, M.P.
11. Cw 7, Simp.
12. $Dw \cdot Cw$ 10, 11, Conj.
13. $(\exists x)[Dx \cdot Cx]$ 12, **EG**
14. $(y)[Dy \supset (Cy \cdot Uy)]$ 2, 13, M.P.
15. $Dz \supset (Cz \cdot Uz)$ 14, **UI**
16. $(Dz \supset Cz) \cdot (Dz \supset Uz)$ 15, Dist.
17. $Dz \supset Cz$ 16, Simp.
18. $(x)[Dx \supset Cx]$ 17, **UG**
19. $(y)[(Ny \cdot Ty) \supset Sy]$ 1, 18, M.P.
20. $(Nu \cdot Tu) \supset Su$ 19, **UI**
21. Au 5, Simp.
22. $Au \supset Nu$ 4, **UI**
23. Nu 22, 21, M.P.
24. Tu 5, Simp.
25. $Nu \cdot Tu$ 23, 24, Conj.
26. Su 20, 25, M.P.
27. Su 6, 7–26, **EI**
28. $(\exists y)[Gy \cdot Cy] \supset Su$ 6–27, C.P.
29. $(Tu \cdot Au) \supset \{(\exists y)[Gy \cdot Cy] \supset Su\}$ 5–28, C.P.
30. $(x)\{(Tx \cdot Ax) \supset \{(\exists y)[Gy \cdot Cy] \supset Sx\}\}$ 29, **UG**

EXERCISES

Construct a formal proof of validity for each of the following arguments, in each case using the suggested notation, and making the symbolic formulas parallel the English as closely as possible:

1. No acrobats are clumsy. Therefore if Al is a waiter then if all waiters are clumsy Al is not an acrobat. (*Ax, Cx, Wx, a.*)

2. All pets are gentle. Therefore if any dogs are excitable and no excitable dogs are gentle they are not pets. (*Px, Gx, Dx, Ex.*)

3. All the accused are guilty. All who are convicted will hang. Therefore, if all who are guilty are convicted then all the accused will hang. (*Ax, Gx, Cx, Hx.*)

★4. If there are any geniuses then all great composers are geniuses. If anyone is temperamental, all geniuses are temperamental. Therefore, if anyone is a temperamental genius, then all great composers are temperamental. (*Gx*: *x* is a genius. *Cx*: *x* is a great composer. *Px*: *x* is a person. *Tx*: *x* is temperamental.)

5. Any car with good brakes is safe to drive and safe to ride in. So if a car is new then if all new cars have good brakes it is safe to drive. (*Cx*: *x* is a car. *Bx*: *x* has good brakes. *Dx*: *x* is safe to drive. *Rx*: *x* is safe to ride in. *Nx*: *x* is new.)

6. Either all the guests enjoyed themselves or some of the guests concealed their real feelings. No honest person would conceal his real feelings. Therefore if the guests were all honest persons then all the guests enjoyed themselves. (*Gx*: *x* is a guest. *Ex*: *x* enjoyed himself. *Cx*: *x* conceals his real feelings. *Hx*: *x* is honest. *Px*: *x* is a person.)

7. Any businessman who is a poet must be a wealthy man. Wealthy men are all conservatives. If some conservative does not like poetry then no poets are conservatives. Therefore if there is a wealthy man who does not like poetry then no businessmen are poets. (*Bx*: *x* is a businessman. *Px*: *x* is a poet. *Wx*: *x* is a wealthy man. *Cx*: *x* is a conservative. *Lx*: *x* likes poetry.)

★8. All radioactive substances either have a very short life or have medical value. No uranium isotope which is radioactive has a very short life. Therefore if all uranium isotopes are radioactive then all uranium isotopes have medical value. (*Rx*: *x* is radioactive. *Sx*: *x* has a very short life. *Mx*: *x* has medical value. *Ux*: *x* is a uranium isotope.)

9. No sane witness would lie if his lying would implicate him in a crime. Therefore if any witness implicated himself in a crime, then if all witnesses were sane, that witness did not lie. (*Sx*: *x* is sane. *Wx*: *x* is a witness. *Lx*: *x* lies. *Ix*: *x* implicates himself in a crime.)

10. If any jewelry is missing then if all the servants are honest it will be returned. If any servant is honest they all are. So if any jewelry is missing then if at least one servant is honest it will be returned. (*Jx*: *x* is jewelry. *Mx*: *x* is missing. *Sx*: *x* is a servant. *Hx*: *x* is honest. *Rx*: *x* will be returned.)

11. If there are any liberals then all philosophers are liberals. If there are any humanitarians, then all liberals are humanitarians. So if there are any humanitarians who are liberals then all philosophers are humanitarians. (*Lx*: *x* is a liberal. *Px*: *x* is a philosopher. *Hx*: *x* is a humanitarian.)

★12. If something is lost then if everyone values his possessions it will be missed. If anyone values his possessions, so does everyone. Therefore if something is lost then if someone values his possessions then something will be missed. (*Lx*: *x* is lost. *Px*: *x* is a person. *Vx*: *x* values his possessions. *Mx*: *x* is missed.)

4.6 LOGICAL TRUTHS INVOLVING QUANTIFIERS

In Chapter 2 truth tables were used not only to establish the *validity* of arguments but also to certify the *logical truth* of propositions (tautologies such as '$A \lor \sim A$'). The notion of a logically true proposition is therefore familiar. As we have seen, not every valid argument can be established by the method of truth tables: some of them are proved valid using quantification rules. Similarly, not every logically true proposition can be certified by the method of truth tables: some of them are *demonstrated* using quantification rules.

The method used in demonstrating the logical truth of tautologies was set forth in Chapter 3. A demonstration of the logical truth of the tautology '$A \supset (A \lor B)$' can be set down as

$$
\begin{array}{lll}
\text{1. } & A & \\
\text{2. } & A \lor B & \text{1, Add.} \\
\text{3. } & A \supset (A \lor B) & \text{1–2, C.P.}
\end{array}
$$

In demonstrating the logical truth of propositions involving quantifiers, we shall have to appeal not only to the original list of elementary valid argument forms and the strengthened principle of Conditional Proof, but to our quantification rules as well. Thus a demonstration of the logical truth of the proposition '$(x)Fx \supset (\exists x)Fx$' can be set down as

$$
\begin{array}{lll}
\text{1. } & (x)Fx & \\
\text{2. } & Fy & \text{1, UI} \\
\text{3. } & (\exists x)Fx & \text{2, EG} \\
\text{4. } & (x)Fx \supset (\exists x)Fx & \text{1–3, C.P.}
\end{array}
$$

(In discussing 'logical truth' we explicitly limit our consideration to possible nonempty universes, just as in discussing *validity*.)

Other logically true propositions involving quantifiers require more complicated demonstrations. For example, the logically true proposition '$(x)Fx \supset \sim(\exists x)\sim Fx$' has the following demonstration:

1. $(\exists x)\sim Fx$	
2. $\sim Fy$	
3. $(x)Fx$	
4. Fy	3, **UI**
5. $(x)Fx \supset Fy$	3–4, C.P.
6. $\sim(x)Fx$	5, 2, M.T.
7. $\sim(x)Fx$	1, 2–6, **EI**
8. $(\exists x)\sim Fx \supset \sim(x)Fx$	1–7, C.P.
9. $(x)Fx \supset \sim(\exists x)\sim Fx$	8, Trans., D.N.

Similarly, the truth of '$\sim(\exists x)\sim Fx \supset (x)Fx$' is demonstrated by the following:

1. $\sim(\exists x)\sim Fx$	
2. $\sim Fy$	
3. $(\exists x)\sim Fx$	2, **EG**
4. $\sim Fy \supset (\exists x)\sim Fx$	2–3, C.P.
5. Fy	4, 1, M.T., D.N.
6. $(x)Fx$	5, **UG**
7. $\sim(\exists x)\sim Fx \supset (x)Fx$	1–6, C.P.

Given the logical truths established by the two preceding demonstrations, we conjoin them to obtain the equivalence '$(x)Fx \equiv \sim(\exists x)\sim Fx$', already noted to be a logical truth in Section 4.1 of the present chapter. Since our proof of this equivalence does not depend upon any peculiarities of the propositional function 'Fx', the equivalence holds for *any* propositional function. And since our proof does not depend upon any peculiarities of the variable 'x', the equivalence holds not only for any propositional function but for any individual variable. The equivalence form $(\nu)\Phi\nu \equiv \sim(\exists\nu)\sim\Phi\nu$ is thus seen to be *logically true*, and can be added to the other logical equivalences in our list of Rules of Inference.

It permits us validly to interchange $(\nu)\Phi\nu$ and $\sim(\exists\nu)\sim\Phi\nu$ wherever they may occur. This connection between the two quantifiers by way of negation will now be adopted as an additional rule of inference, and may be used in constructing formal proofs of validity and demonstrations of logical truth. When it is so used, the letters 'QN' (for *quantifier negation*) should be written to indicate the principle being appealed to. It should be obvious that the forms

$$\sim(\nu)\Phi\nu \equiv (\exists\nu)\sim\Phi\nu$$
$$(\nu)\sim\Phi\nu \equiv \sim(\exists\nu)\Phi\nu$$
$$\sim(\nu)\sim\Phi\nu \equiv (\exists\nu)\Phi\nu$$

are all logically equivalent to each other and to the form **QN**, and are therefore logically true.

Some fairly obvious logical truths are simply stated and easily demonstrated with our present symbolic apparatus. A logically true equivalence, for any propositional functions '*Fx*' and '*Gx*', is

$$[(x)Fx \cdot (x)Gx] \equiv (x)(Fx \cdot Gx)$$

which asserts that: everything has the property F and everything has the property G if and only if everything has both the properties F and G. The demonstrations of the two implications involved may be written side by side:

1.	$(x)Fx \cdot (x)Gx$		1.	$(x)(Fx \cdot Gx)$	
2.	$(x)Fx$	1, Simp.	2.	$Fy \cdot Gy$	1, **UI**
3.	$(x)Gx$	1, Simp.	3.	Fy	2, Simp.
4.	Fy	2, **UI**	4.	Gy	2, Simp.
5.	Gy	3, **UI**	5.	$(x)Fx$	3, **UG**
6.	$Fy \cdot Gy$	4, 5, Conj.	6.	$(x)Gx$	4, **UG**
7.	$(x)(Fx \cdot Gx)$	6, **UG**	7.	$(x)Fx \cdot (x)Gx$	5, 6, Conj.
8.	$[(x)Fx \cdot (x)Gx] \supset (x)(Fx \cdot Gx)$		8.	$(x)(Fx \cdot Gx) \supset [(x)Fx \cdot (x)Gx]$	
	1–7, C.P.			1–7, C.P.	

Another logical truth is in the form of a conditional rather than an equivalence. Written as

$$[(x)Fx \text{ v } (x)Gx] \supset (x)(Fx \text{ v } Gx)$$

it asserts that if either everything is an F or everything is a G, then everything is either an F or a G. Its demonstration involves making several assumptions of limited scope, and can be written as follows:

1.	$(x)Fx$ v $(x)Gx$	
2.	$(x)Fx$	
3.	Fy	2, **UI**
4.	Fy v Gy	3, Add.
5.	$(x)(Fx$ v $Gx)$	4, **UG**
6.	$(x)Fx \supset (x)(Fx$ v $Gx)$	2–5, C.P.
7.	$(x)Gx$	
8.	Gy	7, **UI**
9.	Fy v Gy	8, Add.
10.	$(x)(Fx$ v $Gx)$	9, **UG**
11.	$(x)Gx \supset (x)(Fx$ v $Gx)$	7–10, C.P.
12.	$[(x)Fx \supset (x)(Fx$ v $Gx)] \cdot [(x)Gx \supset (x)(Fx$ v $Gx)]$	6, 11, Conj.
13.	$(x)(Fx$ v $Gx)$ v $(x)(Fx$ v $Gx)$	12, 1, C.D.
14.	$(x)(Fx$ v $Gx)$	13, Taut.
15.	$[(x)Fx$ v $(x)Gx] \supset (x)(Fx$ v $Gx)$	1–14, C.P.

The converse of this conditional is *not* logically true, however. The converse states that if everything is either F or G then either everything is F or everything is G. That this converse is not always true can be seen by replacing 'G' by '$\sim F$', for '$(x)(Fx$ v $\sim Fx)$' is true for any predicate 'F', while there are few predicates for which '$(x)Fx$ v $(x)\sim Fx$' holds. Another logical truth conditional in form is

$$(\exists x)(Fx \cdot Gx) \supset [(\exists x)Fx \cdot (\exists x)Gx]$$

Its demonstration is perfectly straightforward, and can be left as an exercise for the reader. That its converse is not true in general can be seen by again replacing 'G' by '$\sim F$'. For most predicates 'F' the proposition '$(\exists x)Fx \cdot (\exists x)\sim Fx$' is true (e.g. 'something is round and something is not round'), but for any 'F' the proposition '$(\exists x)(Fx \cdot \sim Fx)$' is logically false.

It has already been observed that propositional functions can contain propositions and/or other propositional functions as components.

Examples of such propositional functions are

$$Fx \cdot Ga, \ Fx \vee Fy, \ Gy \vee (z)Hz, \ Gw \supset Fz, \ \ldots$$

When such propositional functions as these are quantified, to obtain

$$(x)[Fx \cdot Ga], \ (x)[Fx \vee Fy], \ (\exists y)[Gy \vee (z)Hz], \ (z)[Gw \supset Fz], \ \ldots$$

we have propositions and/or propositional functions lying within the scopes of quantifiers, although the quantifiers have no real affect on those expressions. When a quantifier with respect to a given variable is prefixed to an expression its only effect is to bind previously free occurrences of that variable. In the expressions written above, the propositions 'Ga' and '$(z)Hz$', and the propositional functions 'Fy' and 'Gw', although lying within the scopes of the quantifiers '(x)', '$(\exists y)$', '(x)' and '(z)', respectively, are not really affected by them. Wherever we have an expression containing a quantifier on the variable μ within whose scope lies either a proposition or a propositional function not containing a free occurrence of μ, the entire expression is logically equivalent to another expression in which the scope of that quantifier does *not* extend over the proposition or propositional function. An example or two will make this clear. In the following, let 'Q' be either a proposition or a propositional function containing no free occurrence of the variable 'x', and 'Fx' any propositional function containing at least one free occurrence of the variable 'x'. Our first equivalence here is between the universal quantification of '$Fx \cdot Q$' and the conjunction of the universal quantification of 'Fx' with 'Q', which is more briefly expressed as

$$(x)(Fx \cdot Q) \equiv [(x)Fx \cdot Q]$$

The demonstration of this equivalence can be written as

1.	$(x)(Fx \cdot Q)$		1.	$(x)Fx \cdot Q$	
2.	$Fx \cdot Q$	1, **UI**	2.	$(x)Fx$	1, Simp.
3.	Fx	2, Simp.	3.	Fx	2, **UI**
4.	$(x)Fx$	3, **UG**	4.	Q	1, Simp.
5.	Q	2, Simp.	5.	$Fx \cdot Q$	3, 4, Conj.
6.	$(x)Fx \cdot Q$	4, 5, Conj.	6.	$(x)(Fx \cdot Q)$	5, **UG**
7.	$(x)(Fx \cdot Q) \supset [(x)Fx \cdot Q]$	1–6, C.P.	7.	$[(x)Fx \cdot Q] \supset (x)(Fx \cdot Q)$	1–6, C.P.

Another logical equivalence holds between the universal quantification of '$Q \supset Fx$' and the conditional statement whose antecedent is 'Q' and whose consequent is the universal quantification of 'Fx'. The first asserts that *given any individual x, Q implies that x has F*, and is equivalent to *Q implies that given any individual x, x has F*. Our symbolic expression of this equivalence is

$$(x)(Q \supset Fx) \equiv [Q \supset (x)Fx]$$

Its demonstration is easily constructed:

1. $(x)(Q \supset Fx)$		1. $Q \supset (x)Fx$	
2. $Q \supset Fx$	1, **UI**	2. Q	
3. Q		3. $(x)Fx$	1, 2, M.P.
4. Fx	2, 3, M.P.	4. Fx	3, **UI**
5. $(x)Fx$	4, **UG**	5. $Q \supset Fx$	2–4, C.P.
6. $Q \supset (x)Fx$	3–5, C.P.	6. $(x)(Q \supset Fx)$	5, **UG**
7. $(x)(Q \supset Fx) \supset$		7. $[Q \supset (x)Fx] \supset$	
$[Q \supset (x)Fx]$	1–6, C.P.	$(x)(Q \supset Fx)$	1–6, C.P.

The same pattern of equivalence holds for the existential quantification of '$Q \supset Fx$' and the conditional statement '$Q \supset (\exists x)Fx$'. The first asserts that *there is at least one individual x such that Q implies that x has F*, and is equivalent to *Q implies that there is at least one individual x such that x has F*, which is asserted by the second. Its demonstration is very easily constructed, and will be left as an exercise.

However, the pattern of equivalence is different when 'Q' occurs as consequent rather than antecedent. Although the universal quantification of '$Fx \supset Q$' implies '$(x)Fx \supset Q$', it is not implied by the latter. There is an equivalence, however, between *given any x, if x has F then Q* and *if there is at least one x such that x has F, then Q*, which was established informally on page 111, and is expressed symbolically as

$$(x)(Fx \supset Q) \equiv [(\exists x)Fx \supset Q]$$

And although the existential quantification of '$Fx \supset Q$' is implied by '$(\exists x)Fx \supset Q$', it does not imply the latter. There is an equivalence, however, between *there is at least one x such that if x has F then Q* and *if given any x, x has F, then Q*, which is expressed symbolically as

$$(\exists x)(Fx \supset Q) \equiv [(x)Fx \supset Q]$$

This logical equivalence supplies an alternative method of symbolizing one of the propositions discussed in Section 4.4:

> If something is wrong with the house then everyone in the house complains.

The translation given there abbreviates to

$$(\exists x)Wx \supset (y)(Py \supset Cy)$$

which, as we have just remarked, is logically equivalent to

$$(x)[Wx \supset (y)(Py \supset Cy)]$$

We shall conclude our discussion of logically true propositions involving quantifiers by turning our attention to four logically true propositions which are neither equivalences nor conditionals. They correspond, in a sense, to our quantification rules:

1. $(y)[(x)Fx \supset Fy]$
2. $(y)[Fy \supset (\exists x)Fx]$
3. $(\exists y)[Fy \supset (x)Fx]$
4. $(\exists y)[(\exists x)Fx \supset Fy]$

The first of these corresponds to **UI**, saying, as it does, that given any individual *y*, if every individual has the property *F*, then *y* does. Its demonstration is almost trivially obvious, proceeding:

1. $(x)Fx$		
2. Fz	1, **UI**	
3. $(x)Fx \supset Fz$	1–2, C.P.	
4. $(y)[(x)Fx \supset Fy]$	3, **UG**	

The second corresponds to **EG**, asserting that if any given individual *y* has the property *F*, then something has *F*. The third and fourth, corresponding to **UG** and **EI**, respectively, are not so immediately obvious, but nevertheless are logically true and quite easily demonstrated. An intuitive explanation can be given by reference to the ancient Athenian general and statesman Aristides, often called 'the just'. So outstanding was Aristides for his rectitude that the Athenians had a saying:

If anyone is just, Aristides is just.

With respect to *any* property, there is always some individual *y* such that if anything has that property, *y* has it. That is what is asserted by the fourth proposition listed above, which corresponds to **EI**. The matter can be put another way. If we turn our attention not to the property of being just, but to its reverse, the property of being corruptible, then the sense of the first Athenian saying is also expressible as

If Aristides is corruptible, then everyone is corruptible.

Again generalizing, we may observe that with respect to *any* property there is always some individual *y* such that if *y* has that property, everything has it. That is what is asserted by the third proposition listed above, which corresponds to **UG**. Its demonstration proceeds:

1.	$\sim(\exists y)[Fy \supset (x)Fx]$	
2.	$(y)\sim[Fy \supset (x)Fx]$	1, **QN**
3.	$\sim[Fy \supset (x)Fx]$	2, **UI**
4.	$Fy \cdot \sim(x)Fx$	3, Impl.
5.	Fy	4, Simp.
6.	$(x)Fx$	5, **UG**
7.	$(x)Fx \ v \ (\exists y)[Fy \supset (x)Fx]$	6, Add.
8.	$\sim(x)Fx$	4, Simp.
9.	$(\exists y)[Fy \supset (x)Fx]$	7, 8, D.S.
10.	$\sim(\exists y)[Fy \supset (x)Fx] \supset (\exists y)[Fy \supset (x)Fx]$	1–9, C.P.
11.	$(\exists y)[Fy \supset (x)Fx] \ v \ (\exists y)[Fy \supset (x)Fx]$	10, Impl., D.N.
12.	$(\exists y)[Fy \supset (x)Fx]$	11, Taut.

Although we shall not prove it until the end of Chapter 9, the methods of proof so far assembled (techniques for 'Natural Deduction', as they are sometimes called) permit the demonstration of all logically true propositions constructed out of truth-functional connectives and the quantification of individual variables. It will also be proved that *only* propositions that are logically true can be demonstrated by these techniques.

EXERCISES

Construct demonstrations for the following, in which 'Q' is either a proposition or a propositional function containing no free occurrence of the variable 'x':

1. $(x)(Fx \supset Q) \equiv [(\exists x)Fx \supset Q]$
2. $(\exists x)(Fx \cdot Gx) \supset [(\exists x)Fx \cdot (\exists x)Gx]$
3. $(x)(Fx \supset Gx) \supset [(x)Fx \supset (x)Gx]$
★4. $[(\exists x)Fx \supset (\exists x)Gx] \supset (\exists x)(Fx \supset Gx)$
5. $(\exists x)(Q \supset Fx) \equiv [Q \supset (\exists x)Fx]$
6. $(\exists x)(Fx \cdot Q) \equiv [(\exists x)Fx \cdot Q]$
7. $(x)(Fx \lor Q) \equiv [(x)Fx \lor Q]$
★8. $(\exists x)(Fx \lor Q) \equiv [(\exists x)Fx \lor Q]$
9. $(\exists x)(Fx \supset Q) \equiv [(x)Fx \supset Q]$
10. $(y)[Fy \supset (\exists x)Fx]$
11. $(\exists y)[(\exists x)Fx \supset Fy]$
★12. $[(\exists x)Fx \lor (\exists x)Gx] \equiv (\exists x)(Fx \lor Gx)$

5

THE
LOGIC
OF
RELATIONS

5.1 SYMBOLIZING RELATIONS

Some propositions containing two or more proper names (of individuals) are correctly interpreted as truth-functional compounds of singular propositions having different subject terms. For example, the proposition

Lincoln and Grant were presidents.

is properly interpreted as the conjunction of the two singular propositions

Lincoln was a president   and   Grant was a president.

But for some other propositions having the same verbal pattern that analysis is wholly unsatisfactory. Thus the proposition

Lincoln and Grant were acquainted.

is definitely *not* a conjunction or any other truth function of the two expressions

Lincoln was acquainted   and   Grant was acquainted.

On the contrary, dividing the proposition in this way destroys its significance, for its meaning is not that both Lincoln and Grant were (or had) acquaintances, but that they were *acquainted with each other*. The given proposition does not assert that Lincoln and Grant both had a certain *property*, but that they stood in a certain *relation*. Lincoln is not said simply to be acquainted (whatever that might mean), but *acquainted with Grant*. Other propositions that express relations between two individuals are

John loves Mary

Plato was a student of Socrates.

Isaac was a son of Abraham.

New York is east of Chicago.

Chicago is smaller than New York.

Relations such as these, that can hold between two individuals, are called 'binary' or 'dyadic'. Other relations may relate three or more individuals. For example, the propositions

Detroit is between New York and Chicago.

Helen introduced John to Mary.

America won the Philippines from Spain.

express *ternary* or *triadic* relations, while *quaternary* or *tetradic* relations are expressed by the propositions

America bought Alaska from Russia for seven million dollars.

Jack traded his cow to the peddler for a handful of beans.

Al, Bill, Charlie, and Doug played bridge together.

Relations enter into arguments in various ways. One example of a relational argument is

Al is older than Bill.

Bill is older than Charlie.

Therefore, Al is older than Charlie.

A slightly more complex example, which involves quantification, is

Helen likes David.

Whoever likes David likes Tom.

Helen likes only good-looking men.

Therefore, Tom is a good-looking man.

A still more complex relational inference, which involves multiple quantification, is:

All horses are animals.
_____

Therefore, the head of a horse is the head of an animal.

The latter is a valid inference that, as De Morgan observed, all the logic of Aristotle will not permit one to draw. Its validation by our apparatus of quantifiers and propositional functions will be set forth in the next section.

Before discussing proofs of validity for relational arguments (and they will require no methods of proof beyond those developed in the preceding chapter) the problem of *symbolizing* relational propositions must be dealt with. Just as a single predicate symbol can occur in different propositions, so a single relation symbol can occur in different propositions. Just as we have the predicate 'human' common to the propositions:

Aristotle is human.
Plato is human.
Socrates is human.

so we have the relation word 'teacher' common to the propositions:

Socrates was a teacher of Plato.
Plato was a teacher of Aristotle.

And just as we regard the three subject-predicate propositions as different substitution instances of the propositional function 'x is human', so we can regard the two relational propositions as different substitution instances of the propositional function 'x was a teacher of y'. Replacing the variable 'x' by the constant 'Socrates' and the variable 'y' by the constant 'Plato' gives us the first proposition; replacing the 'x' by 'Plato' and the 'y' by 'Aristotle' gives the second. The *order* of replacement is of great importance here: if 'x' is replaced by 'Aristotle' and 'y' by 'Plato', the result is the *false* proposition

Aristotle was a teacher of Plato.

Just as a propositional function of one variable like 'x is human' was abbreviated as 'Hx', so a propositional function of two variables like 'x

was the teacher of y' is abbreviated as 'Txy'. Similarly, the propositional function 'x is between y and z' will be abbreviated as '$Bxyz$', and the propositional function 'x traded y to z for w' will be abbreviated as '$Txyzw$'. Our first example of a relational argument involves no quantifiers and is very easily symbolized. Using the individual constants 'a', 'b', and 'c' to denote Al, Bill, and Charlie, and the expression 'Oxy' to abbreviate 'x is older than y', we have

$$Oab$$
$$\underline{Obc}$$
$$\therefore\ Oac$$

Our second argument is not much more difficult, since none of its propositions contains more than a single quantifier. Using the individual constants 'h', 'd', and 't' to denote Helen, David, and Tom, respectively, 'Gx' to abbreviate 'x is a good-looking man', and the symbol 'Lxy' to abbreviate 'x likes y', the argument can be symbolized as

1. Lhd
2. $(x)(Lxd \supset Lxt)$
3. $\underline{(x)(Lhx \supset Gx)}$
    $\therefore\ Gt$

A proof of its validity is so easily constructed that it may well be set down now. Referring back to the numbered premisses, the proof proceeds:

4. $Lhd \supset Lht$ 2, **UI**
5. Lht 4, 1, M.P.
6. $Lht \supset Gt$ 3, **UI**
7. Gt 6, 5, M.P.

Symbolizing relational propositions becomes more complicated when several quantifiers occur in a single proposition. Our discussion of the problem will be simplified by confining attention at first to the two individual constants, 'a', and 'b', and the propositional function 'x attracts y', abbreviated as 'Axy'. The two statements 'a attracts b' and 'b is attracted by a' obviously have the same meaning, the first expressing that meaning by use of the *active voice*, the second by use of the *passive voice.* Both statements translate directly into the single formula '*Aab*'. Similarly, the two statements '*b* attracts *a*' and '*a* is attracted by *b*' are both symbolized by the formula '*Aba*'. These two different substitution instances of '*Axy*' are logically independent of each other, either can be true without entailing the truth of the other.

We are still on elementary and familiar ground when we come to symbolize

'*a* attracts everything'
'everything is attracted by *a*' } as '(*x*)*Aax*',

'*a* attracts something'
'something is attracted by *a*' } as '(∃*x*)*Aax*',

'everything attracts *a*'
'*a* is attracted by everything' } as '(*x*)*Axa*',

'something attracts *a*'
'*a* is attracted by something' } as '(∃*x*)*Axa*'.

But the problem of symbolizing becomes more complex when we dispense entirely with individual constants and consider relational propositions that are completely general. The simplest propositions of this kind are

1. Everything attracts everything.
2. Everything is attracted by everything.
3. Something attracts something.
4. Something is attracted by something.
5. Nothing attracts anything.
6. Nothing is attracted by anything.

which are symbolized by the following formulas:

1. $(x)(y)Axy$
2. $(y)(x)Axy$
3. $(\exists x)(\exists y)Axy$
4. $(\exists y)(\exists x)Axy$
5. $(x)(y){\sim}Axy$
6. $(y)(x){\sim}Axy$

In their English formulations, propositions 1 and 2 are clearly equivalent to each other, as are 3 and 4, and 5 and 6. The first two equivalences are easily established for the corresponding symbolic translations:

1. $(x)(y)Axy$			1. $(\exists x)(\exists y)Axy$	
2. $(y)Awy$	1, **UI**		2. $(\exists y)Awy$	
3. Awv	2, **UI**		3. Awv	
4. $(x)Axv$	3, **UG**		4. $(\exists x)Axv$	3, **EG**
5. $(y)(x)Axy$	4, **UG**		5. $(\exists y)(\exists x)Axy$	4, **EG**
6. $(x)(y)Axy \supset (y)(x)Axy$			6. $(\exists y)(\exists x)Axy$	2, 3–5, **EI**
1–5, C.P.			7. $(\exists y)(\exists x)Axy$	1, 2–6, **EI**
			8. $(\exists x)(\exists y)Axy \supset (\exists y)(\exists x)Axy$	
			1–7, C.P.	

These demonstrate the logical truth of conditionals rather than of equivalences, but their converses can be established by the same patterns of argument. (The equivalence between formulas 5 and 6 is clearly established by the same pattern of argument that proves 1 equivalent to 2.)

When we turn to the next pair of statements

7. Everything attracts something.

8. Something is attracted by everything.

there is no longer any logical equivalence or sameness of meaning. Sentence 7 is not entirely unambiguous, and some exceptional contexts might shift its meaning, but its most natural interpretation is *not* that there is some one thing that is attracted by everything, but rather that everything attracts *something or other*. We symbolize it by way of successive paraphrasings, writing first

$$(x)(x \text{ attracts something})$$

and then symbolizing the expression 'x attracts something' the same way in which we symbolized 'a attracts something'. This gives us the formula

7. $(x)(\exists y)Axy$

Sentence 8 is also susceptible of alternative interpretations, one of which would make it synonymous with sentence 7, meaning that something or other is attracted by any (given) thing. But a perfectly straightforward way of understanding sentence 8 is to take it as asserting that some *one thing* is attracted by all things. It, too, is symbolized in a stepwise fashion, writing first

$$(\exists y)(y \text{ is attracted by everything})$$

and then symbolizing the expression '*y* is attracted by everything' the same way that we symbolized '*a* is attracted by everything'. This gives us the formula

8. $(\exists y)(x)Axy$

There is a certain *misleading* similarity between formulas 7 and 8. They both consist of the propositional function '*Axy*' to which are applied a universal quantifier with respect to '*x*' and an existential quantifier with respect to '*y*'. But the *order* in which the quantifiers are written is different in each case, and that makes a world of difference in their meanings. Formula 7, in which the universal quantifier comes first, asserts that given anything in the universe, there is something or other that it attracts. But formula 8, in which the existential quantifier comes first, asserts that there is some one thing in the universe such that everything in the universe attracts *it*. Where two quantifiers are applied successively to one propositional function, if they are both universal or both existential, their order does not matter, as is shown by the equivalence of formulas 1 and 2, 3 and 4, and 5 and 6. But where one is universal and the other existential, the order of generalization or quantification is very important indeed.

Although formulas 7 and 8 are not equivalent, they are not independent. The former is validly deducible from the latter. The demonstration is easily constructed as follows:

1. $(\exists y)(x)Axy$
2. $(x)Axv$
3. Auv 2, **UI**
4. $(\exists y)Auy$ 3, **EG**
5. $(\exists y)Auy$ 1, 2–4, **EI**
6. $(x)(\exists y)Axy$ 5, **UG**

But the inference is valid only one way. Any attempt to derive formula 8 from 7 must inevitably run afoul of one of the restrictions on **UG**.

The argument

$$(x)(\exists y)Axy$$
$$\therefore\ (\exists y)(x)Axy$$

is easily proved invalid by the method of Section 4.3. For a possible nonempty universe containing just the two individuals a and b, the given argument is logically equivalent to the truth-functional argument

$$(Aaa \text{ v } Aab)\cdot(Aba \text{ v } Abb)$$
$$\therefore\ (Aaa\cdot Aba) \text{ v } (Aab\cdot Abb)$$

which is proved invalid by assigning the truth value **T** to 'Aaa' and Abb', and the truth value **F** to 'Aab' and 'Aba'.

A similar pair of inequivalent propositions may be written as

9. Everything is attracted by something.
10. Something attracts everything.

These are clearly inequivalent when the 'something' in 9, coming at the end, is understood as 'something or other', and the 'something' in 10, coming at the beginning, is understood as 'some one thing'. They are symbolized as

9. $(y)(\exists x)Axy$
10. $(\exists x)(y)Axy$

Relational propositions are sometimes formulated as though they were simple subject-predicate assertions. For example, 'a was struck' is most plausibly interpreted to assert that *something struck a*. Such implicit occurrences of relations are often marked by the passive voice of a transitive verb. Our symbolizing of propositions containing implicit relations should be guided by consideration of the use to which they are to be put. Our purpose in symbolizing arguments is to put them into a form convenient for testing their validity. Our goal, therefore, with respect to a given argument, is not to provide a theoretically complete analysis, but rather to provide one sufficiently complete for the purpose at hand—the testing of validity. Consequently some implicit relations may be left implicit, while others require a more thorough analysis, as may be made clear by an example. Consider the argument

Whoever visited the building was observed. Anyone who had observed Andrews would have remembered him. Nobody remembered Andrews. Therefore, Andrews didn't visit the building.

The first proposition of this argument contains two relations, one explicit, the other implicit. Explicitly, we have the relation of *someone visiting the building*. It is explicit because mention is made of both the visitor and what was visited by him. Implicitly, we have the relation of *someone observing someone*, which is implicit because no mention is made of the someone who does the observing—the omission being marked by the use of the passive voice. However, because the only other occurrence of 'x visited the building' is also as a *unit*, in the conclusion, it need not be treated as a relation at all, but may be symbolized as a simple predicate. On the other hand, 'x observed y', despite its merely implicit occurrence in the first premiss, must be explicitly symbolized as a relation if the argument is to be proved valid. For its second occurrence is not a simple repetition of the original unit; it appears instead as an explicit relation, with the first variable quantified and the second replaced by the proper name 'Andrews'. Using 'a' to denote Andrews, 'Vx' to abbreviate 'x visited the building', 'Oxy' to abbreviate 'x observed y', and 'Rxy' to abbreviate 'x remembers y', a symbolic translation and proof of validity for the given argument may be written as

1. $(x)[Vx \supset (\exists y)Oyx]$
2. $(x)[Oxa \supset Rxa]$
3. $(x)\sim Rxa$ $/ \therefore \sim Va$
4. $Oza \supset Rza$ 2, **UI**
5. $\sim Rza$ 3, **UI**
6. $\sim Oza$ 4, 5, M.T.
7. $(y)\sim Oya$ 6, **UG**
8. $\sim(\exists y)Oya$ 7, **QN**
9. $Va \supset (\exists y)Oya$ 1, **UI**
10. $\sim Va$ 9, 8, M.T.

Our proof of validity for this argument would not have been helped at all by symbolizing 'Andrews visited the building' as a substitution instance of the relational 'x visited y' rather than of the simpler 'Vx'. But our proof of validity depended upon our symbolizing 'was observed' explicitly as a relation.

Most of our previous examples were illustrations of *unlimited* generality, in which it was asserted that *everything* stood in such-and-such a relation, or something did, or nothing did. A great many relational propositions are not so sweeping. Most assertions are more modest, claiming not that *everything* stands in such-and-such a relation, but that everything does *if* it satisfies certain conditions or restrictions. Thus we may say either that

Everything is attracted by all magnets.

or that

Everything made of iron is attracted by all magnets.

The second, of course, is the more modest assertion, being less *general* than the first. While the first is adequately symbolized, where 'Mx' abbreviates 'x is a magnet', as

$$(x)(y)[My \supset Ayx]$$

the second is symbolized, where 'Ix' abbreviates 'x is made of iron', as

$$(x)[Ix \supset (y)(My \supset Ayx)]$$

That this symbolic translation is correct can be seen by paraphrasing the second proposition in English as

Given anything at all, *if* it is made of iron then it is attracted by all magnets.

Perhaps the best way to symbolize relational propositions is by the kind of stepwise process that has already been illustrated. Let us use it again, this time for propositions of limited generality. First let us consider the proposition

Any good amateur can beat some professional.

As a first step we may write

$$(x)\{(x \text{ is a good amateur}) \supset (x \text{ can beat some professional})\}$$

Next, the consequent of the conditional between the braces

x can beat some professional

is symbolized as a generalization or quantified expression:

$$(\exists y)[(y \text{ is a professional})\cdot(x \text{ can beat } y)]$$

Now, using the obvious abbreviations, 'Gx', 'Px', and 'Bxy' for 'x is a good amateur', 'x is a professional', and 'x can beat y', the given proposition is symbolized by the formula

$$(x)[Gx \supset (\exists y)(Py\cdot Bxy)]$$

Using the same method of paraphrasing by successive steps, we may symbolize

Some professionals can beat all amateurs.

first as

$$(\exists x)[(x \text{ is a professional})\cdot(x \text{ can beat all amateurs})]$$

then as

$$(\exists x)\{(x \text{ is a professional})\cdot(y)[(y \text{ is an amateur}) \supset (x \text{ can beat } y)]\}$$

and finally (using abbreviations) as

$$(\exists x)[Px\cdot(y)(Ay \supset Bxy)]$$

The same method is applicable in more complex cases, where more than one relation is involved. We symbolize the proposition

Anyone who promises everything to everyone is certain to disappoint somebody.

first by paraphrasing it as

$$(x)\{[(x \text{ is a person})\cdot(x \text{ promises everything to everyone})]$$
$$\supset [x \text{ disappoints somebody}]\}$$

The second conjunct of the antecedent

x promises everything to everyone

may be further paraphrased, first as

$$(y)[(y \text{ is a person}) \supset (x \text{ promises everything to } y)]$$

and then as

$$(y)[(y \text{ is a person}) \supset (z)(x \text{ promises } z \text{ to } y)]$$

The consequent in our first paraphrase

$$x \text{ disappoints somebody}$$

has its structure made more explicit by being rewritten as

$$(\exists u)[(u \text{ is a person}) \cdot (x \text{ disappoints } u)]$$

The original proposition can now be rewritten as

$$(x)\{\{(x \text{ is a person}) \cdot (y)[(y \text{ is a person}) \supset (z)(x \text{ promises } z \text{ to } y)]\}$$
$$\supset (\exists u)[(u \text{ is a person}) \cdot (x \text{ disappoints } u)]\}$$

Using the obvious abbreviations, '*Px*', '*Pxyz*', '*Dxy*' for '*x* is a person', '*x* promises *y* to *z*', and '*x* disappoints *y*', the proposition can be expressed more compactly in the formula

$$(x)\{\{Px \cdot (y)[Py \supset (z)Pxzy]\} \supset (\exists u)(Pu \cdot Dxu)\}$$

With practice, of course, not all such intermediate steps need be written out explicitly.

Quantification words such as 'everyone', 'anyone', 'everybody', 'anybody', and 'whoever', refer to *all persons* rather than to *all things;* and such quantification words as 'someone' and 'somebody' refer to *some persons* rather than to *some things*. It is frequently desirable to represent this reference in our symbolism. But doing so is not always necessary for the purpose of evaluating arguments containing these words, however, and the choice of symbols is determined on the same grounds on which one decides if a relational clause or phrase is to be symbolized explicitly as a relation or as a mere predicate.

The words 'always', 'never', and 'sometimes' frequently have non-temporal significance, as in the propositions

Good men always have friends.

Bad men never have friends.

Men who have no wives sometimes have friends.

which may be symbolized, using obvious abbreviations, as

$$(x)[(Gx \cdot Mx) \supset (\exists y)Fxy]$$
$$(x)[(Bx \cdot Mx) \supset \sim(\exists y)Fxy]$$
$$(\exists x)\{[Mx \cdot \sim(\exists y)(Wy \cdot Hxy)] \cdot (\exists z)Fxz\}$$

However, some uses of these words are definitely temporal, and when they are, they can be symbolized using the logical machinery already available, as can other temporal words like 'while', 'when', 'whenever', and the like. An example or two should serve to make this clear. Thus the proposition

Dick always writes Joan when they are separated.

asserts that all times when Dick and Joan are separated are times when Dick writes Joan. This can be symbolized using 'Tx' for 'x is a time', '$Wxyz$' for 'x writes y at (time) z', and '$Sxyz$' for 'x and y are separated at (time) z', as

$$(x)\{Tx \supset [Sdjx \supset Wdjx]\}$$

Perhaps the most vivid illustration of the adaptability of the present notation is in symbolizing the following remark, usually attributed to Lincoln:

You can fool some of the people all of the time, and all of the people some of the time, but you cannot fool all of the people all of the time.

The first conjunct: 'You can fool some of the people all of the time' is ambiguous. It may be taken to mean either that *there is at least one person who can always be fooled* or that *for any time there is at least one person (or other) who can be fooled at that time*. Adopting the first interpretation, and using 'Px' for 'x is a person', 'Tx' for 'x is a time', and 'Fxy' for 'you can fool x at (or during) y', the above may be symbolized as

$$\{(\exists x)[Px \cdot (y)(Ty \supset Fxy)] \cdot (\exists y)[Ty \cdot (x)(Px \supset Fxy)]\} \cdot$$
$$(\exists y)(\exists x)[Ty \cdot Px \cdot \sim Fxy]$$

The actual testing of relational arguments presents no new problems once the translations into logical symbolism are effected. The latter is the more troublesome part, and so a number of exercises are provided for the student to do before going on.

EXERCISES

I. Using the following 'vocabulary', translate the given formulas into idiomatic English sentences:

Ax-x is silver	Axy-x helps y
Bx-x is blissful	Bxy-x belongs to y
Cx-x is a cloud	$Bxyz$-x borrows y from z
Dx-x is a dog	Cxy-x can command y
Ex-x is smoke	Dxy-x is done at (or by) y
Fx-x is fire	Exy-x shears y
Gx-x is glass	Fxy-x is fair for y
Hx-x is home	Gxy-x gathers y
Ix-x is ill	Hxy-x hears y
Jx-x is work	Ixy-x lives in y
Kx-x is a lining	Jxy-x is jack of y
Lx-x is a lamb	Kxy-x knows y
Mx-x is moss	Lxy-x likes y
Nx-x is good	Mxy-x is master of y
Ox-x is a fool	Nxy-x loses y
Px-x is a person	Oxy-x is judged by y
Qx-x is a place	$Pxyz$-x blows y to z
Rx-x rolls	Qxy-x keeps company with y
Sx-x is a stone	Rxy-x is like y
Tx-x is a trade	Sxy-x says y
Ux-x is a house	Txy-x should throw y
Vx-x is a woman	$Txyz$-x tempers y to z
Wx-x is wind	Uxy-x comes to y
Xx-x is a time	Vxy-x ventures y
Yx-x is a day	Wxy-x is at (or in) y
Zx-x waits	Xxy-x is parent of y

g-God

Formulas

1. $(x)[Dx \supset (\exists y)(Yy \cdot Byx)]$
2. $(x)[(\exists y)(Py \cdot Fxy) \supset (z)(Pz \supset Fxz)]$
3. $(x)[(Rx \cdot Sx) \supset (y)(My \supset \sim Gxy)]$
4. $(x)[(Px \cdot Axx) \supset (Agx)]$
★5. $(x)[(Px \cdot Zx) \supset (y)(Uyx)]$
6. $(x)[Hx \supset (y)(Qy \supset \sim Ryx)]$
7. $(x)[(Px \cdot \sim Nxg) \supset (y)(\sim Nxy)]$
8. $(x)[(Px \cdot \sim Cxx) \supset (y)(Py \supset \sim Cxy)]$
9. $(x)\{Cx \supset (\exists y)[(Ay \cdot Ky) \cdot Byx]\}$
★10. $(x)[Px \supset (y)(Qxy \supset Oxy)]$
11. $(x)\{Qx \supset [(\exists y)(Ey \cdot Wyx) \supset (\exists z)(Fz \cdot Wzx)]\}$
12. $(x)\{[Px \cdot (y)(Ty \supset Jxy)] \supset (z)(Tz \supset \sim Mxz)\}$
13. $(x)\{[Px \cdot (\exists y)[(Gy \cdot Uy) \cdot Ixy]] \supset (z)(Sz \supset \sim Txz)\}$
14. $(x)\{[Px \cdot (y)(Lxy \supset Sxy)] \supset (\exists z)(Hxz \cdot \sim Lxz)\}$
★15. $(x)\{[Wx \cdot (y)[Py \supset \sim (\exists z)(Nz \cdot Pxzy)]] \supset Ix\}$
16. $(x)\{[Px \cdot (y)(\sim Vxy)] \supset (z)(\sim Gxz)\}$
17. $(x)\{Vx \supset (y)[Xy \supset (\exists z)[(Jz \cdot Bzx) \cdot \sim Dzy]]\}$
18. $(x)\{[Lx \cdot (\exists y)(Py \cdot Eyx)] \supset (z)(Wz \supset Tgzx)\}$
19. $(x)\{Px \supset (\exists y)[Py \cdot (\exists z)(Bxzy)]\}$
★20. $(x)\{Px \supset (\exists y)[Py \cdot (\exists z)(\sim Bxzy)]\}$
21. $(x)\{Px \supset (y)[Py \supset (z)(\sim Bxzy)]\}$
22. $(x)\{Px \supset (y)[Py \supset (\exists z)(\sim Bxzy)]\}$
23. $(x)[(Nx \cdot Dx) \supset (y)(Lxy \supset Myx)]$
24. $(x)[Px \supset (\exists y)(Py \cdot Xyx)] \cdot (\exists u)[Pu \cdot (v)(Pv \supset \sim Xuv)]$
★25. $(x)\{[Qx \cdot (y)\{[(Py \cdot Wyx) \cdot (z)(\sim Kyz)] \supset By\}] \supset$
$(u)\{[(Pu \cdot Wux) \cdot (v)(Kuv)] \supset Ou\}\}$

II. Symbolize the following sentences, in each case using the indicated symbols:

1. Dead men tell no tales. (*Dx*: *x* is dead. *Mx*: *x* is a man. *Tx*: *x* is a tale. *Txy*: *x* tells *y*.)
2. To err is human. (*Ex*: *x* is an error. *Hx*: *x* is human. *Mxy*: *x* makes *y*.)
3. A dead lion is more dangerous than a live dog. (*Lx*: *x* is a lion. *Ax*: *x* is alive. *Dx*: *x* is a dog. *Dxy*: *x* is more dangerous than *y*.)
4. Uneasy lies the head that wears a crown. (*Ux*: *x* lies uneasy. *Hx*: *x* is a head. *Cx*: *x* is a crown. *Wxy*: *x* wears *y*.)
★5. Every rose has its thorn. (*Rx*: *x* is a rose. *Tx*: *x* is a thorn. *Hxy*: *x* has *y*.)

6. Anyone who consults a psychiatrist ought to have his head examined. (*Px*: *x* is a person. *Sx*: *x* is a psychiatrist. *Ox*: *x* ought to have his head examined. *Cxy*: *x* consults *y*.)

7. No one ever learns anything unless he teaches it to himself. (*Px*: *x* is a person. *Lxy*: *x* learns *y*. *Txyz*: *x* teaches *y* to *z*.)

8. Delilah wore a ring on every finger, and had a finger in every pie. (*d*: Delilah. *Rx*: *x* is a ring. *Fxy*: *x* is a finger of *y*. *Oxy*: *x* is on *y*. *Px*: *x* is a pie. *Ixy*: *x* is in *y*.)

9. Any man who hates children and dogs cannot be all bad. (*Mx*: *x* is a man. *Cx*: *x* is a child. *Dx*: *x* is a dog. *Bx*: *x* is all bad. *Hxy*: *x* hates *y*.)

★10. Anyone who accomplishes anything will be envied by everyone. (*Px*: *x* is a person. *Axy*: *x* accomplishes *y*. *Exy*: *x* envies *y*.)

11. To catch a fish one must have some bait. (*Px*: *x* is a person. *Fx*: *x* is a fish. *Bx*: *x* is bait. *Cxy*: *x* catches *y*. *Hxy*: *x* has *y*.)

12. Every student does some problems, but no student does all of them. (*Sx*: *x* is a student. *Px*: *x* is a problem. *Dxy*: *x* does *y*.)

13. Any contestant who answers all the questions put to him will win any prize he chooses. (*Cx*: *x* is a contestant. *Qx*: *x* is a question. *Px*: *x* is a prize. *Axy*: *x* answers *y*. *Pxy*: *x* is put to *y*. *Wxy*: *x* wins *y*. *Cxy*: *x* chooses *y*.)

14. Every son has a father but not every father has a son. (*Px*: *x* is a person. *Mx*: *x* is male. *Pxy*: *x* is a parent of *y*.)

★15. A person is maintaining a nuisance if he has a dog that barks at everyone who visits its owner. (*Px*: *x* is a person. *Nx*: *x* is a nuisance. *Mxy*: *x* maintains *y*. *Dx*: *x* is a dog. *Bxy*: *x* barks at *y*. *Vxy*: *x* visits *y*. *Hxy*: *x* has *y*.)

16. A doctor has no scruples who treats a patient who has no ailment. (*Dx*: *x* is a doctor. *Sx*: *x* is a scruple. *Hxy*: *x* has *y*. *Px*: *x* is a patient. *Ax*: *x* is an ailment. *Txy*: *x* treats *y*.)

17. A doctor who treats a person who has every ailment has a job no one would envy him. (*Dx*: *x* is a doctor. *Px*: *x* is a person. *Txy*: *x* treats *y*. *Ax*: *x* is an ailment. *Hxy*: *x* has *y*. *Jx*: *x* is a job. *Exyz*: *x* envies *y* his *z*.)

18. If a farmer keeps only hens, none of them will lay eggs that are worth setting. (*Fx*: *x* is a farmer. *Kxy*: *x* keeps *y*. *Hx*: *x* is a hen. *Ex*: *x* is an egg. *Lxy*: *x* lays *y*. *Wx*: *x* is worth setting.)

In symbolizing the following, use only the abbreviations: *Px*: *x* is a person. *Sx*: *x* is a store. *Bxyz*: *x* buys *y* from *z*.

19. Everyone buys something from some store (or other).

★20. There is a store from which everyone buys something (or other).

21. Some people make all their purchases from a single store.

22. No one buys everything that it sells from any store.
23. No one buys things from every store.
24. No store has everyone for a customer.
★25. No store makes all its sales to a single person.

5.2 ARGUMENTS INVOLVING RELATIONS

No new principles need be introduced to deal with relational arguments. The original list of nineteen Rules of Inference, together with the strengthened method of Conditional Proof, and our quantification rules plus Quantifier Negation, enable us (if we have sufficient ingenuity) to construct a formal proof of validity for every valid argument in which only individual variables are quantified and only truth-functional connectives occur.

However, a certain change of technique is advisable in working with arguments involving relations. In most of our previous sample proofs and demonstrations, **UI** and **EI** were used to instantiate with respect to a variable different from any quantified in the premiss, and **UG** and **EG** were used to quantify with respect to a variable different from any which occurred free in the premiss. Our inferences were for the most part of the following forms:

$$\frac{(x)Fx}{\therefore Fy}, \quad \frac{(\exists x)Fx}{\therefore Fz}, \quad \frac{Fx}{\therefore (y)Fy}, \quad \frac{Fy}{\therefore (\exists w)Fw}$$

But our statement of the quantification rules does not require that μ and ν be different variables; they may well be the same. And on the whole it is simpler (wherever it is legitimate) to instantiate with respect to the same variable that had been quantified, and to quantify with respect to the same variable that had been free in the premiss. Thus the above inferences may also take the following forms:

$$\frac{(x)Fx}{\therefore Fx}, \quad \frac{(\exists x)Fx}{\therefore Fx}, \quad \frac{Fx}{\therefore (x)Fx}, \quad \frac{Fy}{\therefore (\exists y)Fy}$$

In this way instantiation is accomplished by simply dropping a quantifier, and generalization is accomplished by simply adding a quantifier. Of course our restrictions on the quantification rules must still be observed. For example, where we have two premisses '$(\exists x)Fx$' and

'$(\exists x) \sim Fx$', we can instantiate with respect to one by simply dropping the quantifier, but when that has been done, if **EI** is subsequently used on the other, a new variable must be used instead of 'x', for the latter will already have a free occurrence in the proof under construction. Of course we remain perfectly free to use **UI** to instantiate with respect to any variable or constant we choose. The preceding remarks can be illustrated by constructing a proof of validity for the argument

> There is a man whom all men despise.
> ———————————————————————
> Therefore at least one man despises himself.

Its symbolic translation and proof, using 'Mx' and 'Dxy' to abbreviate 'x is a man' and 'x despises y' may be written as follows:

1. $(\exists x)[Mx \cdot (y)(My \supset Dyx)]$ $/ \therefore$ $(\exists x)(Mx \cdot Dxx)$
2. $Mx \cdot (y)(My \supset Dyx)$
3. $(y)(My \supset Dyx)$ 2, Simp.
4. $Mx \supset Dxx$ 3, **UI**
5. Mx 2, Simp.
6. Dxx 4, 5, M.P.
7. $Mx \cdot Dxx$ 5, 6, Conj.
8. $(\exists x)(Mx \cdot Dxx)$ 7, **EG**
9. $(\exists x)(Mx \cdot Dxx)$ 1, 2–8, **EI**

In the foregoing proof, the only use of a quantification rule accompanied by a change of variable was the use of **UI** in going from line 3 to line 4, which was because we needed the expression 'Dxx' thus obtained.

Another formal proof serves to establish the validity of the third specimen argument stated at the beginning of the present chapter. Its premiss, 'All horses are animals' will be symbolized as '$(x)(Ex \supset Ax)$', where 'Ex' and 'Ax' abbreviate 'x is a horse' and 'x is an animal', respectively. In its conclusion

> The head of a horse is the head of an animal.

the word 'the' has the same sense that it does in such propositions as 'The whale is a mammal' or 'The burnt child dreads the fire'. We may paraphrase it therefore first as

> All heads of horses are heads of animals.

then as

$(x)[(x$ is a head of a horse$) \supset (x$ is a head of an animal$)]$

and finally, writing 'Hxy' for 'x is a head of y', we may express the conclusion by the formula

$$(x)[(\exists y)(Ey \cdot Hxy) \supset (\exists y)(Ay \cdot Hxy)]$$

Once it is symbolized, the argument is easily proved valid by the techniques already available:

1.	$(x)(Ex \supset Ax)$ $\quad / \therefore$ $(x)[(\exists y)(Ey \cdot Hxy) \supset (\exists y)(Ay \cdot Hxy)]$	
2.	$(\exists y)(Ey \cdot Hxy)$	
3.	$Ey \cdot Hxy$	
4.	Ey	3, Simp.
5.	$Ey \supset Ay$	1, **UI**
6.	Ay	5, 4, M.P.
7.	Hxy	3, Simp.
8.	$Ay \cdot Hxy$	6, 7, Conj.
9.	$(\exists y)(Ay \cdot Hxy)$	8, **EG**
10.	$(\exists y)(Ay \cdot Hxy)$	2, 3–9, **EI**
11.	$(\exists y)(Ey \cdot Hxy) \supset (\exists y)(Ay \cdot Hxy)$	2–10, C.P.
12.	$(x)[(\exists y)(Ey \cdot Hxy) \supset (\exists y)(Ay \cdot Hxy)]$	11, **UG**

The first specimen argument presented in this chapter, which dealt with the relation of *being older than*, raises a new problem, which will be discussed in the following section.

EXERCISES

Construct a formal proof of validity for each of the following arguments:

1. Whoever supports Ickes will vote for Jones. Anderson will vote for no one but a friend of Harris. No friend of Kelly has Jones for a friend. Therefore, if Harris is a friend of Kelly, Anderson will not support Ickes. (*Sxy*: x supports y. *Vxy*: x votes for y. *Fxy*: x is a friend of y. *a*: Anderson. *i*: Ickes. *j*: Jones. *h*: Harris. *k*: Kelly.)

2. All circles are figures. Therefore all who draw circles draw figures. (*Cx*: x is a circle. *Fx*: x is a figure. *Dxy*: x draws y.)

3. Any friend of Al is a friend of Bill. Therefore anyone who knows a friend of Al knows a friend of Bill. (*Px*: *x* is a person. *Fxy*: *x* is a friend of *y*. *Kxy*: *x* knows *y*. *a*: Al. *b*: Bill.)

★4. Only a fool would lie about one of Bill's fraternity brothers to him. A classmate of Bill's lied about Al to him. Therefore if none of Bill's classmates are fools, then Al is not a fraternity brother of Bill. (*Fx*: *x* is a fool. *Lxyz*: *x* lies about *y* to *z*. *Cxy*: *x* is a classmate of *y*. *Bxy*: *x* is a fraternity brother of *y*. *a*: Al. *b*: Bill.)

5. Whoever belongs to the Country Club is wealthier than any member of the Elks Lodge. Not everyone who belongs to the Country Club is wealthier than anyone who does not belong. Therefore not everyone belongs either to the Country Club or the Elks Lodge. (*Cx*: *x* belongs to the Country Club. *Ex*: *x* belongs to the Elks Lodge. *Px*: *x* is a person. *Wxy*: *x* is wealthier than *y*.)

★6. It is a crime to sell an unregistered gun. All the weapons that Red owns were purchased by him from either Lefty or Moe. So if one of Red's weapons is an unregistered gun, then if Red never bought anything from Moe, Lefty is a criminal. (*Rx*: *x* is registered. *Gx*: *x* is a gun. *Cx*: *x* is a criminal. *Wx*: *x* is a weapon. *Oxy*: *x* owns *y*. *Sxyz*: *x* sells *y* to *z*. *r*: Red. *l*: Lefty. *m*: Moe.)

7. Everything on my desk is a masterpiece. Anyone who writes a masterpiece is a genius. Someone very obscure wrote some of the novels on my desk. Therefore some very obscure person is a genius. (*Dx*: *x* is on my desk. *Mx*: *x* is a masterpiece. *Px*: *x* is a person. *Gx*: *x* is a genius. *Ox*: *x* is very obscure. *Nx*: *x* is a novel. *Wxy*: *x* wrote *y*.)

8. There is a professor who is liked by every student who likes at least one professor. Every student likes some professor or other. Therefore there is a professor who is liked by all students. (*Px*: *x* is a professor. *Sx*: *x* is a student. *Lxy*: *x* likes *y*.)

★9. No one respects a person who does not respect himself. No one will hire a person he does not respect. Therefore a person who respects no one will never be hired by anybody. (*Px*: *x* is a person. *Rxy*: *x* respects *y*. *Hxy*: *x* hires *y*.)

10. Whoever donates to the United Fund gives all of his donations to the United Fund. Therefore if Jones is a person who does not give all of his donations to the United Fund then he does not donate anything at all to the United Fund. (*Px*: *x* is a person. *Dxyz*: *x* donates *y* to *z*. *f*: The United Fund. *j*: Jones.)

11. Any book which is approved by all critics is read by every literary person. Anyone who reads anything will talk about it. A critic will approve any

book written by any person who flatters him. Therefore if someone flatters every critic then any book he writes will be talked about by all literary persons. (*Bx*: *x* is a book. *Cx*: *x* is a critic. *Lx*: *x* is literary. *Px*: *x* is a person. *Axy*: *x* approves *y*. *Rxy*: *x* reads *y*. *Txy*: *x* talks about *y*. *Fxy*: *x* flatters *y*. *Wxy*: *x* writes *y*.)

12. A work of art which tells a story can be understood by everyone. Some religious works of art have been created by great artists. Every religious work of art tells an inspirational story. Therefore if some people admire only what they cannot understand, then some great artists' creations will not be admired by everyone. (*Ax*: *x* is a great artist. *Px*: *x* is a person. *Sx*: *x* is a story. *Ix*: *x* is inspirational. *Rx*: *x* is religious. *Wx*: *x* is a work of art. *Cxy*: *x* creates *y*. *Axy*: *x* admires *y*. *Txy*: *x* tells *y*. *Uxy*: *x* can understand *y*.)

5.3 SOME PROPERTIES OF RELATIONS

There are many interesting properties that relations themselves may possess. We shall consider only a few of the more familiar ones, and our discussion will be confined to properties of *dyadic* relations.

Dyadic relations may be characterized as *symmetrical*, *asymmetrical*, or *nonsymmetrical*. Various symmetrical relations are designated by the phrases: 'is next to', 'is married to', and 'has the same weight as'. A *symmetrical* relation is a relation such that if one individual has that relation to a second individual, then the second individual must have that relation to the first. A propositional function '*Rxy*' designates a symmetrical relation if and only if

$$(x)(y)(Rxy \supset Ryx)$$

On the other hand, an *asymmetrical* relation is a relation such that if one individual has that relation to a second individual, then the second individual *cannot* have that relation to the first. Various asymmetrical relations are designated by the phrases: 'is north of', 'is older than', and 'weighs more than'. A propositional function '*Rxy*' designates an asymmetrical relation if and only if

$$(x)(y)(Rxy \supset \sim Ryx)$$

Not all relations are either symmetrical or asymmetrical, however. If one individual loves a second, or is a brother of a second, or weighs no more than a second, it does not follow that the second loves the first, or is a brother to the first (possibly being a sister instead), or weighs no more than the first. Nor does it follow that the second does *not* love the first, or is *not* a brother to him, or *does* weigh more than the first. Such relations as these are *nonsymmetrical*, and are defined as those which are neither symmetrical nor asymmetrical.

Dyadic relations may also be characterized as *transitive*, *intransitive*, or *nontransitive*. Various transitive relations are designated by the phrases: 'is north of', 'is an ancestor of', and 'weighs the same as'. A *transitive* relation is a relation such that if one individual has it to a second, and the second to a third, then the first must have it to the third. A propositional function 'Rxy' designates a transitive relation if and only if

$$(x)(y)(z)[(Rxy \cdot Ryz) \supset Rxz]$$

An *intransitive* relation, on the other hand, is a relation such that if one individual has it to a second, and the second to a third, then the first *cannot* have it to the third. Some intransitive relations are designated by the phrases: 'is mother of', 'is father of', and 'weighs exactly twice as much as'. A propositional function 'Rxy' designates an intransitive relation if and only if

$$(x)(y)(z)[(Rxy \cdot Ryz) \supset \sim Rxz]$$

Not all relations are either transitive or intransitive. We define a *nontransitive* relation as one which is neither transitive nor intransitive; examples of nontransitive relations are designated by: 'loves', 'is discriminably different from', and 'has a different weight than'.

Finally, relations may be *reflexive*, *irreflexive*, or *nonreflexive*. Various definitions of these properties have been proposed by different authors, and there seems to be no standard terminology established. It is convenient to distinguish between reflexivity and total reflexivity. A relation is *totally reflexive* if every individual has that relation to itself. For example, the phrase 'is identical with' designates the totally reflexive relation of identity. A propositional function 'Rxy' designates a totally reflexive relation if and only if

$$(x)Rxx$$

On the other hand, a relation is said to be *reflexive* if any individual a has that relation to itself if there is something b such that either Rab or Rba. Obvious examples of reflexive relations are designated by the phrases: 'has the same color hair as', 'is the same age as', and 'is a contemporary of'. A propositional function 'Rxy' designates a reflexive relation if and only if

$$(x)[(\exists y)(Rxy \text{ v } Ryx) \supset Rxx]$$

It is obvious that all totally reflexive relations are reflexive.

An irreflexive relation is a relation which no individual has to itself. A propositional function 'Rxy' designates an irreflexive relation if and only if

$$(x){\sim}Rxx$$

Examples of irreflexive relations are common indeed; the phrases: 'is north of', 'is married to', and 'is parent of' all designate irreflexive relations. Relations which are neither reflexive nor irreflexive are said to be *nonreflexive*. The phrases: 'loves', 'hates', and 'criticizes' designate nonreflexive relations.

Relations may have various combinations of the properties described. The relation of *weighing more than* is asymmetrical, transitive, and irreflexive, while the relation of *having the same weight as* is symmetrical, transitive, and reflexive. However, some properties entail the presence of others. For example, all asymmetrical relations must be irreflexive, as can easily be demonstrated. Let 'Rxy' designate any asymmetrical relation; then by definition:

1. $(x)(y)(Rxy \supset {\sim}Ryx)$

From this premiss we can deduce that R is irreflexive, that is, that $(x){\sim}Rxx$:

2. $(y)(Rxy \supset \sim Ryx)$ 1, **UI**
3. $Rxx \supset \sim Rxx$ 2, **UI**
4. $\sim Rxx \ v \sim Rxx$ 3, Impl.
5. $\sim Rxx$ 4, Taut.
6. $(x)\sim Rxx$ 5, **UG**

Other logical connections among these properties of relations are easily stated and proved, but our present interest lies in another direction.

The relevance of these properties to relational arguments is easily seen. An argument to which one of them is relevant might be stated thus:

Tom has the same weight as Dick.
Dick has the same weight as Harry.
The relation of *having the same weight as* is transitive.
Therefore Tom has the same weight as Harry.

When it is translated into our symbolism as

$$Wtd$$
$$Wdh$$
$$(x)(y)(z)[(Wxy \cdot Wyz) \supset Wxz]$$
$$\therefore Wth$$

the method of proving its validity is immediately obvious. We said that the argument 'might' be stated in the way indicated. But such a statement of the argument would be the rare exception rather than the rule. The ordinary way of propounding such an argument would be to state only the first two premises and the conclusion, on the grounds that *everyone knows* that *having the same weight as* is a transitive relation. Relational arguments are often used, and many of them depend essentially on the transitivity, or symmetry, or one of the other properties of the relations involved. But *that* the relation in question *has* the relevant property is seldom—if ever—stated explicitly as a premiss. The reason is easy to see. In most discussions a large body of propositions can be presumed to be common knowledge. The majority of speakers and writers save themselves trouble by not repeating well-known and perhaps trivially true propositions that their hearers or readers can perfectly well be expected to supply for themselves. An argument which is incompletely expressed, part of it being 'understood', is an *enthymeme.*

Because it is incomplete, an enthymeme must have its suppressed premiss or premisses taken into account when the problem arises of testing its validity. Where a necessary premiss is missing, the inference is technically invalid. But where the unexpressed premiss is easily supplied and obviously true, in all fairness it ought to be included as part of the argument in any evaluation of it. In such a case one assumes that the maker of the argument did have more 'in mind' than he stated explicitly. In most cases there is no difficulty in supplying the tacit premiss that the speaker intended but did not express. Thus the first specimen argument stated at the beginning of this chapter:

> Al is older than Bill.
> Bill is older than Charlie.
> Therefore Al is older than Charlie.

ought to be counted as valid, since it becomes so when the trivially true proposition that *being older than* is a transitive relation, is added as an auxiliary premiss. When the indicated missing premiss is supplied, a formal proof of the argument's validity is very easily set down.

Of course premisses other than relational ones are often left unexpressed. For example, in the argument

> Any horse can outrun any dog. Some greyhounds can outrun any rabbit. Therefore any horse can outrun any rabbit.

not only is the needed premiss about the transitivity of *being able to outrun* left unexpressed, but also the nonrelational premiss that all greyhounds are dogs. When these are added—and they are certainly not debatable issues—the validity of the argument can be demonstrated as follows:

1. $(x)[Hx \supset (y)(Dy \supset Oxy)]$ premises
2. $(\exists y)[Gy \cdot (z)(Rz \supset Oyz)]$ $/ \therefore$ $(x)[Hx \supset (z)(Rz \supset Oxz)]$
3. $(x)(y)(z)[(Oxy \cdot Oyz) \supset Oxz]$ additional premises
4. $(y)(Gy \supset Dy)$

5. Hx
6. Rz
7. $Gy \cdot (z)(Rz \supset Oyz)$
8. Gy 7, Simp.
9. $Gy \supset Dy$ 4, **UI**
10. Dy 9, 8, M.P.
11. $Hx \supset (y)(Dy \supset Oxy)$ 1, **UI**
12. $(y)(Dy \supset Oxy)$ 11, 5, M.P.
13. $Dy \supset Oxy$ 12, **UI**
14. Oxy 13, 10, M.P.
15. $(z)(Rz \supset Oyz)$ 7, Simp.
16. $Rz \supset Oyz$ 15, **UI**
17. Oyz 16, 6, M.P.
18. $Oxy \cdot Oyz$ 14, 17, Conj.
19. $(y)(z)[(Oxy \cdot Oyz) \supset Oxz]$ 3, **UI**
20. $(z)[(Oxy \cdot Oyz) \supset Oxz]$ 19, **UI**
21. $(Oxy \cdot Oyz) \supset Oxz$ 20, **UI**
22. Oxz 21, 18, M.P.
23. Oxz 2, 7–22, **EI**
24. $Rz \supset Oxz$ 6–23, C.P.
25. $(z)(Rz \supset Oxz)$ 24, **UG**
26. $Hx \supset (z)(Rz \supset Oxz)$ 5–25, C.P.
27. $(x)[Hx \supset (z)(Rz \supset Oxz)]$ 26, **UG**

Missing premises are not always so easily noticed and supplied as in the present example. When it is not so obvious which needed premises are missing from an enthymematically expressed argument, then in beginning a proof of its validity it is a good policy to leave a little space just below the given premises, in which additional premises can be written when need arises for their use. The only point to be stressed is that no statement which is as doubtful or debatable as the argument's own conclusion is to be admitted as a supplementary premiss, for in a valid argument that is enthymematically stated only the sheerest platitudes should be left unexpressed for the hearer or reader to fill in for himself.

EXERCISES

Prove the validity of the following enthymemes—adding obviously true premises where necessary:

1. A Cadillac is more expensive than any low-priced car. Therefore no Cadillac is a low-priced car. (Cx: x is a Cadillac. Lx: x is a low-priced car. Mxy: x is more expensive than y.)

2. Alice is Betty's mother. Betty is Charlene's mother. Therefore if Charlene loves only her mother then she does not love Alice. (a: Alice. b: Betty. c: Charlene. Mxy: x is mother of y. Lxy: x loves y.)

★3. Any man on the first team can outrun every man on the second team. Therefore no man on the second team can outrun any man on the first team. (Fx: x is a man on the first team. Sx: x is a man on the second team. Oxy: x can outrun y.)

4. Every boy at the party danced with every girl who was there. Therefore every girl at the party danced with every boy who was there. (Bx: x is a boy. Gx: x is a girl. Px: x was at the party. Dxy: x danced with y.)

★5. Anyone is unfortunate who bears the same name as a person who commits a crime. Therefore anyone who commits a burglary is unfortunate. (Px: x is a person. Ux: x is unfortunate. Cx: x is a crime. Bx: x is a burglary. Cxy: x commits y. Nxy: x bears the same name as y.)

6. All the watches sold by Kubitz are made in Switzerland. Anything made in a foreign country has a tariff paid on it. Anything on which a tariff was paid costs its purchaser extra. Therefore it costs extra to buy a watch from Kubitz. (Wx: x is a watch. Tx: x has a tariff paid on it. Fx: x is a foreign country. Cxy: x costs y extra. Mxy: x is made in y. $Bxyz$: x buys y from z. s: Switzerland. k: Kubitz.)

★7. Vacant lots provide no income to their owners. Any owner of real estate must pay taxes on it. Therefore any owner of a vacant lot must pay taxes on something which provides no income to its owner. (Vx: x is a vacant lot. Rx: x is real estate. Ixy: x provides income to y. Txy: x pays taxes on y. Oxy: x owns y.)

8. All admirals wear uniforms having gold buttons. Therefore some naval officers wear clothes which have metal buttons. (Ax: x is an admiral. Ux: x is a uniform. Gx: x is gold. Bx: x is a button. Nx: x is a naval officer. Cx: x is clothing. Mx: x is metal. Wxy: x wears y. Hxy: x has y.)

9. Whenever Charlie moved to Boston, it was after he had met Al. Whenever Charlie got married, it was before he ever saw Dave. Therefore if Charlie moved to Boston and subsequently got married, then he met Al before he ever saw Dave. (Tx: x is a time. Ax: Charlie met Al at (time) x. Bx: Charlie moved to Boston at (time) x. Mx: Charlie got married at (time) x. Dx: Charlie saw Dave at (time) x. Pxy: x precedes y.)

10. A fish that chases every shiner will be hooked by an angler who uses a shiner for bait. A greedy fish will chase every shiner. So if all anglers are sportsmen, then no pike which is not hooked by a sportsman who uses minnows for bait is greedy. (Fx: x is a fish. Sx: x is a shiner. Cxy: x chases y. Hxy: x hooks y. Ax: x is an angler. Bxy: x uses y for bait. Gx: x is greedy. Px: x is a pike. Rx: x is a sportsman. Mx: x is a minnow.)

5.4   IDENTITY AND THE DEFINITE DESCRIPTION

The notion of *identity* is a familiar one. Perhaps the most natural occasion for its use is in the process of *identification*, as when in a police line-up a witness identifies a suspect, asserting that

The man on the right *is* the man who snatched my purse.

Other identifications are common, as in a geography class when it is asserted that

Mt. Everest *is* the tallest mountain in the world.

or when in a literature class it is asserted that

Scott *is* the author of *Waverley*.

Each of these propositions asserts that a relation obtains between the individuals denoted by its two terms. The relation asserted to hold is that of *identity*. In each of the preceding propositions at least one term was a *definite description*, which is a phrase of the form 'the so-and-so'. In identifications, however, both terms may be proper names. Just as the two propositions

Brutus killed Caesar.

and

Booth killed Lincoln.

assert the relation of *killing* to hold between the individuals denoted by the proper names appearing in them, so the propositions

Lewis Carroll was Charles Lutwidge Dodgson.

and

Mark Twain was Samuel Clemens.

assert the relation of *identity* to hold between the individuals denoted by the proper names appearing in them.

The usual notation for the relation of identity is the ordinary equals-sign '='. It is intuitively obvious that the relation of identity is transitive, symmetrical, and totally reflexive. In our symbolic notation we can write

$$(x)(y)(z)\{[(x = y)\cdot(y = z)] \supset (x = z)\}$$
$$(x)(y)[(x = y) \supset (y = x)]$$
$$(x)(x = x)$$

All of these are immediate consequences of the definition of identity contained in Leibniz's principle of the Identity of Indiscernibles:

$x = y$ if and only if every property of x is a property of y, and conversely.

This principle permits us to infer, from the premisses $\nu = \mu$ and any proposition containing an occurrence of the symbol ν, as conclusion any proposition which results from replacing any occurrences of ν in the second premiss by the symbol μ.[1] Any inference of this pattern is valid, and in a proof should have the letters 'Id.' written beside it. A specimen deduction or two will make this clear. The argument

O. Henry was William Sidney Porter.
O. Henry was a writer.
Therefore William Sidney Porter was a writer.

may be symbolized and proved valid by the following, in which we use the letters 'h' and 'p' to abbreviate the proper names 'O. Henry' and

[1] Here we are using the letters *mu* and *nu* to represent any individual symbols, constants, or variables.

'William Sidney Porter', and the symbol '*Wx*' for '*x* was a writer':

1. $h = p$
2. Wh /∴ Wp
3. Wp 1, 2, Id.

Another illustration is provided by the argument

> George Eliot wrote *The Mill on the Floss*.
> George Eliot is Mary Ann Evans.
> Mary Ann Evans is a lady.
> _____
> Therefore a lady wrote *The Mill on the Floss*.

Using the symbols '*g*', '*f*', '*m*', '*Wxy*', '*Lx*' to abbreviate 'George Eliot', '*The Mill on the Floss*', 'Mary Ann Evans', '*x* wrote *y*', and '*x* is a lady', we may formulate the given argument and demonstrate its validity as follows:

1. Wgf
2. $g = m$
3. Lm /∴ $(\exists x)(Lx \cdot Wxf)$
4. Lg 2, 3, Id.
5. $Lg \cdot Wgf$ 4, 1, Conj.
6. $(\exists x)(Lx \cdot Wxf)$ 5, **EG**

An alternative proof for the second argument would be the following:

4. Wmf 1, 2, Id.
5. $Lm \cdot Wmf$ 3, 4, Conj.
6. $(\exists x)(Lx \cdot Wxf)$ 5, **EG**

A third illustration is provided by the argument:

> Only a bald man wears a wig. Kaplan is a man who wears a wig.
> This man is not bald. Therefore this man is not Kaplan.

Using the symbols '*t*', '*k*', '*Mx*', '*Bx*', '*Wx*', to abbreviate 'this man', 'Kaplan', '*x* is a man', '*x* is bald', and '*x* wears a wig', we may symbolize the present argument and prove its validity as follows:

1. $(x)[(Mx \cdot Wx) \supset Bx]$
2. $Mk \cdot Wk$
3. $\sim Bt$ $/ \therefore \sim(t = k)$
4. $(Mk \cdot Wk) \supset Bk$ 1, **UI**
5. Bk 4, 2, M.P.
6. $\sim(t = k)$ 3, 5, Id.

This last proof serves to show that we use the principle of Identity not only to infer $\Phi\nu$ from $\Phi\mu$ and $\nu = \mu$, but also to infer $\sim(\nu = \mu)$ from $\Phi\nu$ and $\sim\Phi\mu$. For completeness and convenience we include in our statement of the principle of Identity its symmetry and its total reflexiveness, even though its symmetry is readily derived from the others. Our formulation is

Id. $\dfrac{\Phi\mu}{\begin{array}{c}\nu = \mu \\ \hline \therefore \Phi\nu\end{array}}$, $\dfrac{\Phi\mu}{\begin{array}{c}\sim\Phi\nu \\ \hline \therefore \sim(\nu = \mu)\end{array}}$, $\dfrac{\nu = \mu}{\therefore \mu = \nu}$,   and $\dfrac{p}{\therefore \mu = \mu}$

An important use for the identity symbol is in the formulation of certain common types of exceptive statements. If we wish to symbolize the proposition

> Al is on the team and can outrun anyone else on it.

using 'a' for 'Al', 'Tx' for 'x is on the team', and 'Oxy' for 'x can outrun y', we cannot simply write down

$$Ta \cdot (x)(Tx \supset Oax)$$

for this would entail

$$Oaa$$

which is false because *being able to outrun* is an irreflexive relation. The preceding formula does not translate the given proposition, but rather the necessarily false one:

> Al is on the team and can outrun anyone on it.

In this second proposition the important word 'else' is missing. The first proposition does not assert that Al can outrun *everyone* on the team, but everyone *else* on it, that is, everyone on it who is *other than* or *not identical with* Al. The proper translation of the first proposition is

$$Ta \cdot (x)\{[Tx \cdot \sim(x = a)] \supset Oax\}$$

If we adopt the convention of abbreviating $\sim(\nu = \mu)$ as $\nu \neq \mu$, the preceding formula may be written

$$Ta \cdot (x)[(Tx \cdot x \neq a) \supset Oax]$$

Making similar use of the identity sign, we may symbolize the propositions

> Only John loves Mary.

and

> Mary can tolerate anyone but John.

as

$$Ljm \cdot (x)(x \neq j \supset \sim Lxm)$$

and

$$\sim Tmj \cdot (x)[(Px \cdot x \neq j) \supset Tmx]$$

A similar technique can be used in symbolizing the notion expressed by the English phrases 'at most' and 'no more than'. Thus the statement

> There is at most one opening.

interpreted not as asserting that there *is* an opening, but that there is *no more* than one, may be symbolized as

$$(x)(y)[(Ox \cdot Oy) \supset x = y]$$

Similarly, the statement

> No more than two visitors are permitted.

interpreted as leaving open the question of there being any at all, may be symbolized as

$$(x)(y)(z)[(Vx \cdot Vy \cdot Vz) \supset (x = z \vee y = z \vee x = y)]$$

The identity sign is also useful in symbolizing the notion of *at least*. It is not needed for 'at least one', because the existential quantifier by itself suffices for this, the statement

There is at least one applicant.

being symbolized as

$$(\exists x)Ax$$

But to symbolize

There are at least two applicants.

we use the identity sign, writing

$$(\exists x)(\exists y)[Ax \cdot Ay \cdot x \neq y]$$

Putting together the notations for 'at least one' and 'at most one' we have a method for symbolizing definite numerical propositions. Thus the statement

There is one book on my desk.

meaning *exactly* one, is symbolized, using '*Bx*' for '*x* is a book' and '*Dx*' for '*x* is on my desk', as

$$(\exists x)\{Bx \cdot Dx \cdot (y)[(By \cdot Dy) \supset y = x]\}$$

And the statement

Every state elects two Senators.

meaning *exactly* two, is symbolized, using '*Sx*' for '*x* is a state', '*Nx*' for '*x* is a Senator', and '*Exy*' for '*x* elects *y*', as

$$(x)\{Sx \supset (\exists y)(\exists z)[Ny \cdot Nz \cdot Exy \cdot Exz \cdot y \neq z \cdot$$
$$(w)[(Nw \cdot Exw) \supset (w = y \vee w = z)]]\}$$

Finally, the (presumably false) statement

Cerberus has three heads.

is symbolized, using '*Hx*' for '*x* is a head of Cerberus', as

$$(\exists x)(\exists y)(\exists z)\{Hx \cdot Hy \cdot Hz \cdot x \neq y \cdot y \neq z \cdot x \neq z \cdot$$
$$(w)[Hw \supset (w = x \vee w = y \vee w = z)]\}$$

The present notation is adequate for symbolizing arithmetical statements about individuals, but to symbolize propositions of pure arithmetic requires an expanded logical apparatus such as that suggested in the following section.

Very rarely does an individual have two different proper names ν and μ, so that $\nu = \mu$ is a significant and informative statement. However, individuals are often referred to by means of descriptive phrases rather than by their proper names. Thus when a crime has been committed, and the police have not yet learned who committed it, the newspapers are not silenced for want of a name—the individual in question is referred to as 'the kidnapper of the Lindbergh baby', or 'the driver of the missing car'.

The word 'the' has a variety of uses. In one sense it has the force of 'all' or 'any', as in 'The whale is a mammal' or 'The early bird gets the worm'. But in another sense it serves to indicate *existence* and *uniqueness*, as in the phrases

> The author of *Waverley*,
> The man who shot Lincoln,
> The largest city in Illinois,

which denote Scott, Booth, and Chicago, respectively. The standard notation for *this* sense of the word 'the' involves an upside-down iota. The three phrases above are (partially) symbolized as

> $(\imath x)(x$ wrote *Waverley*$)$,
> $(\imath x)(x$ is a man·x shot Lincoln$)$,
> $(\imath x)(x$ is a city in Illinois·x is larger than any other city in Illinois$)$.

In general a formula like '$(\imath x)(x$ wrote *Waverley*$)$' is read as 'the x that wrote *Waverley*', and is treated as a proper name. Thus we can replace the individual variable μ in the propositional function $\Psi\mu$ by $(\imath\nu)(\Phi\nu)$ to obtain $\Psi(\imath\nu)(\Phi\nu)$ as a substitution instance.

Normally, a definite description functions in argument the same way that a proper name does. The principle of Identity permits us to infer the conclusion 'Scott wrote *Marmion*' from the premisses 'Scott is the author of *Waverley*' and 'the author of *Waverley* wrote *Marmion*'. The proposition 'Something is larger than Detroit' follows validly by **EG** from the premiss 'The largest city in Illinois is larger than Detroit'. Of course **EI** instantiates only with a variable, and **UG** generalizes only from a variable, so there is no difference with respect to these two principles between a proper name and a definite description. But with respect to the principle of Universal Instantiation, certain differences and difficulties arise.

Where the letter 'F' designates a property, the symbol complex '$(\imath x)(Fx)$' denotes the individual having the property F *if* there is one and only one such individual. But what if no individual, or more than one individual, has this property? In such a case, since there is no unique individual to be denoted by the expression '$(\imath x)(Fx)$', that expression does not denote. The problem of interpreting phrases which purport to denote but do not really do so can be handled in the following fashion, which is due to Russell.[2] An explicit definition of a symbol is given by presenting another symbol which is equivalent to it in meaning. Thus the symbol 'bachelor' is defined explicitly by equating it to the phrase 'unmarried man'. An alternative method of explaining the meaning of a symbol is to give a *contextual* rather than an explicit definition for it. A contextual definition of a symbol does not explain the symbol's meaning in isolation, but rather explains the meaning of any statement or context in which that symbol occurs. We do not give an explanation of the word 'the' (or the iota symbol) in isolation, but instead we present a method for interpreting any sentence (or formula) in which it appears. A contextual definition is also referred to as a 'definition in use'. Russell's analysis of the definite description consists of a contextual definition, or definition in use, of the word 'the'—in the sense in which it signifies existence and uniqueness. Consider the proposition

The author of *Waverley* was a genius.

It seems to assert three things: first that

There is an individual who wrote *Waverley*,

second that

at most one individual wrote *Waverley*,

---

[2] Cf. 'On Denoting', *Mind*, n.s. vol. 14 (1905). Russell's paper, together with alternative treatments due to G. Frege and P. F. Strawson, is reprinted in Part Three of *Contemporary Readings in Logical Theory*, edited by I. M. Copi and J. A. Gould, New York and London, The Macmillan Company, 1967.

and finally that

that individual was a genius.

The three parts of its meaning can be symbolized—without using the iota—as follows:

$$(\exists x)(x \text{ wrote } Waverley)$$
$$(y)(y \text{ wrote } Waverley \supset y = x)$$

and

$$x \text{ was a genius.}$$

Putting these three parts together, we obtain

$$(\exists x)\{(x \text{ wrote } Waverley)\cdot(y)(y \text{ wrote } Waverley \supset y = x)\cdot$$
$$(x \text{ was a genius})\}$$

Here we have a symbolic translation of the given statement that contains neither the troublesome word 'the' nor any synonym for it. In general, any statement of the form

The so-and-so is such-and-such,

or any formula such as

$$\Psi(\imath x)(\Phi x)$$

is regarded as logically equivalent to

$$(\exists x)\{(x \text{ is a so-and-so})\cdot(y)(y \text{ is a so-and-so} \supset y = x)\cdot$$
$$(x \text{ is a such-and-such})\}$$

or as

$$(\exists x)\{\Phi x\cdot(y)(\Phi y \supset y = x)\cdot\Psi x\}$$

Incidentally, when a property is expressed in the superlative form as 'best', 'fastest', 'heaviest', or the like, any proposition containing it can be expressed using only the comparative forms 'better', 'faster', 'heavier', or the like. Thus the statement

The largest ocean is to the west of America.

can be symbolized, using 'Ox' for 'x is an ocean', 'Wx' for 'x is to the west of America', and 'Lxy' for 'x is larger than y', as

$$(\exists x)\{Ox\cdot(y)[(Oy\cdot y \neq x) \supset Lxy]\cdot Wx\}$$

A definite description is ordinarily used only when it is believed that it does denote. One normally uses the words 'the so-and-so' only when he believes that there exists one and only one so-and-so. But beliefs are often mistaken, and one sometimes uses such a phrase even when it does not denote. When it does not, any sentence which asserts that *the so-and-so* has such-and-such a property, or stands in this or that relation, is false. Thus, even though it might be true that everything has mass, it is *false* that

The immortal man has mass.

for this sentence asserts the existence of exactly one immortal man, whereas there are none. And unless it occurs in a context which makes clear either that some particular mountain is being referred to, or that *mountains in general* are under discussion, the statement

The mountain has mass.

is false, for it asserts that there is only one mountain, whereas in fact there are many. These remarks should serve to make clear that a phrase of the form 'the so-and-so' or a symbol such as '$(\imath x)(Fx)$' cannot be instantiated by the principle of Universal Instantiation alone. In order to deduce the conclusion '$G(\imath x)(Fx)$' from '$(x)Gx$' we require the additional premiss that there is exactly one individual having the property F. Where that premiss is missing, the inference is invalid. But where it is present, the argument is easily proved valid as follows:

1. $(x)Gx$
2. $(\exists x)[Fx \cdot (y)(Fy \supset y = x)]$ /∴ $G(\imath x)(Fx)$
⸺▸3. $Fx \cdot (y)(Fy \supset y = x)$
 4. Gx 1, **UI**
 5. $Fx \cdot (y)(Fy \supset y = x) \cdot Gx$ 3, 4, Conj.
 6. $(\exists x)\{Fx \cdot (y)(Fy \supset y = x) \cdot Gx\}$ 5, **EG**
7. $(\exists x)\{Fx \cdot (y)(Fy \supset y = x) \cdot Gx\}$ 2, 3–6, **EI**
8. $G(\imath x)(Fx)$ 7—definition

Any proposition of the form $\Psi(\imath x)(\Phi x)$ is false either if there is no x that is Φ or if there is more than one of them. In such a proposition the descriptive phrase $(\imath x)(\Phi x)$ is said to have a *primary* occurrence. But a proposition containing a descriptive phrase may be part of another proposition, in which the descriptive phrase is said to have a *secondary* occurrence. A proposition in which $(\imath x)(\Phi x)$ has a secondary occurrence may be true even if there is no x that is Φ or there is more than one of them. One of the simplest examples, $\sim\Psi(\imath x)(\Phi x)$, might mean either that

(1) $$(\exists x)\{\Phi x\cdot(y)(\Phi y \supset y = x)\cdot\sim\Psi x\}$$

or that

(2) $$\sim(\exists x)\{\Phi x\cdot(y)(\Phi y \supset y = x)\cdot\Psi x\}$$

If there is no x that is Φ or there is more than one of them, (1) is false and (2) is true. To make ambiguous propositions definite and unambiguous, Russell proposed using formulas of the form $(\imath x)(\Phi x)$ as a kind of 'scope indicator'. But the rules governing this use are quite complicated, and we shall have no use for them here. Indeed, we shall make no further use of formulas of the form $(\imath x)(\Phi x)$, using instead the explicit symbolic translation involving quantifiers and the identity symbol.

EXERCISES

Prove the validity of the following arguments—using only the identity symbol in addition to the indicated abbreviations:

1. The architect who designed Tappan Hall designs only office buildings. Therefore Tappan Hall is an office building. (Ax: x is an architect. t: Tappan Hall. Dxy: x designed y. Ox: x is an office building.)

★2. The Professor of Greek at Siwash is very learned. Therefore all Professors of Greek at Siwash are very learned. (Px: x is a Professor of Greek. Sx: x is at Siwash. Lx: x is very learned.)

3. The smallest state is in New England. All states in New England are primarily industrial. Therefore the smallest state is primarily industrial. (Sx: x is a state. Nx: x is in New England. Ix: x is primarily industrial. Sxy: x is smaller than y.)

★4. The fastest running person is a Scandinavian. Therefore anyone who is not a Scandinavian can be outrun by someone (or other). (Sx: x is a Scandinavian. Px: x is a person. Fxy: x can run faster than y.)

5. All entrants will win. There will be at most one winner. There is at least one entrant. Therefore there is exactly one entrant. (*Ex*: *x* is an entrant. *Wx*: *x* will win.)

★6. Any fish can swim faster than any smaller one. Therefore if there is a largest fish then there is a fastest fish. (*Fx*: *x* is a fish. *Lxy*: *x* is larger than *y*. *Sxy*: *x* can swim faster than *y*.)

7. Adams and Brown were the only men at the banquet who drank. All the men at the banquet who brought liquor drank. Adams did not bring any liquor. If any man at the banquet drank then some man at the banquet who drank must have brought liquor. All who drank became ill. Therefore the man at the banquet who brought liquor became ill. (*a*: Adams. *b*: Brown. *Mx*: *x* was a man at the banquet. *Dx*: *x* drank. *Lx*: *x* brought liquor. *Ix*: *x* became ill.)

8. Anyone who has climbed Mt. Blanc is braver than anyone who has not. Only the youngest member of our team has climbed Mt. Blanc. Everyone on our team is a veteran. Therefore the bravest member of our team is a veteran. (*Cx*: *x* has climbed Mt. Blanc. *Tx*: *x* is on our team. *Vx*: *x* is a veteran. *Bxy*: *x* is braver than *y*. *Oxy*: *x* is older than *y*.)

9. There is exactly one penny in my right hand. There is exactly one penny in my left hand. Nothing is in both my hands. Therefore there are exactly two pennies in my hands. (*Px*: *x* is a penny. *Rx*: *x* is in my right hand. *Lx*: *x* is in my left hand.)

10. All accompanists were bagpipers. All bagpipers were in the cabin. At most two individuals were in the cabin. There were at least two accompanists. Therefore there were exactly two bagpipers. (*Ax*: *x* was an accompanist. *Bx*: *x* was a bagpiper. *Cx*: *x* was in the cabin.)

5.5 PROPERTY VARIABLES AND PROPERTIES OF PROPERTIES

In all of the preceding discussion, quantification has been confined to individual variables. With the exception of the greek letters *phi* and *psi*, all property symbols and relation symbols introduced thus far have been *constants*. The letters '*W*', '*S*', and '*B*' in our usage of '*Wx*', '*Sxy*', and '*Bxyz*' as abbreviations for '*x* is wise', '*x* is a son of *y*', and '*x* is between *y* and *z*', have denoted definite properties of, or relations between, individuals. However, property variables and relation variables can be introduced also, and they too may be quantified.

If we set aside the capital letters 'F', 'G', 'H', as property or relation variables, then the same quantification techniques that are already familiar will permit symbolizing a greater variety of statements. We shall be able to symbolize statements about all or some properties or relations that individuals may have or stand in. The expression

$$Fx$$

consisting of a property variable and an individual variable juxtaposed in that order may be regarded as a propositional function of *two* variables. By instantiation with respect to both variables we obtain such singular propositions as 'Socrates is mortal' and 'Plato is wise', expressed symbolically as '*Ms*' and '*Wp*'. By instantiation with respect to the property variable and generalization with respect to the individual variable we obtain such familiar singly general propositions as

$$(x)Mx \quad \text{(everything is mortal)}$$
$$(\exists x)Wx \quad \text{(something is wise)}$$

We have seen all these before. A new kind of proposition, however, although still singly general, is obtained by instantiating with respect to the individual variable and generalizing with respect to the property variable. Here we have

$$(F)Fs \quad \text{(Socrates has all properties)}$$
$$(\exists F)Fp \quad \text{(Plato has some property)}$$

Finally, by generalizing with respect to *both* variables, the following doubly general propositions are obtained:

(1) $(x)(F)Fx$ (5) $(F)(x)Fx$
(2) $(x)(\exists F)Fx$ (6) $(F)(\exists x)Fx$
(3) $(\exists x)(F)Fx$ (7) $(\exists F)(x)Fx$
(4) $(\exists x)(\exists F)Fx$ (8) $(\exists F)(\exists x)Fx$

Of these, (1) and (5) are clearly equivalent, (1) stating that

Every individual has every property.

and (5) stating that

Every property belongs to every individual.

Propositions (4) and (8) are also equivalent to each other, with (4) stating that

Some individual has some property.

and (8) stating that

Some property belongs to some individual.

The remaining propositions, however, are all distinct. They may be expressed in English as

(2) Every individual has some property (or other).
(3) There is an individual that has every property.
(6) Every property belongs to some individual (or other).
(7) There is a property that belongs to every individual.

There are no equivalences here, but proposition (3) logically entails proposition (6), and proposition (7) logically entails proposition (2). These implications can be formally established by means of our familiar quantification rules, allowing the symbols 'μ' and 'ν' of the rules to denote property variables as well as individual variables— with the same restrictions on their application, of course.

When property variables are introduced and their quantification permitted, a formal, that is, completely symbolic definition, can be given for the identity symbol. The definition is

$$(x = y) = df (F)(Fx \equiv Fy)$$

From this definition we have

$$(x)(y)[(x = y) \equiv (F)(Fx \equiv Fy)]$$

following as a logical consequence. And from the latter all the properties of the identity relation can be deduced.

For the most part our preceding discussion has concerned only properties of individuals. But individuals are not the only entities that have properties. In Section 5.3 we discussed various properties which can be predicated of *relations*. And properties themselves can have properties: thus the property of being *honest* has the property of being *desirable*, a *virtue* (which is a property) may itself have the property of being *rare*, and the property of being *inconsiderate* is *common*.

Once it has been noted that some properties can be predicated of other properties, the temptation arises to predicate certain properties of themselves. For example, the property of being abstract seems itself to be abstract, whereas the property of being concrete seems not to be itself concrete. Any property that can be truly predicated of itself will be said to be a *predicable* property. Thus being predicable is a property that belongs to all those and only those properties which can be truly predicated of themselves. On the other hand, any property that cannot be truly predicated of itself will be said to be an *impredicable* property. Thus being impredicable is a property which belongs to all those and only those properties that cannot be truly predicated of themselves.

If we now ask whether the property of being impredicable can be truly predicated of itself or not, we are led to the following unhappy conclusion. If the property of being impredicable *can* be truly predicated of itself, then it *has* the property of being impredicable, from which it follows by definition that it *cannot* be truly predicated of itself. On the other hand, if the property of being impredicable *cannot* be truly predicated of itself, then like all other properties which cannot be truly predicated of themselves, it *has* the property of being impredicable, which means that it *can* be truly predicated of itself. We have thus been led to a contradiction.

The contradiction can be derived more clearly by symbolizing the property of being impredicable as 'I', and defining it formally as

$$IF = df \sim FF$$

which definition has the following general proposition as an immediate logical consequence:

$$(F)(IF \equiv \sim FF)$$

From the latter, by the principle of Universal Instantiation, we can instantiate with respect to 'I' itself to obtain

$$II \equiv \sim II$$

which is an explicit contradiction.[3]

---

[3] Cf. Russell's *Principles of Mathematics*, Cambridge, England, 1903, pp. 79–80, 97–98, and 102. Cf. also Carnap's *Logical Syntax of Language*, New York, 1937, p. 211.

Several methods have been proposed for avoiding such contradictions. Perhaps the best known is Russell's (simple) Theory of Logical Types,[4] which can be given the following rough formulation. According to Russell, entities are divided into a hierarchy of different logical types, the lowest of which consists of all individuals, the next of all properties of individuals, the next of all properties of properties of individuals, the next of all properties of properties of properties of individuals, and so on. Relations and their properties give us additional hierarchies, but they will be ignored in the present discussion. The essential point to the theory of types is not merely the division of all entities into different logical types, but the restriction that any property which may significantly be predicated of an entity of one logical type cannot significantly be predicated of any entity of any other logical type. For some properties the theory of types seems perfectly obvious. Thus an individual thing may be orange in color, but it clearly does not make sense to say of any property that *it* is orange in color. And a property may have many instances, but it does not make sense either to affirm or deny of an individual thing that *it* has many instances.

The primary motivation for accepting the theory of logical types, however, it not its naturalness or obviousness, but the fact that it permits the avoidance of such contradictions as that of the alleged property 'impredicable'. According to this theory the type of a property must be higher than the type of any entity of which it can significantly be predicated. Consequently it does not make sense either to affirm or to deny of any property that it belongs to itself; such expressions as '*FF*' and '∼*FF*' must be dismissed as meaningless. Consequently no

---

[4] Russell first formulated his theory of logical types in Appendix B of his *Principles of Mathematics*. A more complex version of the theory, designed to cope with certain other problems as well, will be presented in Appendix C of the present volume. Cf. also Russell's 'Mathematical Logic as Based on the Theory of Types', *American Journal of Mathematics*, vol. 30 (1908), pp. 222–262, reprinted in *Bertrand Russell: Logic and Knowledge. Essays 1901–1950*, edited by Robert Charles Marsh, London, 1956, and Chapter 2 of the Introduction to the first edition of *Principia Mathematica*, by Whitehead and Russell, Cambridge, England, 1910–1913. The best known alternative resolution of the contradiction is the kind of axiomatic set theory first published by E. Zermelo in 'Untersuchungen über die Grundlagen der Mengenlehre I', *Mathematische Annalen*, vol. 65 (1908), pp. 261–281. A brilliant discussion of these alternatives can be found in Willard Van Orman Quine's *Set Theory and Its Logic*, Cambridge, Mass., 1963.

such property as 'impredicable' can be defined, and the contradiction vanishes. The version of the theory of types sketched above—sometimes called the 'Simple Theory of Types'—suffices to rule out all contradictions of this kind. It also has a certain consonance with common sense. However, there are alternative solutions or ways to avoid the contradictions, so the theory of logical types cannot be regarded as *the* solution. It is very widely accepted, however, and we shall follow it in introducing a new type of symbol to represent properties of properties of individuals.

Some words have more than a single meaning, of course, and may in one sense designate a property of individuals, and in another sense designate a property of properties of individuals. Thus the word 'rare' in one sense designates a property of properties of individuals: a property of individuals is rare if it is exemplified by only a few individuals, and in this sense it cannot significantly be affirmed or denied of individuals themselves. But on the other hand, there is a *different* sense of the word 'rare' in which it designates a property of an individual piece of meat that has been cooked for only a short while, and in this sense it cannot significantly be affirmed or denied of any property. To avoid ambiguity we symbolize properties of properties of individuals by boldface italic capital letters '*A*', '*B*', '*C*', . . . , to prevent their being confused with properties of individuals. With this additional symbolic apparatus we can translate into our notation such propositions as 'Unpunctuality is a fault', and 'Truthfulness is a good quality'. Here we use 'Ux', 'Tx', 'FF', and 'GF' to abbreviate 'x is unpunctual', 'x is truthful', 'F is a fault', and 'F is good', and symbolize the two stated propositions as 'FU' and 'GT'. More complex propositions can also be symbolized. The propositions

All useful properties are desirable.

and

Some desirable properties are not useful.

can be symbolized, using the symbols 'UF' for 'F is useful' and 'DF' for 'F is desirable', as

$$(F)(UF \supset DF)$$

and

$$(\exists F)(DF \cdot \sim UF)$$

Finally, the proposition

Tom has all of his mother's good qualities.

can be symbolized, using the additional symbols '*t*' for 'Tom' and '*Mxy*' for '*x* is mother of *y*', either as

$$(F)\{[F(\imath x)(Mxt)\cdot GF] \supset Ft\}$$

or as

$$(F)\{(\exists x)[Mxt\cdot(y)(Myt \supset y = x)\cdot Fx\cdot GF] \supset Ft\}$$

EXERCISES

I. Symbolize the following propositions:

1. Nothing has all properties.
2. Some properties belong to nothing.
★3. No two things have all their properties in common.
4. Any two things have some common property.
5. Napoleon had all the properties of a great general. (*n*: Napoleon. *Gx*: *x* is a great general.)
★6. David has all of his father's faults and none of his virtues. (*d*: David. *Fxy*: *x* is father of *y*. *FF*: *F* is a fault. *VF*: *F* is a virtue.)
7. Jones and Smith share all their good qualities but have no bad qualities in common. (*j*: Jones. *s*: Smith. *GF*: *F* is a good quality. *BF*: *F* is a bad quality.)
8. Nothing which possesses every rare property has any ordinary property. (*RF*: *F* is rare. *OF*: *F* is ordinary.)
★9. A man who possesses all virtues is a virtuous man, but there are virtuous men who do not possess all virtues. (*Mx*: *x* is a man. *Vx*: *x* is a virtuous individual. *VF*: *F* is a virtue.)
10. Everyone has some unusual property or other; it would be an unusual person who had no unusual properties. (*Px*: *x* is a person. *Ux*: *x* is an unusual individual. *UF*: *F* is an unusual property.)

II. Prove the following:

1. $[(x)(F)Fx] \equiv [(F)(x)Fx]$
★2. $[(\exists x)(\exists F)Fx] \equiv [(\exists F)(\exists x)Fx]$
3. $[(\exists x)(F)Fx] \supset [(F)(\exists x)Fx]$
4. $[(\exists F)(x)Fx] \supset [(x)(\exists F)Fx]$
5. $[(\exists R)(x)(\exists y)Rxy] \supset [(x)(\exists y)(\exists R)Rxy]$

*6. Every (dyadic) relation which is transitive and irreflexive is asymmetric.

7. All intransitive dyadic relations are irreflexive.

8. Any dyadic relation which every individual has to some individual or other is totally reflexive if it is both symmetric and transitive.

9. From the premiss '$(x)(y)[(x = y) \equiv (F)(Fx \equiv Fy)]$' (which is true by definition), deduce that the identity relation is symmetric, without using the principle Id.

*10. From the same premiss as in 9 and under the same restriction deduce that the identity relation is totally reflexive.

11. From the same premiss as in 9 and under the same restriction deduce that the identity relation is transitive.

12. If circles are ellipses then circles have all properties of ellipses.

6

DEDUCTIVE
SYSTEMS

6.1 DEFINITION AND DEDUCTION

In the preceding chapters a number of principles of logic have been set forth. These principles embody some knowledge about logic, but they do not constitute a *science* of logic, for *science* is *organized* knowledge. No mere list or catalog of propositions is ever said to constitute a system of knowledge or a science. We have scientific knowledge only when our propositions are organized in a systematic way, to display their interrelations. If a system of logic or a science of logical principles is to be achieved, those principles must be arranged or organized in a systematic fashion. This task will be attempted, on a limited scale, in the following chapters. But first it will be of interest to consider the general questions of what interrelations are important, and how propositions may be organized into a system or science.

All knowledge that we possess can be formulated in propositions, and these propositions are composed of terms. In any science, some propositions can be deduced from or proved on the basis of other propositions. For example, Galileo's laws of falling bodies and Kepler's laws of planetary motion are all derivable from Newton's more general laws of gravitation and motion, and the discovery of these deductive inter-relationships was an exciting phase in the development of the *science* of physics. Thus one important relationship among the propositions of a science is deducibility. Propositions that embody knowledge about a subject become a *science* of that subject when they are arranged or ordered by displaying some of them as conclusions deduced from others.

In any science, some of the terms involved in its propositions can be explained or defined on the basis of other terms. For example, in physics again, *density* is defined as *mass per unit volume*, *acceleration* is defined as the *time rate of change in velocity*, and *velocity* is in turn defined as the *time rate of change of position*. This definition of some terms by means of others also serves to reveal interrelations among the proposi-tions. It shows their concern with a common subject matter, and integrates the concepts of the science just as deductions integrate its laws or statements. Propositions that embody knowledge are helped to become a *science* when some of the words or symbols they contain are defined in terms of their other symbols.

The recognition of definition and deduction as important to science may suggest a specious ideal for scientific systems. It may be imagined that in an ideal science *all* propositions should be *proved*, by deducing them from others, and *all* terms should be *defined*. But this would be 'ideal' only in the sense of being impossible to realize. Terms can be defined only by means of other terms, whose meanings are presupposed and must be antecedently understood if the definitions are to explain the meanings of the terms being defined. And deductions can establish their conclusions only on the basis of premises, which must already have been verified if the conclusions are really to be established by the proofs. Hence, if all terms or symbols of a system are to be defined *within the system*, there must be either infinite sequences of definitions, or circular definitions, as in a pocket dictionary which defines the word 'big' as meaning *large*, and the word 'large' as meaning *big*. Circular definitions are obviously worthless, and infinite sequences of definitions are worthless also, for no term will really be explained until the end is reached, and an infinite sequence has no end. Similarly, to prove *all* propositions there must be either infinite regressions of proofs or circular proofs. And these are equally objectionable.

It must be admitted that *within* a system of propositions which constitutes a science, not all propositions can be proved, and not all terms can be defined. It is not that there is some particular proposition that cannot be proved, or some particular term that cannot be defined, but rather that they cannot *all* be proved or defined without a vicious regression or circularity arising. The ideal of science, then, cannot be a system in which *every* proposition is proved and *every* term defined, but is rather one in which a minimum number of propositions suffice for the deduction of all the rest, and a minimum number of terms suffice for the definition of all the others. This ideal of knowledge is described as a *deductive system*.

6.2   EUCLIDEAN GEOMETRY

Euclidean Geometry is the oldest example of systematized knowledge or science. Of historical interest and importance in its own right, it has the advantage (for our purpose) of being an example with which the reader has already come into contact during his high school training.

It is generally recognized that geometry, as a science, was originated and developed by the Greeks. Among the most important of the contributors to its development were the mathematicians Pythagoras and Euclid. And yet, geometrical truths were known to the Egyptians thousands of years earlier, as attested by their pyramids, already ancient in the time of Pythagoras (6th century B.C.). Records reveal that the Babylonians, even earlier, were familiar with various principles of geometry. If a considerable body of geometrical knowledge was already possessed before their time, in what sense did the Greeks originate the science of geometry? The answer has already been indicated. Before Pythagoras, man's geometrical knowledge consisted of a collection or catalog of almost wholly isolated facts. Geometrical truths constituted a mere list of useful empirical rules-of-thumb for surveying land or constructing bridges or buildings, and there was no system to their knowledge of geometrical truths. By introducing order into the subject, the Greeks transformed it from a mere body of isolated bits of knowledge into a science.

System was introduced into geometry by the deduction of some of its propositions from others. The propositions of geometry were ordered by listing earlier those which could be used as premises in the demonstrations of those which were put later. This systematization of geometry was begun by Pythagoras and continued by his successors. It culminated in the *Elements* of Euclid (c.300 B.C.), in which all geometrical propositions were arranged in order, beginning with Axioms, Definitions, and Postulates, and continuing with Theorems deduced from the initial propositions. Geometry was cast by the Greeks into the form of a deductive system. Theirs was the first deductive system ever devised, and so great was the achievement that it has served as a model for scientific thought down to the present time. Even today the most advanced sciences are those which most nearly approximate the form of a deductive system. These are the sciences which have achieved a relatively small number of very general principles from which a relatively large number of other laws and special cases may be derived. Parts of physics have actually been formulated as deductive systems, and similar attempts have been made, with somewhat less impressive results, in parts of biology and psychology also. Perhaps the boldest attempt in this direction was that of Spinoza, whose most important work, the *Ethics*, was written in 'geometrical' form. Starting with axioms and definitions, Spinoza attempted to deduce the rest of his metaphysical and ethical doctrines as theorems provable on the basis of those initial assumptions.

Euclid begins his geometry with definitions of some of the terms used in its development. Thus Definition 1 reads: 'A point is that which has no parts', and Definition 2 reads: 'A line is length without breadth'.[1] Euclid does not attempt to define *all* his terms, of course. The first two definitions define the terms 'point' and 'line' respectively. The words *used* in these definitions, such as 'parts', 'length', and 'breadth' are not themselves defined but are among the *undefined terms* of the system for Euclid. As more new terms are introduced their definitions make use

[1] These and the following are quoted from the Todhunter edition of *The Elements of Euclid*, No. 891 of Everyman's Library, London and New York.

of previously defined terms as well as the original undefined ones. Thus Definition 4: 'A straight line is . . . [a line] . . . which lies evenly between its extreme points', makes use not only of such undefined terms as 'evenly' and 'between', but also the previously defined terms 'point' and 'line'.

The use of *defined* terms is, from the point of view of logic, a matter of convenience only. Theoretically, every proposition that contains defined terms can be translated into one that contains only *undefined* ones by replacing each occurrence of a defined term by the sequence of undefined terms which was used to define it. For example, Postulate 1: 'Let it be granted that a straight line may be drawn from any one point to any other point', which contains the defined terms 'straight', 'line', and 'point', can be expressed without using those defined terms as: 'Let it be granted that a length without breadth which lies evenly between its extreme parts which (themselves) have no parts may be drawn from any one thing which has no parts to any other thing which has no parts'. But this version of the Postulate is extremely awkward. Although they are theoretically eliminable, in actual practice a considerable economy of space, time, and effort is effected by using relatively brief defined terms to replace lengthy sequences or combinations of undefined ones.

In setting up his deductive system of geometry, Euclid divided his unproved propositions into two groups, one called 'Axioms', the other called 'Postulates'. He gave, however, no reason for making this division, and there seems to be no very clear basis for distinguishing between them. Possibly he felt that some were more *general* than others, or psychologically more *obvious*. The contemporary practice is to draw no such distinction, but to regard all the unproved, initial propositions of a deductive system as having the same standing, and to refer to them all, indifferently, as 'axioms' or as 'postulates', without attaching any difference in meaning to those two terms.

Every deductive system, on pain of falling into circularity or a vicious regression, must contain some axioms (or postulates) which are assumed but not proved within the system. They need not be *precarious* assumptions, or *mere* assumptions. They may be very carefully and convincingly established—but they are *not proved within the system itself.* Any argument intended to establish the truth of the axioms is definitely *outside* the system, or *extrasystematic*.

The older conception of Euclidean geometry held not only that all of its theorems followed logically from its axioms, and were therefore just as *true* as the axioms, but also that the axioms were *self-evident*. It is in this tradition to regard any statement as 'axiomatic' only when its truth is beyond all doubt, being evident in itself and not requiring any proof. It should be clear from what has already been said, however, that we are *not* using the word 'axiom' in *that* sense. No claim is made that the axioms of any system are self-evidently true. Any proposition of a deductive system is an axiom of that system if it is assumed rather than proved in that system. This modern point of view has arisen largely as a consequence of the historical development of geometry and physics.

The self-evident truth of the Euclidean axioms (and postulates) was long believed. It was not believed quite whole-heartedly, however. Most of the axioms, such as Axiom 9: 'The whole is greater than its part', were not questioned; but while there was no doubt about the *truth* of Axiom 12 (the famous 'parallel Postulate'), there was considerable scepticism about its 'self-evidence'. Axiom 12 reads: 'If a straight line meet two straight lines, so as to make the two interior angles on the same side of it taken together less than two right angles, these straight lines, being continually produced, shall at length meet on that side on which are the angles which are less than two right angles'.[2] Proclus, a fifth century A.D. commentator, wrote of it: 'This ought even to be struck out of the Postulates altogether; for it is a theorem involving many difficulties . . . '.[3] That is, although its *truth* was not questioned, its *self-evidence* was denied, which was deemed sufficient reason to relegate it from its exalted position as axiom to the less dignified status of a mere theorem.

The history of mathematics is filled with attempts to prove the proposition in question as a theorem, either by deducing it from the remain-

[2] Listed as Postulate 5 by Sir Thomas L. Heath, in *The Thirteen Books of Euclid's Elements*, Cambridge, Eng., Cambridge University Press, 1926. For an interesting discussion of the history of the parallel postulate, the reader is referred to pages 202 ff. of Volume I of that work.

[3] *Ibid.*, p. 202.

ing axioms of Euclid, or from those axioms supplemented by some more nearly 'self-evident' additional assumption. The latter kind of attempt was pretty uniformly unsuccessful, because every additional or alternative assumption strong enough to permit the deduction of the parallel postulate turned out to be no more self-evident than Euclid's own hypothesis. The first kind of attempt failed also; it was just not possible to deduce the parallel postulate from the others. The most fruitful attempt was that of the Italian mathematician Gerolamo Saccheri (1667–1733), who *replaced* the parallel postulate by alternative, contrary assumptions, and then sought to derive a contradiction from them together with Euclid's other axioms. Had he succeeded in doing so, he would have obtained a *reductio ad absurdum* proof of the parallel postulate. He derived many theorems that he regarded as *absurd* because they were so different from common sense or ordinary geometrical intuition. He believed himself to have succeeded thus in demonstrating the parallel postulate, and in 'vindicating Euclid'. But his derived theorems, while 'absurd' in the sense of violating ordinary geometrical intuitions, were *not* 'absurd' in the logical or mathematical sense of being self-contradictory. Instead of proving the parallel postulate, Saccheri (unknowingly) did something more important: he was the first to set up and develop a system of non-Euclidean geometry.

The parallel postulate is in fact *independent* of the other Euclidean postulates—although it was not *proved* to be so until the modern period. It is independent of the other postulates in the sense that neither it nor its denial is deducible from them. Alternative systems of 'geometry', non-Euclidean geometries, were subsequently developed, notably by Lobachevsky and Riemann. These were long regarded as ingenious fictions, mere mathematical playthings, in contrast with the Euclidean geometry which was 'true' of the real space about us. But subsequent physical and astronomical research along lines suggested by Einstein's theory of relativity has tended to show that—to the extent that the question is significant—'real' or physical space is more probably non-Euclidean than Euclidean. In any event, the truth or falsehood of its axioms is a purely *external* property of any deductive system. The truth of its propositions is an extrasystematic consideration. It is no doubt important to the extent that a deductive system is ordered *knowledge;* but when we concentrate our attention on the system as such, its *order* is its more important characteristic.

From the purely mathematical or logical point of view, a deductive system can be regarded as a vast and complex argument. Its premises are the axioms, and its conclusion is the conjunction of all the theorems deduced. As with any other argument, the logical question does not concern the truth or falsehood of the premises, but the validity of the inference. Granted the truth of the axioms, does the truth of the theorems necessarily follow? That is the question with which the logician and the mathematician are concerned. The answer is, of course, yes—*if* the demonstrations of the theorems are all valid arguments. Hence the most important aspect of any deductive system is the cogency with which its theorems are proved. In the rigorous development of deductive systems in abstraction from the extrasystematic explanation of their undefined terms, the question of truth or falsehood is obviously irrelevant.

6.3 FORMAL DEDUCTIVE SYSTEMS

There are serious errors in the system of geometry set forth by Euclid in his *Elements.* Indeed, a mistake occurs in his very first proof. The flaw in his proof, paradoxically enough, was the result of his knowing too much about his subject. He did not appeal to his explicitly stated axioms alone as premises, but depended also upon what might be called his geometrical intuition.[4] Where a chain of argument involves familiar notions, there is always the danger of assuming more than the explicitly stated premises warrant. That is particularly serious in the development of a deductive system, for any attempted systematization which appeals to new and unacknowledged assumptions in the derivations of its theorems thereby *fails* to achieve its aim. In a deduc-

---

[4] Euclid's proof and a brief discussion of his mistake can be found on pages 241–243 of Volume I of *The Thirteen Books of Euclid's Elements,* by Heath, *op. cit.* An example of how the same type of error can lead to conclusions that are false or even self-contradictory can be found on pages 77–78 of *Mathematical Recreations and Essays,* by W. W. Rouse Ball, New York, The Macmillan Co., 1940.

tive system the theorems must be deduced *rigorously* from the stated postulates. If they are not, however true they may be, the result falls short of the goal of systematization.

Since lapses from rigor are most often occasioned by too great familiarity with the subject matter, mathematicians have found it helpful to minimize or eliminate such familiarity in the interest of achieving greater rigor. In the case of geometry, that end is accomplished by abstracting from the meanings of such geometrical words as 'point', 'line', and 'plane', and developing the theorems as purely formal consequences of the postulates. The familiar geometrical words, with all their associations and suggestions, are replaced by arbitrary symbols. Instead of deductive systems explicitly and avowedly concerned with geometrical entities, mathematicians today develop *formal* deductive systems whose primitive or undefined terms include arbitrary, uninterpreted symbols, usually letters of the Greek or Latin alphabets. Since the undefined terms of a *formal* deductive system include arbitrary symbols, its postulates are not propositions at all, but mere formulas, and so are the theorems.

Deductive relationships can exist, of course, among mere formulas as well as among propositions. Thus the formula 'all F's are H's' is logically deducible from the formulas 'all F's are G's' and 'all G's are H's'. Since the postulates and theorems of a formal deductive system are formulas rather than propositions, the proofs of theorems can proceed unhampered by familiar associations and unconscious assumptions. Moreover, since the formulas are not propositions, the question of truth is strictly irrelevant and does not arise.

More than rigor is gained by the formal development of deductive systems. Since some of the symbols of a formal deductive system are arbitrary uninterpreted symbols, it may be possible to give them different, alternative interpretations. And since the theorems are formal consequences of the axioms, any interpretation of the arbitrary symbols which makes the axioms true will necessarily make the theorems true also. The additional advantage of generality is thus gained. An example may help to make this clear. Given some knowledge about astronomy, it may be desired to set up a deductive system for that subject. To avoid the errors into which familiarity with the subject matter may lead in deducing theorems from the axioms chosen, the system may be developed *formally*. Instead of taking, say, 'stars' and 'planets' among the undefined terms, one may take '*A*'s and '*B*'s. The axioms and theorems will contain these symbols, and when the system is developed, all its formulas may be interpreted by letting the symbol '*A*' designate stars and the symbol '*B*' designate planets. Now, if the axioms are *true* when so interpreted, the theorems must be true also, and the formal system with this interpretation will constitute a science or deductive system of astronomy. But it may be possible to find a *different* interpretation of the symbols '*A*' and '*B*' which also makes the axioms true (and hence the theorems also). The formulas of the system might be made into different but equally true statements by letting the symbol '*A*' designate atomic nuclei and the symbol '*B*' designate electrons. Could this be done (and at one stage in the recent history of atomic physics it seemed highly plausible), the original formal system with this second interpretation would constitute a science or deductive system of atomic physics. Hence developing a deductive system formally, *i.e.*, not interpreting its undefined terms until after its theorems have all been derived, not only helps achieve rigor in its development, but also achieves greater generality because of the possibility of finding alternative interpretations for it. This kind of advantage is often realized in pure mathematics. For example, different interpretations of its arbitrary primitive symbols will transform the same formal deductive system into the theory of real numbers, on the one hand, or into the theory of points on a straight line, on the other. That fact provides the theoretical foundation for the branch of mathematics called *Analytical Geometry*.

As the term is being used here, a *formal deductive system* is simply a deductive system, consisting of axioms and theorems, some of whose undefined or primitive terms are arbitrary symbols whose interpretation is completely extrasystematic. In addition to those special undefined terms, and others defined by means of them, the formulas (axioms and theorems) of the system contain only such logical terms as 'if . . . then', 'and', 'or', 'not', 'all', 'are', and the like, and possibly (unless the system is intended for arithmetic itself) such arithmetical terms as 'sum' and 'product', and numerical symbols.

6.4 PROPERTIES OF FORMAL DEDUCTIVE SYSTEMS

Usually, though not always, a formal deductive system is set up with some particular interpretation 'in mind'. That is, the investigator has some knowledge about a certain subject, and wishes to set up a system adequate for its expression. When the formal system has been constructed, the question naturally arises as to whether or not it is adequate to the formulation of all the propositions it is intended to express. If it is, it may be said to be 'expressively complete' *with respect to that subject matter*. We are here discussing what can be *said* in the system, *not* what can be proved. With respect to a given subject matter, a formal deductive system is 'expressively complete' when it is possible to assign meanings to its undefined terms in such a way that every proposition about that subject matter can be *expressed* as a formula of the system. Whether the *true* propositions can be *proved as theorems* or not is another question, which will be discussed below.

A system is said to be *inconsistent* if two formulas, one of which is the denial or contradictory of the other, can both be proved as theorems within it. A system is *consistent* if it contains no formula such that both the formula and its negation are provable as theorems within it. As was shown in Chapter 3, a contradiction logically entails any proposition whatever. Hence a derivative definition or criterion for consistency can be formulated as follows: Any system is consistent if it contains (that is, can express) a formula that is not provable as a theorem within it. This is known as the 'Post criterion for consistency', having been enunciated by the American mathematician and logician, E. L. Post. Consistency is of fundamental importance. An inconsistent deductive system is worthless, for all of its formulas are provable as theorems, including those which are explicit negations of others. When the undefined terms are assigned meanings, these contradictory formulas become contradictory propositions, and cannot possibly all be true. And since they cannot possibly be true, they cannot serve as a systematization of knowledge—for knowledge is expressed in true propositions only.

If one succeeds in deriving both a formula and its negation as theorems of a system, that proves the system inconsistent. But if one tries and does not succeed in deriving both a formula and its negation as theorems, that does *not* show the system to be consistent, for it may only reflect a lack of ingenuity at making proofs on the part of the investigator. How then can the consistency of a deductive system be established? One method of proving the consistency of a formal deductive system is to find an interpretation of it in which all its axioms and theorems are true propositions. Since its theorems are logical consequences of its axioms, any interpretation which makes its axioms true will make its theorems true also. Hence it is sufficient for the purpose of proving a system consistent to find an interpretation which makes all of its axioms true.

The axioms of a deductive system are said to be *independent* (or to exhibit *independence*) if no one of them can be derived as a theorem from the others. A deductive system which is not consistent is logically objectionable and utterly worthless, but there is no *logical* objection to a deductive system whose axioms are not independent. However, it is often felt that making more assumptions than necessary for the development of a system is extravagant and inelegant, and should be avoided. When a formula need not be assumed as an axiom, but can be proved as a theorem, it *ought* to be proved and not assumed, for the sake of 'economy'. A set of axioms which are not independent is said to be 'redundant'. A redundant set of axioms is aesthetically inelegant, but it is not logically 'bad'.

If one of the axioms of a system *can* be derived from the remaining ones, the set of axioms is thereby shown to be redundant. But if one tries and is not able to derive any of the axioms from the remaining ones, they are *not* thereby shown to be independent, for the failure to find a demonstration may be due only to the investigator's lack of ingenuity. To prove any particular axiom independent of the others, it suffices to find an interpretation which makes the axiom in question *false* and the remaining ones all *true*. Such an interpretation will prove that the axiom in question is not derivable as a theorem from the others, for if it were, it would be made true by any assignment of meanings which made the others true. If such an interpretation can be found for each axiom, this will prove the set of axioms to be independent.

The notion of *deductive completeness* is a very important one. The term 'completeness' is used in various senses. In the least precise sense of the term we can say that a deductive system is complete if all the *desired* formulas can be proved within it. We may have an extrasystematic criterion for the truth of propositions about the subject matter for which we constructed the deductive system. If we have, then we may call that system complete when all of its formulas which become true propositions on the intended interpretation are provable formulas or theorems of the system. (In any sense of the term, an *inconsistent* system will be *complete*, but in view of the worthlessness of inconsistent systems, we shall confine our attention to *consistent* systems in the following discussion.)

There is another conception of *completeness* which can be explained as follows. Any formal deductive system will have a certain collection of special undefined or primitive terms. Since any terms definable within the system are theoretically eliminable, being replaceable in any formula in which they occur by the sequence of undefined terms by means of which they were defined, we shall ignore defined terms for the present. All formulas which contain only these special undefined terms (and logical terms) are expressible within the system. We may speak of the totality of undefined terms as the *base* of the system, and the formulas expressible in the system are all formulas constructed *on that base*. In general, the totality of formulas constructed on the base of a given system can be divided into three groups: first, all formulas which are provable as theorems within the system; second, all formulas whose negations are provable within the system; and third, all formulas such that neither they nor their negations are provable within the system. For *consistent* systems the first and second groups are *disjoint*, that is, have no formulas in common. Any system whose third group is empty, containing no formulas at all, is said to be *deductively complete*. An alternative way of phrasing this sense of completeness is to say that every formula of the system is such that either it or its negation is provable as a theorem.

Another definition of 'completeness', roughly equivalent to the preceding one, is that a deductive system is complete when every formula constructed on its base is either a theorem or else its addition as an axiom would make the system inconsistent.

An example of an incomplete deductive system would be Euclidean geometry minus the parallel postulate. For the parallel postulate is itself a formula constructible on the base of the Euclidean system, yet it is not derivable as a theorem from the remaining ones, and the system remains consistent when the parallel postulate is added. It is clear that although completeness is an important property, an incomplete deductive system may be very interesting and valuable. For by investigating the incomplete system of Euclidean geometry without the parallel postulate, we can discover those properties possessed by space independently of the question of whether it is Euclidean or non-Euclidean. Perhaps a more cautious and less misleading formulation of the same point is to say that by investigating the incomplete system we can discover the *common features* of Euclidean and non-Euclidean geometries. Yet for many purposes, a complete system is to be preferred.

6.5 LOGISTIC SYSTEMS

Most important of all properties for a deductive system to possess is that of rigor. A system has rigor when no formula is asserted to be a theorem unless it is logically entailed by the axioms. It is for the sake of rigor that arbitrary rather than familiar symbols are taken as undefined or primitive terms, and the system developed *formally*. Listing clearly all the undefined terms, and explicitly stating all the axioms used as premises for the theorems, will help to specify precisely which formulas are to be esteemed as theorems and which are not. With the increased emphasis on rigor that characterizes the modern period, critical mathematicians have seen that this is not enough. To achieve rigor, more is required.

A system is rigorous only when its theorems are proved logically, or derived logically from its axioms. It has now been realized that however clearly its axioms are stated, a formal system will lack rigor unless the notion of *logical proof* or *logical derivation* is specified precisely also. All deductive systems of the sort that have been mentioned, even formal deductive systems which contain logical terms in addition to their own special uninterpreted symbols, depend upon 'ordinary logic' for their development. They *assume* logic, in the sense that their theorems are supposed to follow *logically* from their axioms. But they do not specify what this 'logic' is. Hence all earlier deductive systems, for geometry, or physics, or psychology, or the like, contain concealed assumptions which are not explicitly stated. These hidden assumptions are the rules or principles of logic to which one appeals in constructing proofs or derivations of theorems. Hence all such deductive systems fall short of complete rigor, for not all of their presuppositions are acknowledged. Therefore their developments are not entirely rigorous, but more or less loose. The question naturally arises: How can this looseness be eliminated, and greater rigor be achieved? The answer is obvious enough. A deductive system will be developed more rigorously when it is specified not only what axioms are assumed as premises in deriving the theorems, but also what principles of inference are to be used in the derivations. The axioms must be supplemented by a list of valid argument forms, or principles of valid inference.

The demand for rigor and for system does not stop even here, however. For the sake of rigor, in addition to its own special axioms, a deductive system must specify explicitly what forms of inference are to be accepted as valid. But it would be unsystematic—and probably impossible—simply to list or catalog *all* required rules of logic or valid modes of inference. A deductive system of logic itself must be set up. Such a deductive system will have deduction itself as its subject matter. A system of this type, often referred to as a *logistic system*, must differ from the ordinary, less formal varieties in several important respects. Since its subject matter is deduction itself, the logical terms 'if . . . then', 'and', 'or', 'not', and so on, cannot occur in it with their ordinary meanings simply assumed. In their stead must be uninterpreted symbols. And the logical principles or rules of inference that *it* assumes for the sake of deducing logical theorems from logical axioms must be few in number and explicitly stated.

A second fundamental difference between logistic systems and other formal deductive systems is that in the latter the notion of a significant or 'well formed' formula need not be specified, whereas it is absolutely required in a logistic system. In an ordinary (nonformal) deductive system, it will be obvious which sequences of its words are significant propositions of English (or of whatever the natural language is in which the system is expressed). In a formal but nonlogistical deductive system, the sequences of its symbols are easily divided into those which 'make sense' and those which do not, for they will contain such ordinary logical words as 'if . . . then', 'and', 'or', or 'not', by whose disposition in the sequence it can be recognized as significant or otherwise. An example will make this clear. In a formal deductive system which contains 'A', 'B', and 'C' as uninterpreted primitive symbols, the sequence of symbols 'If any A is a B, then it is a C' is clearly a complete and 'significant' formula which may or may not be provable as a theorem. But the sequence of symbols 'If any A is a B' is obviously *incomplete*, while the sequence 'And or or A B not not if' is clearly nonsense. These are recognized as 'complete' or 'well formed', as 'incomplete' or 'ill formed' by the presence in them of *some* symbols whose meanings are understood. In a logistic system, however, *all* symbols are uninterpreted: there are no familiar words within its formulas (or sequences of symbols) to indicate which are 'well formed' and which are not. Where the symbols 'A', 'B', '$\sim$', and '$\supset$' are uninterpreted, there must be some method of distinguishing between a well formed formula like '$A \supset \sim B$' and one like '$AB \supset \sim$', which is not well formed. By our knowledge of the normal interpretations of these symbols we can recognize the difference and classify them correctly, but for the *rigorous* development of our system we must be able to do this in abstraction from the (intended) meanings of the symbols involved.

The matter may be expressed in the following terms. As ordinarily conceived, a nonformal deductive system (interpreted, like Euclidean geometry) is an arrangement or organization of propositions about some specified subject matter. Consisting of propositions, it is a *language* in which the subject matter may be discussed. Understanding the language, we can divide all sequences of its words into those which are meaningful statements and those which are meaningless or nonsensical. This division is effected in terms of meanings and is thus done *nonformally*. In a logistic system the situation is different, for prior to the extrasystematic assignment of meanings or interpretation, *all* sequences of symbols are without meaning. Yet we want, prior to and independent of its interpretation, a comparable division of all of its formulas into two groups. When meanings are assigned to the primitive symbols of a logistic system, some of its formulas will become statements expressing propositions, while others will not. We may informally characterize a formula which on the intended interpretation becomes a significant statement as a 'well formed formula' (customarily abbreviated '*wff*'). Any formulas which on the intended interpretation do *not* become significant statements are *not* well formed formulas. In a logistic system there must be a *purely formal* criterion for distinguishing well formed formulas from all others. To characterize the criterion as 'purely formal' is to say that it is *syntactical* rather than *semantical*, pertaining to the formal characteristics and arrangements of the symbols in abstraction from their meanings. Thus a logistic system must contain only uninterpreted symbols, and must provide a criterion for dividing sequences of these symbols into two groups, the first of which will contain all well formed formulas, the second containing all others. Of the well formed formulas, some will be designated as Axioms (or Postulates) of the logistic system.

It is also desired to divide all well formed formulas which are not axioms into two groups, those which are theorems and those which are not. The former are those which are derivable from the axioms or postulates, *within the system*. Although uninterpreted, the well formed formulas of a logistic system constitute a 'language' in which derivations or proofs can be set down. Some well formed formulas will be assumed as postulates, and other well formed formulas will be derived from them as theorems. It might be proposed to define 'theorem' as any *wff* which is the conclusion of a valid argument whose premisses include only axioms of the system. This proposed definition of 'theorem' will be acceptable only if the notion of a *valid* argument within the logistic system can be defined formally. Because all *wffs* of the system are uninterpreted, the ordinary notion of validity cannot be used to characterize arguments within the system, for the usual notion of validity is *semantical*, an argument being regarded as valid if and only if the *truth* of its premisses entails the *truth* of its conclusion. Consequently, a purely formal or syntactical *criterion of validity* must be provided for arguments expressed *within the system*. 'Valid' arguments within the system may have not merely postulates or already established theorems as premisses and new theorems as conclusions, but may have as premisses *any wffs*, even those which are neither postulates nor theorems, and as conclusions *wffs* which are not theorems. Of course it is desired that any argument within the system which is syntactically 'valid' will become, on the intended or 'normal' interpretation, a semantically valid argument.

Any logistic system, then, will contain the following elements: (1) a list of primitive symbols which, together with any symbols defined in terms of them, are the only symbols which occur within the system; (2) a purely formal or syntactical criterion for dividing sequences of these symbols into formulas which are well formed (*wffs*) and those which are not; (3) a list of *wffs* assumed as postulates or axioms; (4) a purely formal or syntactical criterion for dividing sequences of well formed formulas into 'valid' and 'invalid' arguments; and (5), derivatively from (3) and (4), a purely formal criterion for distinguishing between theorems and nontheorems of the system.

Different logistic systems may be constructed as systematic theories of different parts of logic. The simplest logistic systems are those which formalize the logic of truth-functional compound statements. These systems are called *propositional calculi* or, less frequently, *sentential calculi*. One particular propositional calculus will be presented and discussed in the following chapter.

7

A
PROPOSITIONAL
CALCULUS

7.1 OBJECT LANGUAGE AND METALANGUAGE

The logistic system to be constructed in this chapter is intended to be adequate to the formulation of arguments whose validity depends upon the ways in which statements are truth functionally compounded. Our logistic system will be a *language*, although for the sake of rigor in developing its theorems, it will be regarded as uninterpreted. We shall *talk about* this language. It will be the *object* of our discussion, and is therefore called the 'object language'. Because it is uninterpreted, its symbols and formulas have no meaning, and we cannot *use* it until it is given an interpretation—which will be postponed until after its development. We must therefore use a *different* language in order to talk about our object language. The language *used* in talking about a language is called a 'metalanguage'. In any investigation of language, there is an object language which is the *object* of investigation, and there is a metalanguage which is *used* by the investigators in talking about the object language.

An object language may be discussed from alternative points of view.

195

Its relationship to its users may be investigated, as in a study of dialect changes in English usage and pronunciation in various parts of the country. Or the meaning or interpretation of a language may be investigated, as in compiling a dictionary, and in this latter inquiry a *semantical* metalanguage must be used. Finally the formal structure of a language may be investigated, as in a grammar textbook, or in describing the development of theorems in an uninterpreted logistic system, for which a *syntactical* metalanguage or *Syntax Language* is used. In discussing the object language to be constructed here, we shall sometimes need to use a semantical metalanguage, and sometimes a syntactical one. In discussing its adequacy for expressing all truth-functional compound statements, and its consistency and completeness, we shall have to use a semantical metalanguage, for these topics involve its intended interpretation. But in describing the purely formal criteria for its well formed formulas and the syntactical 'validity' of its arguments, only a Syntax Language need be used, for no references to meanings are made in these connections.

The language to be used as metalanguage in discussing our logistic system will be ordinary English, plus elementary arithmetic, with the addition of some special symbolic devices which will be introduced and explained as they are needed. It is assumed, of course, that the reader understands the metalanguage, for the entire discussion occurs within it. Only this one metalanguage will be used, and it will function in some parts of our inquiry as a semantical metalanguage, in other parts as a Syntax Language.

It should be emphasized that 'object language' and 'metalanguage' are *relative terms*. Any language, no matter how simple or how complex, is an object language when it is being talked *about*. And any language (which must be an interpreted, or meaningful one, of course) is a metalanguage when it is being *used* to discuss an object language. Since *our* object language is uninterpreted, we cannot use it as a metalanguage, but in another context, where the object language is an interpreted or meaningful language, one and the same language can function as both object language and metalanguage. Thus in our first chapter the English language was being discussed (and hence was the object language), and the discussion was carried on in English (which was therefore the metalanguage also). A sufficiently rich or complex language can succeed in formulating the whole of its own syntax, and a good deal of its own semantics. But no language, on pain of contradiction, can express the whole of its own semantics; certainly not the truth conditions for all of its own statements. That limitation can easily be shown.

That no language can express exhaustively its own semantics is shown by the following version of the 'Paradox of the Liar'.[1] Consider the following English statement:

The sentence printed on page 197, line 10 of this book is not true.

Let us abbreviate the preceding statement by the letter 'S'. Now just as it is obvious that 'Snow is white' is true if and only if *snow is white*, so it is equally obvious that

'S' is true if and only if *the sentence printed on page* 197, *line* 10 *of this book is not true.*

But counting the lines and looking at the page number verifies that 'S' is identical with *the sentence printed on page* 197, *line* 10 *of this book.* Hence

'S' is true if and only if 'S' *is not true.*

which is an explicit contradiction. That such a contradictory result can appear as a consequence of apparently innocent assumptions ought not to be regarded as a joke or a sophistry. It is a serious matter which reveals that the assumptions were not so innocent as they appeared. The source of the trouble is generally agreed to lie in the attempt to formulate the truth conditions for the statements of a language within that language itself. At least, if we distinguish sharply between object language and metalanguage, and do not try to make an object language serve as its own semantical metalanguage, the contradiction does not arise. An alternative method of avoiding such contradictions is discussed in Appendix C at the end of this book.

[1] Due to J. Lukasiewicz.

7.2   PRIMITIVE SYMBOLS AND WELL FORMED FORMULAS

We now proceed to construct our logistic system. There are two kinds of primitive symbols in our propositional calculus: 'propositional' symbols and 'operator' symbols. We use just four of the latter kind, these being

$$\cdot, \sim, (,).$$

We want infinitely many propositional symbols, for which we use the first four capital letters of the alphabet (in boldface type), with and without subscripts:

$$A \quad A_1 \quad A_2 \quad A_3 \quad \ldots$$
$$B \quad B_1 \quad B_2 \quad B_3 \quad \ldots$$
$$C \quad C_1 \quad C_2 \quad C_3 \quad \ldots$$
$$D \quad D_1 \quad D_2 \quad D_3 \quad \ldots$$

These are the only symbols that our propositional calculus will contain, and in proving theorems and deriving conclusions from premisses *within the system* they are to be regarded as being completely uninterpreted. They may be thought of, prior to the assignment of meanings, as being repeatable and recognizable *marks* rather than 'symbols' at all—though it will be convenient to refer to them as 'symbols'.

Of course we are guided in setting up our logistic system by the interpretation we intend eventually to give it. This intended interpretation controls our choice of primitive symbols, and also governs our syntactical definition of 'well formed formula'. A *formula* of our system is defined to be any finite sequence of primitive symbols of our system. The set of *all* formulas of our system includes such sequences as the following:

$$B_1$$
$$(A) \cdot (A)$$
$$\sim (D) \sim (\sim)$$
$$\sim ((A_1) \cdot (C_3))$$
$$B_2 B_3 A_7 \sim (\ )(\ ) \cdot (\ )$$
$$)))(($$

$$\cdot \quad \cdot \quad \cdot \quad \cdot \quad \cdot \quad \cdot \quad \cdot \quad \cdot \quad \cdot \quad \cdot \quad \cdot \quad \cdot \quad \cdot$$

Only some of these are to count as well formed formulas, however. Our definition of 'well formed formula' will be stated, of course, in our Syntax Language. It is convenient to introduce some special symbols into our Syntax Language, as an aid in discussing the logistic system clearly and economically. While the first four capital letters of the alphabet, with and without subscripts, printed in boldface type, are symbols in our object language, those same letters printed in light face italic type are symbols in our metalanguage. Their meanings in the latter follows the convention that a light face italic letter which is an element of our metalanguage denotes or means that same letter printed in boldface, which is an element of our object language. In addition we introduce the capital letters 'P', 'Q', 'R', 'S', . . . , with and without subscripts, and refer to them as 'propositional variables'. Whereas the propositional symbols *in* our propositional calculus are uninterpreted and have *no meaning*, the propositional variables 'P', 'Q', 'R', 'S', . . . *in* our Syntax Language *are interpreted* and *do have meaning*. Every propositional variable of our Syntax Language, until further notice, denotes any formula of our object language—subject to the following restriction. In any sentence or sequence of sentences of our Syntax Language, two distinct propositional variables, say 'P' and 'Q', may denote either two distinct formulas of our object language, say 'B_1' and '$\sim((A_1)\cdot(C_3))$', or one and the same formula of our object language. But in any one context, although a propositional variable may denote *any* formula of the object language, it must continue to denote that same formula wherever it occurs in that context. Thus the propositional variables 'P', 'Q', 'R', 'S', . . . of our metalanguage may have substituted for them *any name* in the metalanguage of *any formula* of the object language. We also introduce the symbols '$\cdot$', '$\sim$', '$($', and '$)$' into the Syntax Language, and explain their meanings as follows. Where any propositional variable, say 'P', of our Syntax Language denotes in some context a particular formula of our object language, say 'A', then the symbol '$\sim(P)$' of our Syntax Language will in that context denote the formula '$\sim(A)$' of our object language. And where any propositional variables, say 'P' and 'Q', denote in some context two formulas of our object language, say 'A' and '$\sim(B_2)$' respectively, then the symbol '$(P)\cdot(Q)$' of our Syntax Language will in that context denote the formula '$(A)\cdot(\sim(B_2))$' of our object language.

We cannot simply give a list of all well formed formulas of our object language, since there are infinitely many of them. It is necessary to give an inductive or *recursive* definition of 'well formed formula', which can be stated as follows, using the symbolic conventions explained in the preceding paragraph.

Recursive Definition of Well Formed Formula[2]

(a) Any propositional symbol is a *wff*.

(b) If any formula P is a *wff*, then $\sim(P)$ is a *wff*.

(c) If any formulas P and Q are both *wffs*, then $(P)\cdot(Q)$ is a *wff*.

(No formula of the object language shall be considered to be a *wff* unless its being so follows from these rules.)

This definition permits infinitely many well formed formulas, but it provides an *effective* criterion for recognizing them. No matter how long a (finite) sequence of symbols of the object language may be, our recursive definition permits us to decide in a finite number of steps whether or not it is a well formed formula. Let us take a relatively simple example to illustrate this:

$$\sim((A)\cdot(\sim(B)))$$

The question to be decided is whether the foregoing is a *wff* or not. By part (b) of the recursive definition, it is a *wff* provided that $(A)\cdot(\sim(B))$ is a *wff*. The latter is a *wff* by part (c) of the definition, provided that both A and $\sim(B)$ are *wffs*. The first of these is a *wff* by part (a) of the definition, and by part (b), the second is a *wff* provided that B is a *wff*,

---

[2] Alternatives are available here, as elsewhere, in developing logistic systems. In place of the recursive definition in the text we might have used the following:

(a) If P is a propositional symbol, then (P) is a *wff*.

(b) If P is a *wff*, then $(\sim P)$ is a *wff*.

(c) If P and Q are *wffs*, then $(P\cdot Q)$ is a *wff*. (No formula is a *wff* unless its being so follows from these rules.)

This alternative definition of *wff* would make different formulas *wffs*, but the resulting logistic system could be developed equally well.

which it is by part (a) of the definition. Thus the formula in question *is a wff*. From here on we shall use the propositional variables '*P*', '*Q*', '*R*',' *S*', and so on, of our Syntax Language to denote only *well formed* formulas of our object language.

EXERCISES

Using the Recursive Definition for Well Formed Formulas, show which of the following are *wffs* of our object language:

1. $(\sim(A_1))\cdot(A_1)$
★2. $\sim(\sim((B_1)\cdot(\sim(C_3))))$
3. $\sim(\sim((B_2)\cdot(\sim(D_4))))$
★4. $\sim((\sim(D_3))\cdot(\sim(D_4)))$
5. $(\sim((\sim)\cdot(C_2)))\cdot(\sim((B_3)\cdot(B_3)))$
6. $\sim(((A)\cdot(B))\cdot(\sim(B)))$
7. $\sim((A)\cdot(B))\cdot(\sim((A)\cdot(A)))$
★8. $(\sim(\sim(A))\cdot(B)\cdot(C))))\cdot(((\sim(A))\cdot(B))\cdot(\sim(C)))$
9. $\sim((\sim((A)\cdot(\sim(B))))\cdot(\sim((\sim((B)\cdot(C)))\cdot(\sim(\sim((C)\cdot(A)))))))$
10. $\sim(((\sim((A)\cdot(\sim(B))))\cdot(A))\cdot(\sim(\sim((A)\cdot(\sim(B))))))$

On the intended or 'normal' interpretation of our logistic system its propositional symbols are to be symbolic translations of English statements that contain no other statements as (truth-functional) component parts. Where *P* is the symbolic translation of any English statement whatever, $\sim(P)$ is the symbolic translation of its negation. And where *P* and *Q* are the symbolic translations of any two English statements whatever, $(P)\cdot(Q)$ is the symbolic translation of their conjunction. The question now arises: Is our logistic system adequate, when normally interpreted, to express all truth-functionally compound statements? A system which is adequate to express all truth functions will be said to be '*functionally complete*'.[3]

We begin our discussion by showing that our logistic system (which we call 'R.S.', since it is Rosser's System[4]) is adequate to the formulation of some familiar truth functions. Negations and conjunctions

[3] This is a special case of the 'expressive completeness' mentioned in Chapter 6.
[4] The author is greatly indebted to Professor J. Barkley Rosser of Cornell University for permission to include the following material. The calculi presented here and in Chapter 9 are early versions of logistic systems which appear in revised form in Professor Rosser's *Logic for Mathematicians*, New York, McGraw-Hill, 1953.

have already been mentioned, but there are also disjunctions, conditionals, and equivalences to be considered. Where two English
statements translate into P and Q, their *weak* disjunction (which is true
if either or both are true) is expressible in R.S. as $\sim((\sim(P))\cdot(\sim(Q)))$.
Since it is a very common function we introduce an abbreviation for it
into our Syntax Language, defining 'P v Q' to denote identically the
same *wffs* of the object language R.S. as are denoted by '$\sim((\sim(P))\cdot(\sim(Q)))$'.[5] Where two English statements translate into P and Q, their
strong disjunction (which is true if either one is true but not both) is
expressible in R.S. as $(\sim((P)\cdot(Q)))\cdot(\sim((\sim(P))\cdot(\sim(Q))))$.

The symbolic translation of an English truth-functional conditional
statement whose antecedent has the symbolic translation P and whose
consequent has the symbolic translation Q will be $\sim((P)\cdot(\sim(Q)))$.
This notion too is quite common, so we introduce the symbol '$\supset$' into
our Syntax Language, using '$P \supset Q$' to denote identically the same
wffs of R.S. as are denoted by '$\sim((P)\cdot(\sim(Q)))$'. Where two English
statements have the symbolic translations P and Q, the statement that
they are (materially) equivalent, that is, that they have the same truth
values, or that each (materially) implies the other, has the symbolic
translation $(P \supset Q)\cdot(Q \supset P)$, which is identically the same *wff* of R.S.
as $(\sim((P)\cdot(\sim(Q))))\cdot(\sim((Q)\cdot(\sim(P))))$. Since material equivalence too
is a frequently used notion, we introduce the symbol '$\equiv$' into our
Syntax Language, defining '$P \equiv Q$' as an abbreviation for '$(P \supset Q)\cdot(Q \supset P)$'.

At this point two notational conventions will be adopted for our
metalanguage. The first is dispensing with the dot (for conjunction), so

---

[5] Since 'P v Q' is an abbreviation of '$\sim((\sim(P))\cdot(\sim(Q)))$', it is proper to say that
P v Q is, or is identical with, $\sim((\sim(P))\cdot(\sim(Q)))$, but *not* that P v Q is an abbreviation of the latter, for there are no abbreviations in the object language itself. (The
symbol 'v' is a significant symbol of the Syntax Language, but *does not even occur* in the
object language, although we could introduce it there if we wished.) A parallel may
help make this clear. Since 'U.S.S.R.' is an abbreviation of 'Union of Soviet
Socialist Republics', the U.S.S.R. is identical with the Union of Soviet Socialist
Republics, but is not an abbreviation of anything at all, being a large nation cover-
ing one-sixth of the globe. Since 'U.S.S.R.' denotes a large nation, the U.S.S.R. *is*
a large nation, and has no *meaning* in any literal or semantical sense. Similarly, since
in any context 'P v Q' denotes a *wff* of R.S., in that context P v Q *is* a *wff* of R.S., and
since R.S. is uninterpreted, its *wffs* are meaningless, and P v Q in particular is
meaningless.

that $(P)(Q)$ is identically the same formula of the object language as $(P)\cdot(Q)$. The other notational convention is to replace parentheses by brackets or braces wherever such replacement is conducive to easier reading.

Even using brackets and braces, too many punctuation marks make reading difficult, so two further conventions which permit a minimum use of punctuation will be adopted. The first convention is to assign the following *order of precedence* to the symbols

of our Syntax Language. Of these, each has *greater precedence* or greater scope than any listed to its right. What is intended here can be explained by the following examples. The otherwise ambiguous expression '$\sim\!PQ$' denotes $(\sim(P))\cdot(Q)$ rather than $\sim((P)\cdot(Q))$, because the connective '$\cdot$' (which we have agreed to represent by juxtaposition) has greater scope than the operator '$\sim$'; the scope of the connective '$\cdot$' extends over that of the '$\sim$' symbol. The otherwise ambiguous expression '$P \vee QR$' denotes $P \vee (Q\cdot R)$ rather than $(P \vee Q)\cdot R$, because the connective '$\vee$' has, by our convention, precedence over the connective '$\cdot$', and its scope extends over that of the latter. The otherwise ambiguous expression '$P \supset Q \vee RS$' denotes $P \supset [Q \vee (R\cdot S)]$, because '$\supset$' has precedence over both '$\vee$' and '$\cdot$', and '$\vee$' has precedence over '$\cdot$'. And the otherwise ambiguous expression '$P \supset Q \equiv \sim\!Q \supset \sim\!P$' denotes $[P \supset Q] \equiv [(\sim\!Q) \supset (\sim\!P)]$, because '$\equiv$' has precedence over '$\supset$' and '$\sim$', and '$\supset$' has precedence over '$\sim$'. Our second convention is that of *association to the left*, which means that where the convention of *order of precedence* does not suffice to remove the ambiguity of an expression, its parts should be grouped by parentheses *to the left*. That is, when an expression contains two (or more) occurrences of the same connective, and their relative scopes within the expression are not otherwise indicated, the occurrence to the right shall be understood to have the wider (or widest) scope. This too is best explained by means of an example or two. Since all of its connectives have *equal* order of precedence, the ambiguity of the expression '$P \supset Q \supset P \supset P$' cannot be resolved by our first convention. According to our second convention, however, we interpret it as denoting $[(P \supset Q) \supset P] \supset P$. Part, but not all of the ambiguity of the expression '$P \equiv Q \equiv PQ \lor {\sim}P{\sim}Q$' is resolved by the convention regarding order of precedence. Once this convention has been appealed to, we know that it denotes *either* $[P \equiv Q] \equiv [(P{\cdot}Q) \lor ({\sim}P{\cdot}{\sim}Q)]$ *or* $P \equiv \{Q \equiv [(P{\cdot}Q) \lor ({\sim}P{\cdot}{\sim}Q)]\}$. We decide that the former is meant by consulting the second convention, which instructs us to associate to the left.

EXERCISES

Write the following expressions of the Syntax Language in unabbreviated form, complete with parentheses:

1. $P \lor {\sim}P$
★2. ${\sim}{\sim}P \supset P$
3. $PQ \supset P$
4. $PQ \lor R$
★5. $P \supset (Q \supset P)$

6. $P \supset Q \supset P$
7. $P \supset (P \lor Q)$
★8. $(P \supset PQ) \supset (P \supset Q)$
9. $(P \supset Q)(Q \supset R) \supset (P \supset R)$
10. $P \supset {\sim}P \equiv {\sim}P$

The preceding remarks show how to express some truth functions in R.S. But to prove that R.S. is *functionally complete*, that is, adequate to express *all* possible truth functions of any number of statements, more is required. We must have a method in our semantical metalanguage of expressing all possible truth functions, and then must prove that all of these, or all their substitution instances, can be expressed in our object language R.S. also, in its normal or standard interpretation. Such a method of expressing all possible truth functions is provided by *truth tables*, which were introduced in Chapter 2. The method and notation of truth tables is therefore imported into our semantical metalanguage, and will be used freely in discussing the various semantical properties possessed by R.S. on its standard interpretation.

Truth functions may have one, two, or any number of arguments (in the mathematical sense in which an 'argument' is an independent variable). Thus $f(P)$ is a truth function of P if and only if its truth or falsehood is completely determined by the truth or falsehood of P. Similarly, $f(P,Q)$ is a truth function of P and Q if and only if its truth value is determined solely by the truth values of P and Q.

There are exactly four different truth functions of a single argument, and these may be expressed by the following truth tables:

P	$f_1(P)$		P	$f_2(P)$		P	$f_3(P)$		P	$f_4(P)$
T	F		T	T		T	F		T	T
F	T		F	F		F	F		F	T

The functions $f_1(P)$, $f_2(P)$, $f_3(P)$, and $f_4(P)$ are completely defined by these four truth tables. They are the *only* truth functions of a single argument, and are called 'mónadic', 'unary', or 'singulary' functions.[6] That they can be expressed in R.S. in its intended or normal interpretations is easily seen. First we note that the intended or normal interpretations of $\sim P$ and PQ are given by the truth tables

P	$\sim P$
T	F
F	T

and

P	Q	PQ
T	T	T
T	F	F
F	T	F
F	F	F

That R.S. is adequate to express $f_1(P)$, $f_2(P)$, $f_3(P)$, and $f_4(P)$ is proved by actually formulating them in R.S. The function $f_2(P)$ is true when P is true and false when P is false, and is therefore expressible in R.S. as P itself. The function $f_1(P)$ is false when P is true and true when P is false, and is therefore expressible in R.S. as $\sim P$. The function $f_3(P)$ is false no matter which truth value P assumes, and is therefore expressible in R.S. as $\sim PP$. The function $f_4(P)$ is true in every case and can therefore be expressed in R.S. as the negation of $f_3(P)$, that is, as $\sim(\sim PP)$. We have thereby shown that all singulary truth functions are expressible in R.S.

There are, of course, more truth functions of two arguments than of one argument. These are defined by the following truth tables:

---

[6] Here we are using 'truth function' in the strict and proper sense of a nonlinguistic correlation between or among truth values.

P	Q	$f_1(P,Q)$		P	Q	$f_2(P,Q)$		P	Q	$f_3(P,Q)$		P	Q	$f_4(P,Q)$
T	T	F		T	T	T		T	T	T		T	T	T
T	F	T		T	F	F		T	F	T		T	F	T
F	T	T		F	T	T		F	T	F		F	T	T
F	F	T		F	F	T		F	F	T		F	F	F

P	Q	$f_5(P,Q)$		P	Q	$f_6(P,Q)$		P	Q	$f_7(P,Q)$		P	Q	$f_8(P,Q)$
T	T	F		T	T	F		T	T	F		T	T	T
T	F	F		T	F	T		T	F	T		T	F	F
F	T	T		F	T	F		F	T	T		F	T	F
F	F	T		F	F	T		F	F	F		F	F	T

P	Q	$f_9(P,Q)$		P	Q	$f_{10}(P,Q)$		P	Q	$f_{11}(P,Q)$		P	Q	$f_{12}(P,Q)$
T	T	T		T	T	T		T	T	F		T	T	F
T	F	F		T	F	T		T	F	F		T	F	F
F	T	T		F	T	F		F	T	F		F	T	T
F	F	F		F	F	F		F	F	T		F	F	F

P	Q	$f_{13}(P,Q)$		P	Q	$f_{14}(P,Q)$		P	Q	$f_{15}(P,Q)$		P	Q	$f_{16}(P,Q)$
T	T	F		T	T	T		T	T	F		T	T	T
T	F	T		T	F	F		T	F	F		T	F	T
F	T	F		F	T	F		F	T	F		F	T	T
F	F	F		F	F	F		F	F	F		F	F	T

These are *all* the truth functions of two arguments, and are called 'dyadic' or 'binary' functions. That they are all expressible in R.S. is easily shown by actually expressing them by means of the $\sim$ and $\cdot$ symbols: for example, $f_{14}(P,Q)$ is expressible as PQ, while $f_1(P,Q)$ is expressible as $\sim(PQ)$.

EXERCISES

1. Express each of the dyadic truth functions $f_1(P,Q)$, $\star f_2(P,Q)$, . . . , $\star f_5(P,Q)$, . . . , $\star f_{11}(P,Q)$, . . . , $f_{16}(P,Q)$ as *wffs* of R.S.
2. There are 256 triadic (or ternary) truth functions: $f_1(P,Q,R)$, $f_2(P,Q,R)$, . . . , $f_{256}(P,Q,R)$, each of which is completely determined (or defined) by a different eight-row truth table. Take any ten of them and express each as a *wff* of R.S.

To prove the functional completeness of R.S. it is necessary to show that *any* truth function of *any* number of arguments is expressible by means of $\sim$ and $\cdot$. Any truth function of n arguments is expressible by means of a truth table having n initial columns and 2^n rows. Thus any truth function $f(P_1, P_2, \ldots, P_{n-1}, P_n)$ is completely specified by writing a 'T' or an 'F' in every one of the 2^n places in the last column of the following truth table:

	P_1	$P_2 \ldots P_{n-1}$	P_n	$f(P_1, P_2, \ldots, P_{n-1}, P_n)$
Row 1:	T	T ... T	T	
Row 2:	T	T ... T	F	
. . . .				
Row $2^n - 1$:	F	F ... F	T	
Row 2^n:	F	F ... F	F	

The truth function $f(P_1, P_2, \ldots, P_{n-1}, P_n)$ must have either an **F** in just one row of its truth table, or **F**'s in more than one row of its truth table, or **F**'s in no rows of its truth table. In any case the truth function can be represented by a *wff* of R.S.

CASE 1. $f(P_1, P_2, \ldots, P_{n-1}, P_n)$ has an **F** in just one row of its truth table. If the **F** occurs in the first row then the function is represented in R.S. by the *wff* $\sim(P_1 \cdot P_2 \cdot \ldots \cdot P_{n-1} \cdot P_n)$, which has an **F** in the first row of its truth table and **T**'s in all other rows. If the **F** occurs in the second row then the function is represented in R.S. by the *wff* $\sim(P_1 \cdot P_2 \cdot \ldots \cdot P_{n-1} \cdot \sim P_n)$. The 2^n distinct truth functions the ith of which has an **F** in its ith row and **T**'s in all its others are represented in R.S. by the 2^n *wffs*

$$S_1: \sim(P_1 \cdot P_2 \cdot \ldots \cdot P_{n-1} \cdot P_n)$$
$$S_2: \sim(P_1 \cdot P_2 \cdot \ldots \cdot P_{n-1} \cdot \sim P_n)$$
$$\cdot \cdot \cdot \cdot \cdot \cdot \cdot \cdot \cdot \cdot \cdot \cdot \cdot \cdot \cdot \cdot$$
$$S_2^{m-1}: \sim(\sim P_1 \cdot \sim P_2 \cdot \ldots \cdot \sim P_{n-1} \cdot P_n)$$
$$S_2^m: \sim(\sim P_1 \cdot \sim P_2 \cdot \ldots \cdot \sim P_{n-1} \cdot \sim P_n)$$

CASE 2. $f(P_1, P_2, \ldots, P_{n-1}, P_n)$ has **F**'s in more than one row of its truth table. If it has **F**'s in the k $(1 < k \leq 2^n)$ rows $i_1, i_2, \ldots, i_k$, then it is represented in R.S. by the *wff* $S_{i_1} \cdot S_{i_2} \cdot \ldots \cdot S_{i_k}$.

CASE 3. $f(P_1, P_2, \ldots, P_{n-1}, P_n)$ has **F**'s in no row of its truth table. Such a tautologous function is represented in R.S. by the *wff* $\sim(\sim P_1 \cdot P_1 \cdot P_2 \cdot \ldots \cdot P_{n-1} \cdot P_n)$.

The preceding cases exhaust the possibilities, so we have proved that any truth function of any number of arguments is expressible in R.S. This is not a theorem *of* or *in* R.S., but a theorem *about* it, established in our semantical metalanguage. We may therefore list it as

METATHEOREM I. *R.S. is functionally complete.*

We could have chosen to present a logistic system other than R.S. In addition to parentheses and the propositional symbols P, Q, R, S and so on, we could have selected as primitive operators any of the following pairs of symbols: '$\sim$' and 'v', '$\sim$' and '$\supset$', '$\cdot$' and 'v', '$\cdot$' and '$\supset$', or 'v' and '$\supset$', instead of '$\sim$' and '$\cdot$'. It is instructive to inquire whether or not any of those alternative choices of primitives would have made the resulting system functionally complete (on the normal interpretation of the symbols '$\sim$', '$\cdot$', 'v', '$\supset$', which we shall denote by '$\sim$', '$\cdot$', 'v', '$\supset$'). Before addressing ourselves to these problems it will be well to explain briefly the two kinds of mathematical induction we shall use in establishing results about (not *in*) R.S.

We shall use the term 'weak induction' to refer to the more commonly used type of mathematical induction. The schema for weak induction is

$f(1)$
for any arbitrary m, if $f(m)$ then $f(m + 1)$
therefore $f(m)$ for every m

It is frequently used in proving theorems in elementary algebra. For example, one proves that the sum of the first n odd integers is equal to n^2 by first proving the two premisses of the above schema and then drawing the general conclusion indicated. The first premiss, which we shall call the 'α-case', is here established as the trivial equation $1 = 1^2$. Then the second premiss, which we shall call the 'β-case', is established by assuming $f(m)$ true for an arbitrary integer m and from this assumption deriving the conclusion that $f(m + 1)$ is true. In this particular proof, the β-case assumption is

$$1 + 3 + 5 + \ldots + (2m - 1) = m^2$$

We derive the desired conclusion by adding $(2m + 1)$ to both sides of the equation and performing an elementary regrouping and factoring of terms:

$$1 + 3 + 5 + \ldots + (2m - 1) + (2m + 1) = m^2 + (2m + 1)$$
$$1 + 3 + 5 + \ldots + (2m - 1) + [2(m + 1) - 1] = (m + 1)^2$$

which shows that for an arbitrary m, if the sum of the first m odd integers is m^2, then the sum of the first $(m + 1)$ odd integers is $(m + 1)^2$. We thus have established the β-case; from it and the α-case, by *weak induction*, we draw the desired conclusion that for every m, the sum of the first m odd integers is equal to m^2. Weak induction may be thought of as summarizing an unending sequence of arguments of the form *Modus Ponens*:

$$\frac{\begin{array}{l} f(1) \\ \text{if } f(1) \text{ then } f(2); \end{array}}{\therefore f(2)} \qquad \frac{\begin{array}{l} f(2) \\ \text{if } f(2) \text{ then } f(3); \ldots ; \end{array}}{\therefore f(3)}$$

$$\frac{\begin{array}{l} f(m) \\ \text{if } f(m) \text{ then } f(m + 1); \ldots \end{array}}{\therefore f(m + 1)}$$

The term 'strong induction' will be used to refer to the somewhat less frequently encountered type of mathematical induction whose schema is

$$\frac{\begin{array}{l} f(1) \\ \text{for any arbitrary } m, \text{ if } f(k) \text{ for every } k < m, \text{ then } f(m) \end{array}}{\text{therefore } f(m) \text{ for every } m}$$

Strong induction may also be thought of as summarizing an unending sequence of arguments of the form *Modus Ponens*:

$$\frac{\begin{array}{l} f(1) \\ \text{if } f(1) \text{ then } f(2); \end{array}}{\therefore f(2)} \qquad \frac{\begin{array}{l} f(1) \text{ and } f(2) \\ \text{if } f(1) \text{ and } f(2) \text{ then } f(3); \ldots ; \end{array}}{\therefore f(3)}$$

$$\frac{\begin{array}{l} f(1) \text{ and } f(2) \text{ and } \ldots \text{ and } f(m - 1) \\ \text{if } f(1) \text{ and } f(2) \text{ and } \ldots \text{ and } f(m - 1) \text{ then } f(m); \ldots \end{array}}{\therefore f(m)}$$

To illustrate the use of strong induction, we shall prove that a symbolic logic based on the propositional symbols P, Q, R, S, . . . and the operators · and v is *not* functionally complete. We do so by proving that no well formed formula[7] of the system based on ·, v, and P, Q, R, S, . . . can express a truth function which has the value *true* when all of its arguments have the value *false*. In our proof we use strong induction on the number of symbols in the well formed formula $g(P, Q, R, . . .)$, ignoring parentheses, and counting each occurrence of P, Q, R, . . . , ·, and v as one symbol.

α-CASE: In case $g(P, Q, R, . . .)$ contains just one symbol, to be well formed it must be either P alone, or Q alone, or R alone, or . . . . Where the arguments P, Q, R, . . . all have the value *false*, $g(P, Q, R, . . .)$ will also have the value *false*, since it is one of them. Hence any well formed formula of the present system which contains exactly one symbol cannot have the value *true* when its arguments all have the value *false*.

β-CASE: Here we assume that any well formed formula $g(P, Q, R, . . .)$ containing less than m symbols cannot have the value *true* when all of its arguments have the value *false*, and we shall prove, under this assumption, that any well formed formula containing exactly m symbols cannot have the value *true* when all its arguments have the value *false*. Consider any formula $g(P, Q, R, . . .)$ which contains exactly m symbols (where $m > 1$). To be well formed, $g(P, Q, R, . . .)$ must be either

$$g_1(P, Q, R, . . .) \cdot g_2(P, Q, R, . . .)$$

or

$$g_1(P, Q, R, . . .) \text{ v } g_2(P, Q, R, . . .)$$

where $g_1(P, Q, R, . . .)$ and $g_2(P, Q, R, . . .)$ are well formed formulas containing less than m symbols. By the β-case assumption, when P, Q, R, . . . are all *false*, both $g_1(P, Q, R, . . .)$ and $g_2(P, Q, R, . . .)$ will have the value *false* also. Now given any two propositions which are *false*, both their disjunction and their conjunction are *false;* hence in this case $g(P, Q, R, . . .)$ has the value *false* also. This establishes the β-case.

---

[7] We assume a recursive definition analogous to that stated on page 200.

Having established both the α and β cases, by strong induction we infer that no well formed formula of the system based on $\cdot$, v, P, Q, R, . . . can express a truth function which has the value *true* when all of its arguments have the value *false*. Hence the system is *not* functionally complete.

EXERCISES

Prove the functional completeness or incompleteness of the logistic systems based on the propositional symbols P, Q, R, S, . . . , parentheses, and the operators:

★1. v and $\sim$ 3. $\supset$ and $\sim$

★2. $\supset$ and $\cdot$ 4. $\supset$ and v

5. $\sim$ and $+$, where $+$ is the symbol for exclusive disjunction, defined by the truth table:

P	Q	$P + Q$
T	T	F
T	F	T
F	T	T
F	F	F

★6. $\supset$ and $+$ 9. $+$ and $\cdot$

7. v and $+$ 10. $\equiv$ and $\sim$

8. $+$ and $\equiv$

7.3 AXIOMS AND DEMONSTRATIONS

The rules for our system and the proofs of the theorems within it will be much simplified if we assume infinitely many well formed formulas as axioms or postulates. Of course we cannot actually write out an infinite list of axioms *within our object language*, but we can use our Syntax Language to specify exactly which *wffs* of R.S. are axioms and which are not. There can be no objection to having an infinite number of axioms if there is an *effective* process for determining whether or not any given *wff* is an axiom. The infinite list of axioms of R.S. may be written as

Axiom 1. $P \supset (P \cdot P)$
Axiom 2. $(P \cdot Q) \supset P$
Axiom 3. $(P \supset Q) \supset [\sim(Q \cdot R) \supset \sim(R \cdot P)]$

Each of these syntactical formulas (formulas within our Syntax Language) represents or designates an infinite list of *wffs* of R.S. Thus Axiom 1 designates all the following:

$$\sim((A) \cdot (\sim((A) \cdot (A))))$$
$$\sim((B) \cdot (\sim((B) \cdot (B))))$$
$$\sim((C) \cdot (\sim((C) \cdot (C))))$$
$$\sim((D) \cdot (\sim((D) \cdot (D))))$$
$$\sim((A_1) \cdot (\sim((A_1) \cdot (A_1))))$$

. . . .

$$\sim((\sim(A)) \cdot (\sim((\sim(A)) \cdot (\sim(A)))))$$
$$\sim((\sim(B)) \cdot (\sim((\sim(B)) \cdot (\sim(B)))))$$

. . . .

$$\sim(((A) \cdot (D)) \cdot (\sim(((A) \cdot (D)) \cdot ((A) \cdot (D)))))$$
$$\sim(((A_3) \cdot (B_7)) \cdot (\sim(((A_3) \cdot (B_7)) \cdot ((A_3) \cdot (B_7)))))$$

. . . .

. . . .

and infinitely many more *wffs* of R.S. It designates, in fact, every *wff* of R.S. which is of the indicated pattern; and it is effectively decidable of any given finite sequence of symbols of R.S. whether it is of this pattern or not. Three patterns are set forth, and every *wff* of R.S. which exemplifies any one of these patterns is assumed as an axiom.

That these axioms are reasonable assumptions is evidenced by the fact that on the normal interpretation of the symbols $\sim$ and $\cdot$ they are all tautologies.

Our logistic system is intended, upon interpretation, to be adequate to the formulation of arguments. Arguments, as we know, consist of premisses and conclusions, all of which are expressed in statements. Corresponding to such arguments we have in our logistic system sequences of well formed formulas of which the last formula is the 'conclusion'. It is desired to set up a criterion which will enable us to distinguish formally between two kinds of sequences of *wffs* within R.S.:

those which become valid arguments when interpreted normally and those which do not.

In Chapter 3 a valid argument was characterized as one for which a formal proof or demonstration could be given. A formal proof of an argument's validity was described as a sequence of statements each of which was either a premiss or followed from preceding statements by an elementary valid argument, and whose last statement was the conclusion of the argument being proved valid. Thus the question of the validity of *any* argument was 'reduced' to the question of the validity of certain elementary argument forms or rules of inference. Something like that will be proposed for R.S., but it is not desirable to make such a wholesale set of assumptions about valid elementary inferences as was made in Chapter 3, where nineteen rules of inference were postulated, plus rules of Conditional Proof and Indirect Proof. However, *some* rule of inference must be assumed for our logistic system or there will be no inference at all legitimized within it. One rule of inference will suffice for the validation of all arguments and (hence) for the proof of all theorems within R.S. We assume *Modus Ponens*, and state it (in our Syntax Language, of course) as

RULE 1.   From P and $P \supset Q$ to infer Q.

Examples of arguments *in* R.S. which are legitimized as *valid* by the assumption of this rule of inference are

$$\sim((A)\cdot(\sim(B))) \qquad \sim(((A_1)\cdot(A_2))\cdot(\sim(\sim(C))))$$
$$A \qquad\qquad \text{and} \qquad (A_1)\cdot(A_2)$$
$$B \qquad\qquad\qquad\qquad \sim(C)$$

The assumption of *Modus Ponens* as Rule 1 (abbreviated as R 1) of our logistic system, *by itself*, permits only a special variety of arguments having two premisses to be regarded as valid. But R.S. is adequate to the expression of *all* formally valid arguments that are certifiable by means of truth tables, including extended ones containing any number of premisses. So it is desirable to introduce a method for validating extended arguments in R.S. by showing how their conclusions follow from their premisses by *repeated* applications of R 1. Here our treatment is roughly analogous to that for extended arguments presented in

Chapter 3, although with some important differences. We define a *demonstration* of the validity of an argument having as premises the formulas P_1, P_2, . . . , P_n and as conclusion the formula Q, to be a sequence of well formed formulas S_1, S_2, . . . , S_k such that: every S_i is either one of the premises P_1, P_2, . . . , P_n, or is one of the axioms of R.S., or follows from two preceding S's by R 1; and such that S_k is Q. As before, an argument is to be regarded as valid if and only if there exists a *demonstration* of its validity. A special notation is introduced (into the Syntax Language) to represent this idea. We introduce the special symbol '$\vdash$' (which may be read 'yields') so that

$$P_1, P_2, \ldots , P_n \vdash Q$$

asserts that there is a demonstration of the validity of the argument having P_1, P_2, . . . , P_n as premises and Q as conclusion. For example all of the infinitely many arguments denoted by

$$P \supset Q$$
$$\sim(QR)$$
$$\sim(RP)$$

are valid because $P \supset Q$, $\sim(QR) \vdash \sim(RP)$, the demonstration consisting of the following sequence of S's:

S_1: $(P \supset Q) \supset [\sim(QR) \supset \sim(RP)]$
S_2: $P \supset Q$
S_3: $\sim(QR) \supset \sim(RP)$
S_4: $\sim(QR)$
S_5: $\sim(RP)$

in which S_1 is Axiom 3, S_2 is the first premiss of the argument, S_3 follows from S_1 and S_2 by R 1, S_4 is the second premiss, S_5 follows from S_3 and S_4 by R 1, and S_5 is the conclusion. Any such sequence of S's will be called a *demonstration* that P_1, P_2, . . . , $P_n \vdash Q$, and each S_i will be called a *line* of the demonstration. Where a demonstration is given for the validity of all arguments in R.S. of a particular form, as in the example cited, any particular argument of that form may be regarded as having been validated by that demonstration, and the general form may be regarded as a *derived rule of inference*.

The definition of *demonstration* given in the preceding paragraphs should have made it clear that the axioms of R.S. function as 'understood' premisses of every argument formulated within the system. Where those axioms are the *only* premisses of an argument, then (if it is valid) the conclusion is a *theorem* of the system. That a given formula Q is a theorem is expressed by writing '$\vdash Q$'. The notation '$\vdash Q$' is defined more strictly as the assertion that there exists a demonstration of Q, which is a sequence of well formed formulas $S_1, S_2, \ldots, S_k$ such that: every S_i is either an axiom of R.S. or follows from two preceding S's by R 1, and S_k is Q.

It should be noted that *demonstration*, either of a theorem or of the validity of an argument, is an *effective* notion. Given any sequence of S's, however long, it can be decided quite mechanically, in a finite number of operations, whether or not it is a *demonstration*. It can be decided effectively of any S whether or not it is an axiom (and whether or not it is one of the premisses, if an argument is involved). And if some S, say S_j, is neither an axiom nor a premiss, then since only a finite number of S's precede S_j in the sequence, a finite number of inspections will reveal whether or not two of the preceding lines are S_i and $S_i \supset S_j$, for only if these occur earlier in the sequence of S's will S_j follow from two preceding lines by R 1.

With this definition of *theorem*, the three axioms and the one rule of R.S. can be regarded as a sort of symbolic machine for generating well formed formulas. Each axiom itself generates an infinite number of *wffs*, and by repeated applications of R 1 to them infinitely many more *wffs* are produced as theorems. Two questions quite naturally arise at this point. First, is the system consistent? And second, are all the theorems (on the normal interpretation of the primitive symbols) tautologies?

A logistic system which is a propositional calculus (such as R.S.) will be called *analytic* if and only if all of its theorems become tautologies on their normal interpretations. R.S. is analytic, on this definition, provided that $\vdash P$ implies that P is tautologous. We shall now prove that R.S. has this property.

METATHEOREM II. *R.S. is analytic* (*that is, if* $\vdash P$ *then* P *is a tautology*).

Proof: We use strong induction on the number of uses of R 1 in the demonstration that $\vdash P$.

α-CASE: Suppose P results from a single use of R 1. Then R 1 must be applied to the axioms. The axioms are all tautologies, as is easily verified by actually constructing truth tables for them. Hence P results from applying R 1 to S and $S \supset P$, where S and $S \supset P$ are both tautologies. Clearly P must be a tautology in this case, for if it were not, there would be an **F** in at least one row of its truth table, say row j. But since S is a tautology, it has all **T**'s in its truth table, including of course, a **T** in row j. Hence in the jth row, S would have a **T** and P an **F**, so that $S \supset P$ would have an **F**—contrary to the fact that it is tautologous and has only **T**'s in its truth table. Hence the Metatheorem is true for m uses of R 1 where $m = 1$.

β-CASE: Here we assume the Metatheorem to be true for any number $k < m$ uses of R 1. Consider the status of any P whose demonstration involves m uses of R 1. The formula P is either an axiom (in which case it is clearly a tautology) or must result from earlier lines S and $S \supset P$ by the mth use of R 1. The earlier line S is either an axiom (in which case it is clearly a tautology) or is obtained by $k < m$ uses of R 1, and hence is a tautology by the assumption of the β-case. Similarly, the earlier line $S \supset P$ must also be a tautology. Now, because S and $S \supset P$ are tautologies, P must be one also, by the argument of the α-case.

From α and β, by strong induction we conclude that if $\vdash P$ (by *any* number of applications of R 1) then P is a tautology, which means that R.S. is analytic.

Having established the analyticity of R.S., its consistency follows immediately, and may be regarded as a mere corollary of Metatheorem II. In proving it, we use the Post criterion for consistency, according to which a deductive system is consistent if it contains a formula which is not provable in it as a theorem.

COROLLARY: *R.S. is consistent.*

Proof: The formula $P \cdot \sim P$ is a *wff* of R.S. but is not a tautology, therefore by Metatheorem II it is not a theorem of R.S. Hence R.S. contains a formula which is not provable as a theorem, so R.S. is consistent by the Post criterion.

We define the 'deductive completeness' of a logistic system for the propositional calculus as the converse of the property of analyticity. An *analytic* system is one all of whose theorems are tautologies; a propositional calculus will be called *deductively complete* in case all tautologies are provable as theorems within it. The deductive completeness of R.S. is more difficult to establish than the first two Metatheorems, and requires that we first develop some theorems of the system. The proof, then, will be postponed to Section 7.6, following the development of R.S. itself in Section 7.5, after proving the independence of the axioms of R.S. in the next section.

7.4 INDEPENDENCE OF THE AXIOMS

A set of axioms is said to be independent if each of them is independent of the others, that is, if none of them can be derived as theorems from the others. To prove the independence of each axiom it suffices to find a characteristic of *wffs* of the system such that:

1. the axiom to be proved independent lacks that characteristic,
2. all other axioms have that characteristic, and
3. the characteristic in question is hereditary with respect to the

rules of inference of the system.

Roughly the same sense of 'hereditary' is used here that was explained in Section 3.3: a characteristic is *hereditary with respect to a set of rules of inference* if and only if whenever it belongs to one or more formulas it also belongs to every formula deduced from them by means of those rules of inference.

To prove the independence of Ax. 1 of R.S. we introduce a three-element model in terms of which the symbols and *wffs* of R.S. can be interpreted. The three elements are the 'values' 0, 1, and 2, which play roles analogous to those of the truth values **T** and **F**. Every propositional symbol has one of these three values assigned to it. Every *wff* that is not a propositional symbol will have one of the three values **0, 1, 2** in accordance with the following tables:

P	~P		P	Q	P·Q
0	2		0	0	0
1	1		0	1	1
2	0		0	2	2
			1	0	1
			1	1	2
			1	2	2
			2	0	2
			2	1	2
			2	2	2

The defined symbol '⊃', whose definition is given by

$$P \supset Q = \mathrm{df} \sim (P \cdot \sim Q)$$

has, pursuant to that definition, the table

P	Q	P ⊃ Q
0	0	0
0	1	1
0	2	2
1	0	0
1	1	0
1	2	1
2	0	0
2	1	0
2	2	0

The characteristic of *wffs* that we utilize here is that of having the value **0** regardless of the values assigned to its component propositional symbols. This characteristic is easily seen to belong to Ax. 2 and Ax. 3 of R.S. by the following tables (analogous to that introduced on page 31).

(P	·	Q)	⊃	P
0	0	0	0	0
0	1	1	0	0
0	2	2	0	0
1	1	0	0	1
1	2	1	0	1
1	2	2	0	1
2	2	0	0	2
2	2	1	0	2
2	2	2	0	2

(P	⊃	Q)	⊃	[~	(Q	·	R)	⊃	~	(R	·	P)]
0	0	0	0	2	0	0	0	0	2	0	0	0
0	0	0	0	1	0	1	1	0	1	1	1	0
0	0	0	0	0	0	2	2	0	0	2	2	0
0	1	1	0	1	1	1	0	1	2	0	0	0
0	1	1	0	0	1	2	1	1	1	1	1	0
0	1	1	0	0	1	2	2	0	0	2	2	0
0	2	2	0	0	2	2	0	2	2	0	0	0
0	2	2	0	0	2	2	1	1	1	1	1	0
0	2	2	0	0	2	2	2	0	0	2	2	0
1	0	0	0	2	0	0	0	0	1	0	1	1
1	0	0	0	1	0	1	1	0	0	1	2	1
1	0	0	0	0	0	2	2	0	0	2	2	1
1	0	1	0	1	1	1	0	0	1	0	1	1
1	0	1	0	0	1	2	1	0	0	1	2	1
1	0	1	0	0	1	2	2	0	0	2	2	1
1	1	2	0	0	2	2	0	1	1	0	1	1
1	1	2	0	0	2	2	1	0	0	1	2	1
1	1	2	0	0	2	2	2	0	0	2	2	1
2	0	0	0	2	0	0	0	0	0	2	2	2
2	0	0	0	1	0	1	1	0	0	1	2	2
2	0	0	0	0	0	2	2	0	0	2	2	2
2	0	1	0	1	1	1	0	0	0	0	2	2
2	0	1	0	0	1	2	1	0	0	1	2	2
2	0	1	0	0	1	2	2	0	0	2	2	2
2	0	2	0	0	2	2	0	0	0	0	2	2
2	0	2	0	0	2	2	1	0	0	1	2	2
2	0	2	0	0	2	2	2	0	0	2	2	2

The characteristic is easily seen to be hereditary with respect to R 1 of R.S. by consulting the table given for '$\supset$'. In the only row in which both P and $P \supset Q$ have the value 0, Q also has the value 0. Hence if the characteristic belongs to one or more *wffs* it also belongs to every *wff* deduced from them by R 1.

Finally it is readily seen that the characteristic in question does *not* belong to Ax. 1 When P is assigned the value 1, $P \supset (P \cdot P)$ has the value 1 rather than 0, for $1 \supset (1 \cdot 1)$ is $1 \supset 2$, which is 1. Hence Ax. 1 is independent.

To prove the independence of Ax. 2 of R.S. we use the same three-element model and the same table for '$\sim P$'. The difference lies in the table for '$P \cdot Q$', which follows, along with the derivative table for '$P \supset Q$'.

P	Q	$P \cdot Q$	$P \supset Q$
0	0	0	0
0	1	0	2
0	2	2	2
1	0	0	0
1	1	0	2
1	2	2	2
2	0	2	0
2	1	2	0
2	2	2	0

The characteristic of *wffs* that we utilize here is that of having the value 0 regardless of the values assigned to its component propositional symbols. This characteristic is easily seen to belong to Ax. 1 and Ax. 3 of R.S. by the following tables.

P	$\supset$	$(P$	$\cdot$	$P)$
0	0	0	0	0
1	0	1	0	1
2	0	2	2	2

(P	⊃	Q)	⊃	[∼	(Q	·	R)	⊃	∼	(R	·	P)]
0	0	0	0	2	0	0	0	0	2	0	0	0
0	0	0	0	2	0	0	1	0	2	1	0	0
0	0	0	0	0	0	2	2	0	0	2	2	0
0	2	1	0	2	1	0	0	0	2	0	0	0
0	2	1	0	2	1	0	1	0	2	1	0	0
0	2	1	0	0	1	2	2	0	0	2	2	0
0	2	2	0	0	2	2	0	2	2	0	0	0
0	2	2	0	0	2	2	1	2	2	1	0	0
0	2	2	0	0	2	2	2	0	0	2	2	0
1	0	0	0	2	0	0	0	0	2	0	0	1
1	0	0	0	2	0	0	1	0	2	1	0	1
1	0	0	0	0	0	2	2	0	0	2	2	1
1	2	1	0	2	1	0	0	0	2	0	0	1
1	2	1	0	2	1	0	1	0	2	1	0	1
1	2	1	0	0	1	2	2	0	0	2	2	1
1	2	2	0	0	2	2	0	2	2	0	0	1
1	2	2	0	0	2	2	1	2	2	1	0	1
1	2	2	0	0	2	2	2	0	0	2	2	1
2	0	0	0	2	0	0	0	0	0	0	2	2
2	0	0	0	2	0	0	1	0	0	1	2	2
2	0	0	0	0	0	2	2	0	0	2	2	2
2	0	1	0	2	1	0	0	0	0	0	2	2
2	0	1	0	2	1	0	1	0	0	1	2	2
2	0	1	0	0	1	2	2	0	0	2	2	2
2	0	2	0	0	2	2	0	0	0	0	2	2
2	0	2	0	0	2	2	1	0	0	1	2	2
2	0	2	0	0	2	2	2	0	0	2	2	2

The characteristic is easily seen to be hereditary with respect to R 1 of R.S. by consulting the table for '⊃'. In the only row in which both P and $P \supset Q$ have the value 0, Q also has the value 0. Hence if the characteristic belongs to one or more *wffs* it also belongs to every *wff* deduced from them by R 1.

Finally, it is readily seen that the characteristic in question does not belong to Ax. 2. When P and Q are both assigned the value 1, $(P \cdot Q) \supset P$

has the value **2** rather than **0** for **(1·1)** ⊃ **1** is **0** ⊃ **1** which is **2**. Hence Ax. 2 is independent.

To prove the independence of Ax. 3 of R.S. we use the same three-element model and the same table for '∼P'. The difference lies in the table for 'P·Q', which follows, along with the derivative table for 'P ⊃ Q'.

P	Q	P·Q	P ⊃ Q
0	0	0	0
0	1	1	1
0	2	2	2
1	0	2	0
1	1	2	0
1	2	2	0
2	0	2	0
2	1	2	0
2	2	2	0

The characteristic of *wffs* that we utilize here is that of having the value **0** regardless of the values assigned to its component propositional symbols. This characteristic is easily seen to belong to Ax. 1 and Ax. 2 of R.S. by the following tables.

P	⊃	(P	·	P)
0	0	0	0	0
1	0	1	2	1
2	0	2	2	2

(P	·	Q)	⊃	P
0	0	0	0	0
0	1	1	0	0
0	2	2	0	0
1	2	0	0	1
1	2	1	0	1
1	2	2	0	1
2	2	0	0	2
2	2	1	0	2
2	2	2	0	2

The characteristic is easily seen to be hereditary with respect to R 1 of R.S. by consulting the table for '⊃'. In the only row in which P and $P \supset Q$ have the value 0, Q also has the value 0. Hence if the characteristic belongs to one or more *wffs* it also belongs to every *wff* deduced from them by R 1.

Finally, it is readily seen that the characteristic in question does *not* belong to Ax. 3. When P and Q are both assigned the value 1 and R is assigned the value 0, $(P \supset Q) \supset [\sim(Q \cdot R) \supset \sim(R \cdot P)]$ has the value 1 rather than 0 for $(1 \supset 1) \supset [\sim(1 \cdot 0) \supset \sim(0 \cdot 1)]$ reduces successively to $0 \supset [\sim 2 \supset \sim 1]$, to $0 \supset [0 \supset 1]$, to $0 \supset 1$, and finally to 1. Hence Ax. 3 is independent.

7.5 DEVELOPMENT OF THE CALCULUS

In the actual development of derived rules and theorems of our object language we regard all of its symbols as completely uninterpreted, being motivated by the desire for rigor in its development. *When interpreted normally*, the formulas $\sim RP$ and $P \sim R$ are logically equivalent. But as *wffs* of R.S., *in its development*, they cannot be so regarded, and the *wff* $\sim RP \equiv P \sim R$ cannot be accepted as a theorem until it has been formally derived from the axioms of the system.

It is convenient to begin with the demonstration of a derived rule of inference for R.S., which will validate infinitely many arguments in it. We state it as

DR 1. $P \supset Q, Q \supset R \vdash \sim(\sim RP)$.

Its demonstration requires a sequence of just five well formed formulas, the third of which we shall write twice, once in unabbreviated and once in abbreviated form:

$$S_1: (P \supset Q) \supset [\sim(Q \sim R) \supset \sim(\sim RP)]$$
$$S_2: P \supset Q$$
$$S_3: \sim(Q \sim R) \supset \sim(\sim RP)$$
$$S_3': (Q \supset R) \supset \sim(\sim RP)$$
$$S_4: Q \supset R$$
$$S_5: \sim(\sim RP)$$

That this sequence of S's is a demonstration is easily verified. The first line, S_1, is Axiom 3 of R.S. It is true that there is an apparent difference between S_1 and our syntactical formulation of Axiom 3:

$$S_1: (P \supset Q) \supset [\sim(Q \sim R) \supset \sim(\sim RP)]$$
$$\text{Ax. 3: } (P \supset Q) \supset [\sim(QR) \supset \sim(RP)]$$

because S_1 contains $\sim R$ wherever Axiom 3 contains R. The point is that we are here *talking about* well formed formulas *of* R.S. Both S_1 and Axiom 3 denote infinitely many *wffs* of R.S., and every *wff* of R.S. which is denoted by S_1 *is also denoted by Axiom* 3. We can put the matter another way. Our first derived rule (DR 1) validates infinitely many arguments formulable within R.S., for example:

$$\sim((A) \cdot (\sim(B)))$$
$$\sim((B) \cdot (\sim(C))) \quad \text{and}$$
$$\sim((\sim(C)) \cdot (A))$$

$$\sim((B) \cdot (\sim(C)))$$
$$\sim((C) \cdot (\sim(D)))$$
$$\sim((\sim(D)) \cdot (B))$$

as well as

$$\sim((A) \cdot (\sim(A)))$$
$$\sim((A) \cdot (\sim(A))) \quad \text{and}$$
$$\sim((\sim(A)) \cdot (A))$$

$$\sim(((A) \cdot (B)) \cdot (\sim(\sim(C))))$$
$$\sim((\sim(C)) \cdot (\sim((D_1) \cdot (D_2))))$$
$$\sim((\sim((D_1) \cdot (D_2))) \cdot ((A) \cdot (B)))$$

The sequence of S's in the given demonstration denotes infinitely many sequences of *wffs* of R.S., one for each of the different arguments whose validity is being demonstrated. The first line in the demonstration *in* R.S. for the first of the four examples given is the *wff* of R.S. denoted by S_1 when 'P', 'Q', and 'R' are taken to denote 'A', 'B', and 'C', respectively. But this is identically the same *wff* of R.S. denoted by our syntactical formulation of Axiom 3 when 'P', 'Q', and 'R' in it are taken to denote 'A', 'B', and '$\sim C$', respectively. Hence the first *wff* of the demonstration sequence is one of the infinitely many axioms of R.S. supplied by Axiom 3. The situation is the same with respect to the demonstration of the validity of every other argument *in* R.S. which is validated by DR 1.

It is readily seen that the other lines of the sequence conform to the requirements laid down in our definition of demonstration. The two premisses of the argument occur as S_2 and S_4, while S_3 follows from S_1

and S_2 by R 1, and S_5 follows from $S_3(S'_3)$ and S_4 by R 1. It is helpful to write in the 'justification' for each line in a demonstration: 'Ax. 3' to the right of S_1, 'premiss' to the right of S_2, and so on. These labels are not part of the demonstration, but are helpful to both the writer and the reader.

At this point the question naturally arises as to whether derived rules of inference can be appealed to in deriving theorems from the axioms of the system. It is most conveniently discussed in connection with an actual example. Let us take as our first theorem of R.S. the formula

TH. 1. $\vdash \sim(\sim PP)$

This *formula* follows directly from Axioms 1 and 2 by means of our first derived rule, DR 1. A sequence of formulas which has already been demonstrated to be a valid argument (by our demonstration of DR 1) is

$$S_1: P \supset PP \qquad \text{Ax. 1}$$
$$S_2: PP \supset P \qquad \text{Ax. 2}$$
$$S_3: \sim(\sim PP) \qquad \text{DR 1}$$

That S_2 is Ax. 2 should be clear from the previous discussion. Every *wff* of R.S. denoted by our syntactical formulation of Ax. 2, '$PQ \supset P$', is an axiom, and every *wff* of R.S. denoted by the syntactical expression '$PP \supset P$' is (also) denoted by '$PQ \supset P$', so S_2 denotes infinitely many of the axioms of R.S. that are denoted by our syntactical formulation of Ax. 2. And that S_3 really follows by DR 1 from S_1 and S_2 is seen by observing that DR 1 validates any argument of the form

$$P \supset Q$$
$$Q \supset R$$
$$\sim(\sim RP)$$

no matter what *wffs* of R.S. the formulas P, Q, and R may be. Thus DR 1 includes the case in which 'P' and 'R' denote identically the same formulas, while 'Q' and 'PP' also denote the same *wffs*.

Although the sequence S_1, S_2, S_3 may be regarded as a '*proof*' of Theorem 1, it does not constitute a *demonstration*, for by definition a *demonstration* involves the use of R 1 exclusively. But if we have a 'proof' in which a derived rule is used, as DR 1 is used in the given sequence, the *demonstration of the derived rule* can be *inserted* into the sequence to change it into a demonstration proper. Thus in place of S_3 in the given sequence, the demonstration of DR 1 can be substituted to give us

$$S_1: P \supset PP \qquad\qquad\qquad\qquad\qquad\qquad\quad \text{Ax. 1}$$
$$S_2: PP \supset P \qquad\qquad\qquad\qquad\qquad\qquad\quad \text{Ax. 2}$$
$$S_3: (P \supset PP) \supset [\sim(PP \sim P) \supset \sim(\sim PP)] \quad \text{Ax. 3}$$
$$S_4: \sim(PP \sim P) \supset \sim(\sim PP) \qquad\qquad\qquad\quad \text{R 1}$$
$$S_4': (PP \supset P) \supset \sim(\sim PP)$$
$$S_5: \sim(\sim PP) \qquad\qquad\qquad\qquad\qquad\qquad\quad \text{R 1}$$

This sequence *is* a demonstration; because S_1, S_2, and S_3 are axioms, S_4 follows by R 1 from S_1 and S_3, and S_5 follows by R 1 from S_2 and S_4. Moreover, the present demonstration results from the earlier 'proof' by certain changes which are indicated in the proof itself. The original sequence, which we call a 'proof', is not a demonstration, but a *description* of a demonstration that can be given. A proof may be regarded as a prescription or recipe for the construction of a demonstration.

The situation is analogous to that which occurs when later theorems of a deductive system are derived not directly from the axioms but from earlier, already established theorems. Here again an example will aid the discussion. We shall take as our second theorem the formula

Th. 2. $\vdash \sim\sim P \supset P$

which follows directly from Theorem 1 by definition. Its proof may be written as:

$$S_1: \sim(\sim\sim P \sim P) \qquad \text{Th. 1}$$
$$S_1': \sim\sim P \supset P \qquad\qquad \text{df.}$$

This sequence is clearly *not* a *demonstration*, but it *is* a *proof*, for it tells us exactly how to construct a demonstration of Th. 2. In place of S_1 we need only write our demonstration of Th. 1—or rather the demonstration of that version of it which is relevant to the desired conclusion, Th. 2. The general statement of Th. 1 is

$$\vdash \sim(\sim PP)$$

which denotes every *wff* which is of this form, no matter which *wff* the syntactical variable '*P*' denotes. Every *wff* denoted by '$\sim(\sim\sim P\sim P)$' is of that form, and is therefore included among the infinitely many provable formulas of R.S. that are labeled Theorem 1. The demonstration described by the indicated proof of Th. 2 can be written as follows:

S_1: $\sim P \supset \sim P\sim P$	Ax. 1
S_2: $\sim P\sim P \supset \sim P$	Ax. 2
S_3: $(\sim P \supset \sim P\sim P) \supset [\sim(\sim P\sim P\sim\sim P) \supset \sim(\sim\sim P\sim P)]$	Ax. 3
S_4: $\sim(\sim P\sim P\sim\sim P) \supset \sim(\sim\sim P\sim P)$	R 1
S_4': $(\sim P\sim P \supset \sim P) \supset \sim(\sim\sim P\sim P)$	df.
S_5: $\sim(\sim\sim P\sim P)$	R 1
S_5': $\sim\sim P \supset P$	df.

In general, proofs are shorter and therefore easier to write out than are demonstrations. Since any proof can be made into a demonstration by replacing any line that is a previously established theorem by the demonstration of that theorem, and any line that results from the use of a derived rule by the demonstration of that rule, proofs can be regarded as shorthand notations for demonstrations. However, proofs are *different*, and should not be *confused* with demonstrations.

Before proceeding with the development of additional theorems and derived rules for R.S., it should be remarked that Th. 2 can be equally well expressed as $\vdash \sim P \text{ v } P$, which is a version of the principle of the Excluded Middle. For by our definition of the symbol 'v', '$\sim P \text{ v } P$' is an abbreviation of '$\sim(\sim\sim P\sim P)$', which has (Th. 2) '$\sim\sim P \supset P$' as an alternative abbreviation. In the latter form it constitutes part of the principle of Double Negation.

Some additional theorems of R.S., together with their proofs (*not* demonstrations) are these:

TH. 3. $\vdash \sim(QR) \supset (R \supset \sim Q)$

Proof: $\vdash \sim\sim Q \supset Q$	Th. 2
$\vdash (\sim\sim Q \supset Q) \supset [\sim(QR) \supset \sim(R\sim\sim Q)]$	Ax. 3
$\vdash \sim(QR) \supset \sim(R\sim\sim Q)$	R 1
$\vdash \sim(QR) \supset (R \supset \sim Q)$	df.

Tн. 4. $\vdash R \supset \sim\sim R$

   Proof: $\vdash \sim(\sim RR) \supset (R \supset \sim\sim R)$ Th. 3

          $\vdash \sim(\sim RR)$ Th. 1

          $\vdash R \supset \sim\sim R$ R 1

Tн. 5. $\vdash (Q \supset P) \supset (\sim P \supset \sim Q)$

   Proof: $\vdash \sim(Q\sim P) \supset (\sim P \supset \sim Q)$ Th. 3

          $\vdash (Q \supset P) \supset (\sim P \supset \sim Q)$ df.

It will be observed that Th. 5 is part of the principle of Transposition, and that Theorems 2 and 4 are parts of the principle of Double Negation. But although both $P \supset \sim\sim P$ and $\sim\sim P \supset P$ have been proved to be theorems, *the* principle of Double Negation, $P \equiv \sim\sim P$, which abbreviates $(P \supset \sim\sim P)\cdot(\sim\sim P \supset P)$, is not (yet) proved to be a theorem. It would follow from Theorems 2 and 4 by the principle of Conjunction, $P, Q \vdash P\cdot Q$, but the latter has not (yet) been established as a valid principle of inference or derived rule for R.S. These remarks are intended to throw additional light on the meaning of the '$\vdash$' symbol. Writing '$\vdash P$' asserts that there is a sequence of *wffs* ending with P which is a demonstration. Writing '$\vdash P$ and $\vdash Q$' asserts that there are *two* sequences of *wffs*, both demonstrations, one ending with P, the other ending with Q. But writing '$\vdash P\cdot Q$' asserts that there is a *single* sequence of *wffs* which is a demonstration and ends with $P\cdot Q$. This assertion, although different, follows from the preceding by the principle of Conjunction, which will be established as DR 14.

The next derived rule is proved as follows:

DR 2. $\sim P \supset \sim Q \vdash Q \supset P$

   Proof: $(\sim P \supset \sim Q) \supset [\sim(\sim QQ) \supset \sim(Q\sim P)]$ Ax. 3

          $\sim P \supset \sim Q$ premiss

          $\sim(\sim QQ) \supset \sim(Q\sim P)$ R 1

          $\sim(\sim QQ)$ Th. 1

          $\sim(Q\sim P)$ R 1

          $Q \supset P$ df.

Although Theorem 5, $\vdash (Q \supset P) \supset (\sim P \supset \sim Q)$, is part of the principle of Transposition, DR 2, $\sim P \supset \sim Q \vdash Q \supset P$, is not. That principle asserts that $(Q \supset P) \equiv (\sim P \supset \sim Q)$, which is our abbreviation for $[(Q \supset P) \supset (\sim P \supset \sim Q)] \cdot [(\sim P \supset \sim Q) \supset (Q \supset P)]$. The left-hand conjunct is Theorem 5, but the right-hand conjunct is *not* DR 2. There is an important difference between

$$\sim P \supset \sim Q \vdash Q \supset P \quad \text{and} \quad \vdash (\sim P \supset \sim Q) \supset (Q \supset P)$$

The first asserts that there is a sequence of *wffs* each of which is either $\sim P \supset \sim Q$ or an axiom or follows from two preceding *wffs* by R 1, and whose last *wff* is $Q \supset P$. The second asserts that there is a sequence of *wffs* each of which is an axiom or follows from two preceding *wffs* by R 1, and whose last *wff* is $(\sim P \supset \sim Q) \supset (Q \supset P)$. (The second has not yet been established.) Of course there is some connection between them, as there is between any two statements such as $P \vdash Q$ and $\vdash P \supset Q$. Given the latter, the former is easily established, for to the sequence of *wffs* $S_1, S_2, \ldots, S_k$ (where S_k is $P \supset Q$), which constitutes a demonstration for $\vdash P \supset Q$, we need only add P as S_{k+1} and derive Q as S_{k+2}, for it follows from S_k and S_{k+1} by R 1. But although $\vdash P \supset Q$ follows from $P \vdash Q$, the proof that it does is less simple. It will be established as Metatheorem III (the 'Deduction Theorem'); but until it has been proved it cannot be assumed to hold for R.S.

Some additional derived rules, together with their proofs, are these:

DR 3. $P \supset Q \vdash RP \supset QR$

Proof:	$(P \supset Q) \supset [\sim(QR) \supset \sim(RP)]$	Ax. 3
	$P \supset Q$	premiss
	$\sim(QR) \supset \sim(RP)$	R 1
	$RP \supset QR$	DR 2

DR 4. $P \supset Q, R \supset S \vdash \sim[\sim(QS)(PR)]$

Proof:	$P \supset Q$	premiss
	$SP \supset QS$	DR 3
	$R \supset S$	premiss
	$PR \supset SP$	DR 3
	$\sim[\sim(QS)(PR)]$	DR 1

DR 5. $P \supset Q, Q \supset R, R \supset S \vdash P \supset S$

Proof:

$R \supset S$	premiss
$(R \supset S) \supset (\sim S \supset \sim R)$	Th. 5
$\sim S \supset \sim R$	R 1
$(\sim S \supset \sim R) \supset [\sim(\sim RP) \supset \sim(P \sim S)]$	Ax. 3
$\sim(\sim RP) \supset \sim(P \sim S)$	R 1
$P \supset Q$	premiss
$Q \supset R$	premiss
$\sim(\sim RP)$	DR 1
$\sim(P \sim S)$	R 1
$P \supset S$	df.

The last derived rule mentioned may be thought of as a 'generalized' Hypothetical Syllogism. In developing R.S. it is convenient to establish DR 5 before proving the familiar Hypothetical Syllogism $P \supset Q$, $Q \supset R \vdash P \supset R$. The latter will be established as DR 6. For ease in proving the next derived rule it is desirable to prove three additional theorems first. Their proofs are left as exercises for the reader:

★Th. 6. $\vdash (R \sim \sim P) \supset (PR)$
Th. 7. $\vdash P \supset P$
Th. 8. $\vdash RP \supset PR$

It is convenient to state and prove a corollary of Theorem 7:

Th. 7, Cor. $\vdash P \vee \sim P$

Proof:

$\sim P \supset \sim P$	Th. 7
$\sim(\sim P \sim \sim P)$	df.
$P \vee \sim P$	df.

It will be instructive for the reader to construct a *demonstration* (not merely a proof) for Theorem 7. It is so obvious a tautology as to seem trivial, and yet its demonstration in R.S. is not short.

Together, DR 5 and Theorem 7 provide an easy proof of the validity of the Hypothetical Syllogism

★DR 6. $P \supset Q, Q \supset R \vdash P \supset R$

Some additional theorems and derived rules are useful in proving the next Metatheorem.

TH. 9. $\vdash \sim(PR) \supset \sim(RP)$
DR 7. $P \supset Q, R \supset S \vdash PR \supset QS$

It is convenient to record two corollaries of DR 7:

DR 7, COR. 1. $P \supset Q \vdash PR \supset QR$
DR 7, COR. 2. $R \supset S \vdash PR \supset PS$
DR 8. $P \supset Q, P \supset R \vdash P \supset QR$
★TH. 10. $\vdash (PQ)R \supset P(QR)$

A useful corollary of Th. 10 is the other half of the principle of Association for '$\cdot$':

TH. 10, COR. $\vdash P(QR) \supset (PQ)R$
DR 9. $P \supset R, Q \supset S \vdash (P \vee Q) \supset (R \vee S)$
★DR 10. $P \supset R, Q \supset R \vdash (P \vee Q) \supset R$
TH. 11. $\vdash (P \vee Q) \supset (Q \vee P)$
TH. 12. $\vdash (P \vee Q) \vee R \supset P \vee (Q \vee R)$

A useful corollary of Th. 12 is the other half of the principle of Association for '$\vee$':

TH. 12, COR. $\vdash P \vee (Q \vee R) \supset (P \vee Q) \vee R$
TH. 13. $\vdash [P \supset (Q \supset R)] \supset [PQ \supset R]$
★TH. 14. $\vdash [PQ \supset R] \supset [P \supset (Q \supset R)]$

These last two theorems are the two halves of the principle of Exportation, but before the principle itself can be derived from them, the principle of Conjunction must be established (as DR 14).

DR 11. $P \supset Q, P \supset (Q \supset R) \vdash P \supset R$
TH. 15. $\vdash P \supset (Q \supset PQ)$
TH. 16. $\vdash P \supset (Q \supset P)$

Having established these derived rules and theorems, we are now able to prove the Deduction Theorem for R.S. as

METATHEOREM III.   *If $P_1, P_2, \ldots, P_{n-1}, P_n \vdash Q$ then $P_1, P_2, \ldots, P_{n-1} \vdash P_n \supset Q$.*

Proof: We assume that P_1, P_2, . . . , P_{n-1}, $P_n \vdash Q$, that is, that there is a demonstration or sequence of *wffs* S_1, S_2, . . . , S_s such that each S_i is either an axiom, or a $P_i(i = 1, 2, . . . , n)$, or follows from two previous S's by R 1, and S_s is Q. Now consider the sequence of *wffs* $P_n \supset S_1$, $P_n \supset S_2$, . . . , $P_n \supset S_s$. If we can 'fill in' *wffs* before each $P_n \supset S_i$ in such a way that the resulting total sequence is a demonstration from P_1, P_2, . . . , P_{n-1}, so each line of the resulting total sequence is either an axiom or a $P_i(i = 1, 2, . . . , n - 1)$, or follows from two previous lines by R 1, then since $P_n \supset S_s$ is $P_n \supset Q$, we shall have a demonstration that P_1, P_2, . . . , $P_{n-1} \vdash P_n \supset Q$. That we *can* 'fill in' to get the desired demonstration is proved by weak induction on the number of formulas $P_n \supset S_i$ involved.

(α) In case $i = 1$, we have only the formula $P_n \supset S_1$ to consider. By assumption, S_1 is either an axiom or a $P_i(i = 1, 2, . . . , n)$.

CASE 1. S_1 is an axiom. Here we fill in with the demonstration of Theorem 16, $\vdash S_1 \supset (P_n \supset S_1)$, and S_1 itself. From the last two formulas we derive $P_n \supset S_1$ by R 1, so the total sequence of *wffs* up to and including $P_n \supset S_1$ is a demonstration that $\vdash P_n \supset S_1$ and hence that P_1, P_2, . . . , $P_{n-1} \vdash P_n \supset S_1$.

CASE 2. S_1 is a $P_i(i = 1, 2, . . . , n - 1)$. Here we fill in with the demonstration of Theorem 16, $\vdash S_1 \supset (P_n \supset S_1)$, and S_1 itself. From the last two formulas we derive $P_n \supset S_1$ by R 1, so the total sequence of *wffs* up to and including $P_n \supset S_1$ is a demonstration that $S_1 \vdash P_n \supset S_1$. Since S_1 is a $P_i(i = 1, 2, . . . , n - 1)$ we have a demonstration that P_1, P_2, . . . , $P_{n-1} \vdash P_n \supset S_1$.

CASE 3. S_1 is P_n. Here we fill in with the demonstration of Theorem 7, $\vdash P_n \supset P_n$, that is, $\vdash P_n \supset S_1$, so the total sequence of *wffs* up to and including $P_n \supset S_1$ is a demonstration that $\vdash P_n \supset S_1$, and hence that P_1, P_2, . . . , $P_{n-1} \vdash P_n \supset S_1$.

(β) Now suppose that we have properly filled in all the lines up to and including $P_n \supset S_{k-1}$, so we have a sequence of *wffs* which is a demonstration that P_1, P_2, . . . , $P_{n-1} \vdash P_n \supset S_{k-1}$. Under this assumption we show how to fill in to include $P_n \supset S_k$ in the sequence, which will then be a demonstration that P_1, P_2, . . . , $P_{n-1} \vdash P_n \supset S_k$. By assumption, S_k is an axiom, a $P_i (i = 1, 2, . . . , n)$, or resulted in the original demonstration from the application of R 1 to two previous S's, say S_i and $S_j (i, j < k)$.

CASE 1. S_k is an axiom. Insert the demonstration of Theorem 16, $\vdash S_k \supset (P_n \supset S_k)$, and S_k itself, and derive $P_n \supset S_k$ by R 1. The entire sequence will then be a demonstration that P_1, P_2, . . . , $P_{n-1} \vdash P_n \supset S_k$.

CASE 2. S_k is $P_i (i = 1, 2, . . . , n - 1)$. Insert the demonstration of Theorem 16, $\vdash S_k \supset (P_n \supset S_k)$, and S_k itself, and derive $P_n \supset S_k$ by R 1. The entire sequence will then be a demonstration that P_1, P_2, . . . , $P_{n-1} \vdash P_n \supset S_k$.

CASE 3. S_k is P_n. Insert the demonstration of Theorem 7, $\vdash P_n \supset P_n$, that is, $\vdash P_n \supset S_k$, and the entire sequence will be a demonstration that P_1, P_2, . . . , $P_{n-1} \vdash P_n \supset S_k$.

CASE 4. S_k resulted (in the original demonstration that P_1, P_2, . . . , $P_n \vdash Q$), from the application of R 1 to two earlier S's, say S_i and S_j, where $i, j < k$ and S_i is of the form $S_j \supset S_k$. By the assumption of the β-case we have already filled in up to and including both $P_n \supset S_j$ and $P_n \supset (S_j \supset S_k)$. By DR 11, stated as

$$P \supset Q, P \supset (Q \supset R) \vdash P \supset R$$

we have

$$P_n \supset S_j, P_n \supset (S_j \supset S_k) \vdash P_n \supset S_k$$

Insert the demonstration of this derived rule, whose last line is $P_n \supset S_k$, and the entire sequence will then be a demonstration that P_1, P_2, . . . , $P_{n-1} \vdash P_n \supset S_k$.

Now by weak induction we conclude that we can fill in for *any* number of lines $P_n \supset S_i$ in such a way that the resulting sequence will be a demonstration that P_1, P_2, . . . , $P_{n-1} \vdash P_n \supset S_i$. We can therefore do it for the demonstration of P_1, P_2, . . . , P_{n-1}, $P_n \vdash Q$ no matter how many lines S_1, S_2, . . . , S_s it contains. And since S_s is Q, we can construct a demonstration that P_1, P_2, . . . , $P_{n-1} \vdash P_n \supset Q$. This concludes our proof of the Deduction Theorem.

An immediate consequence is

MT III, Corollary: *If* $P \vdash Q$ *then* $\vdash P \supset Q$.

An equally obvious corollary is the more general conclusion that: The Deduction Theorem holds for *any* propositional calculus which has only the rule *Modus Ponens* and which contains demonstrations for $P \supset P$, $P \supset (Q \supset P)$, and $(P \supset Q) \supset \{[P \supset (Q \supset R)] \supset (P \supset R)\}$.

The way in which Metatheorem III (abbreviated 'D.T'.) may be used in proofs is indicated in the following proof of DR 6. First we demonstrate the relatively trivial DR 6′: $P \supset Q$, $Q \supset R$, $P \vdash R$ by the steps

$P \supset Q$	premiss
P	premiss
Q	R 1
$Q \supset R$	premiss
R	R 1

Then we can prove DR 6 by simply applying the D.T. once, the proof reading

$P \supset Q$, $Q \supset R$, $P \vdash R$	DR 6′
$P \supset Q$, $Q \supset R \vdash P \supset R$	D.T.

Since the D.T. gives us an effective method of constructing a new demonstration for DR 6 on the basis of the old one for DR 6′, the preceding two step proof is a perfectly adequate prescription for the desired demonstration. It should not be thought that effort has been 'wasted' in constructing more difficult proofs of our earlier theorems, for they had to be established first in order to prove the Deduction Theorem itself.

Some additional theorems and derived rules of R.S. are

Th. 17. $\vdash P \supset (Q \vee P)$
★Th. 17, Cor. $\vdash P \supset (P \vee Q)$
Th. 18. $\vdash (P \vee Q)R \supset (PR \vee QR)$

This theorem constitutes a part of the principle of Distribution—the distribution of '·' with respect to 'v'.

DR 12. $P \supset \sim Q \vdash P \supset \sim(QR)$

DR 13. $P \supset \sim R \vdash P \supset \sim(QR)$

★DR 14. $P, Q \vdash PQ$

Here, finally, we have the principle of Conjunction. It permits us to establish the principle of Double Negation as our next theorem, which follows directly from Th. 2 and Th. 4 by DR 14.

TH. 19. $\vdash P \equiv \sim\sim P$

Theorem 19, by itself, however, does not permit us to replace $\sim\sim P$ by P wherever it may occur in the interior of a larger *wff*. That is, where we are able to demonstrate a *wff* $\vdash (- - - \sim\sim P \ . \ . \ .)$ the mere equivalence of $\sim\sim P$ and P does not permit us simply to infer that $\vdash (- - - P \ . \ . \ .)$. The inference would be valid, but we must *prove* that it is valid within R.S. The legitimacy of any such replacement is asserted by our next Metatheorem. Before stating and proving it we shall find it convenient to establish the following:

DR 15. $P \equiv Q \vdash \sim P \equiv \sim Q$

DR 16. $P \equiv Q, R \equiv S \vdash PR \equiv QS$

DR 16, COR. $P \equiv Q, R \equiv S \vdash P \vee R \equiv Q \vee S$

Proofs will be left as exercises for the reader.

Now we are ready to prove the Substitution Theorem for R.S.

METATHEOREM IV.   (*Substitution Theorem.*) *Let P_1, P_2, . . . , P_n be any wffs, let Q be any wff that does not occur in any P_i, and let S be any wff which contains no components other than Q and $P_i (1 \leq i \leq n)$. Where S^* is a wff which results from replacing any number of occurrences of Q in S by R, then $Q \equiv R \vdash S \equiv S^*$.*

Proof: Strong induction is used on the number of symbols in S, counting each occurrence of $\cdot$, $\sim$, Q, or any P_i as a single symbol.

(α) $n = 1$. In this case S is either Q alone or a P_i alone.

CASE 1. S is Q and S^* is R. It is obvious that $Q \equiv R \vdash Q \equiv R$, which can be written $Q \equiv R \vdash S \equiv S^*$.

CASE 2. S is Q and S^* is Q also. Since $\vdash Q \equiv Q$ by Th. 7 and DR 14, $\vdash S \equiv S^*$, whence $Q \equiv R \vdash S \equiv S^*$.

CASE 3. S is a P_i. In this case S^* also is the same P_i. Since $\vdash P_i \equiv P_i$ by Th. 7 and DR 14, $\vdash S \equiv S^*$ whence $Q \equiv R \vdash S \equiv S^*$.

(β) Here the Metatheorem is assumed to be true for any S containing $< n$ symbols. Consider any S containing exactly n symbols ($n > 1$). It is clear that S must be either of the structure $\sim S_1$ or $S_1 \cdot S_2$.

CASE 1. S is of the structure $\sim S_1$. Because S contains n symbols, S_1 contains $< n$ symbols, so by the β-case assumption, $Q \equiv R \vdash S_1 \equiv S_1^*$, where S_1^* is a *wff* which results from replacing any number of occurrences of Q in S_1 by R. But $S_1 \equiv S_1^* \vdash \sim S_1 \equiv \sim S_1^*$ by DR 15, and since $\sim S_1^*$ is obviously the same as S^*, we have $Q \equiv R \vdash S \equiv S^*$.

CASE 2. S is of the structure $S_1 \cdot S_2$. Here S_1 and S_2 each contains $< n$ symbols, so by the β-case assumption, $Q \equiv R \vdash S_1 \equiv S_1^*$ and $Q \equiv R \vdash S_2 \equiv S_2^*$. But by DR 16, $S_1 \equiv S_1^*, S_2 \equiv S_2^* \vdash S_1 \cdot S_2 \equiv S_1^* \cdot S_2^*$ and since any $S_1^* \cdot S_2^*$ is an S^*, $Q \equiv R \vdash S \equiv S^*$.

Hence by strong induction we infer that regardless of the number of symbols in S, $Q \equiv R \vdash S \equiv S^*$.

MT IV, COROLLARY: *If Q, R, S, and S^* are as in* Metatheorem IV, *then $Q \equiv R$, $S \vdash S^*$.*

The proof of the corollary is obvious.

Of the list of Rules of Inference used in proving the validity of arguments back in Chapter 3, the first nine were elementary valid argument forms proper, and the last ten were equivalences whose intersubstitutability was assumed. Of the first nine, the first, *Modus Ponens*, is the primitive rule R 1 of R.S. The third, the Hypothetical Syllogism, has already been established as DR 6; and the eighth, the principle of Conjunction, has been proved as DR 14. The remaining six can easily be proved as derived rules of R.S. They may be listed as

DR 17. $P \supset Q, \sim Q \vdash \sim P$ (*Modus Tollens*)
DR 18. $P \vee Q, \sim P \vdash Q$ (Disjunctive Syllogism)
DR 19. $PQ \vdash P$ (Simplification)
DR 19, Cor. $PQ \vdash Q$
★DR 20. $(P \supset Q)(R \supset S), P \vee R \vdash Q \vee S$ (Constructive Dilemma)
DR 21. $(P \supset Q)(R \supset S), \sim Q \vee \sim S \vdash$
$$\sim P \vee \sim R$$ (Destructive Dilemma)
DR 22. $P \vdash P \vee Q$ (Addition)

The various equivalences which made up the last ten of the nineteen Rules of Inference can easily be established. The principle of Double Negation has already been proved as Theorem 19. The various principles of Commutation and Association are obtained by simply applying DR 14 to already established theorems and corollaries.

Th. 20. $\vdash P \vee Q \equiv Q \vee P$ (Commutation of 'v')
Th. 21. $\vdash PQ \equiv QP$ (Commutation of '·')
Th. 22. $\vdash [P \vee (Q \vee R)] \equiv [(P \vee Q) \vee R]$ (Association of 'v')
Th. 23. $\vdash P(QR) \equiv (PQ)R$ (Association of '·')

The principle of Transposition is obtainable by DR 14 from Theorem 5 and the result of applying the Deduction Theorem to DR 2.

Th. 24. $\vdash (P \supset Q) \equiv (\sim Q \supset \sim P)$ (Transposition)

The proof of the principle of Exportation is even more obvious.

Th. 25. $\vdash [(PQ) \supset R] \equiv [P \supset (Q \supset R)]$ (Exportation)

The proofs of the final group of theorems of the R.S. will be left as exercises for the reader.

Th. 26. $\vdash P \equiv PP$ (Tautology)
Th. 26, Cor. $\vdash P \equiv P \vee P$ (Tautology)
Th. 27. $\vdash \sim(PQ) \equiv (\sim P \vee \sim Q)$ (De Morgan's Theorem)
Th. 28. $\vdash \sim(P \vee Q) \equiv (\sim P \sim Q)$ (De Morgan's Theorem)
Th. 29. $\vdash (P \supset Q) \equiv (\sim P \vee Q)$ (Material Implication)
★Th. 30. $\vdash P(Q \vee R) \equiv PQ \vee PR$ (Distribution of '·' over 'v')
Th. 30, Cor. $\vdash (P \vee Q)R \equiv PR \vee QR$
Th. 31. $\vdash (P \equiv Q) \equiv [PQ \vee \sim P \sim Q]$ (Material Equivalence)
Th. 32. $\vdash P \vee QR \equiv (P \vee Q)(P \vee R)$ (Distribution of 'v' over '·')

With the establishment of this final group of theorems, R.S. has been shown to contain all of the logical principles appealed to in validating extended arguments in Chapter 3. Containing also, as it does, the Deduction Theorem and the principle of Double Negation, it is adequate also to the methods of Conditional Proof and Indirect Proof discussed in Chapter 3. It still remains to be demonstrated that the system is *deductively complete*, which will be established in the next section.

7.6   DEDUCTIVE COMPLETENESS

In Theorems 22, 23, and 30 we already have the Association of 'v' and '·', and the Distribution of '·' with respect to 'v'. But as stated, these properties have been established only for cases involving exactly three *wffs*. In proving the deductive completeness of R.S. it is convenient to make use of more general Association and Distribution principles. These will be established as our next three Metatheorems. The first of them will establish the general Association and Commutation of the conjunction symbol, '·', stating that no matter in what order or grouping any number of *wffs* are conjoined, the resulting *wff* will be equivalent to the result of conjoining them in any other order or grouping. We may state this formally as follows:

METATHEOREM V.   *Let $P_1, P_2, \ldots, P_n$ be any wffs and let Q and R be any two wffs constructed out of them by means of '·'. If each $P_i (1 \leq i \leq n)$ occurs exactly once in each of the wffs Q and R, then $\vdash Q \equiv R$.*

Proof: We use strong induction on the number of 'factors' P_i in Q and R.[8]

α) Where $n = 1$, Q and R are identically the same *wff* P_1 so $\vdash Q \equiv R$ by Th. 7 and DR 14.

β) Here we assume the Metatheorem true for every $k < n$ factors $P_1, P_2, \ldots, P_k$. Now consider Q and R each constructed out of $n > 1$ factors $P_1, P_2, \ldots, P_n$. Q has the structure $S \cdot T$ and R has the structure $X \cdot Y$.

---

[8] The following proof is due to my friend and former student Michael Ikezawa.

Each of the *wffs* S and T contains at least one of the factors P_1, P_2, . . . , P_n. We can assume that P_1 is a factor of S, because if not we can apply Th. 21 and relabel to obtain $\vdash Q \equiv S \cdot T$ where S now does contain P_1 as a factor.

Because T contains at least one of P_2, P_3, . . . , P_n as a factor, S contains $< n$ of the factors P_1, P_2, . . . , P_n. Hence by the β-case assumption $\vdash S \equiv P_1 \cdot S'$, where S' is a *wff* that contains all the factors of S except P_1. Now by MT IV, Cor. we have

$$\vdash Q \equiv (P_1 \cdot S') \cdot T$$

and by Th. 23 and MT IV, Cor.

$$\vdash Q \equiv P_1 \cdot (S' \cdot T)$$

By the same reasoning we derive

$$\vdash R \equiv P_1 \cdot (X' \cdot Y)$$

Now each of the *wffs* $S' \cdot T$ and $X' \cdot Y$ contains the $n - 1$ factors P_2, P_3, . . . , P_n, so by the β-case assumption

$$\vdash S' \cdot T \equiv X' \cdot Y$$

By Th. 7 and DR 14 we have $\vdash P_1 \equiv P_1$, and by DR 16 we have

$$\vdash P_1 \cdot (S' \cdot T) \equiv P_1 \cdot (X' \cdot Y)$$

and by MT IV, Cor.

$$\vdash Q \equiv R$$

Metatheorem V now follows by strong induction.

The next principle concerns the general Association and Commutation of the disjunction symbol 'v'. No matter in what order or grouping any *wffs* are connected by 'v', the resulting disjunction or 'logical sum' will be equivalent to the result of connecting them by 'v' in any other order or grouping. We may state this formally as

METATHEOREM VI. *Let P_1, P_2, . . . , P_n be any wffs and let Q and R be any two wffs constructed out of them by means of 'v'. If each $P_i (1 \leq i \leq n)$ occurs exactly once in each of the wffs Q and R, then $\vdash Q \equiv R$.*

The proof will be left as an exercise for the reader.

MT VI, Cor.   *If Q and R are as in* Metatheorem VI, *then $Q \vdash R$.* The proof of the corollary is obvious.

Finally, we wish to establish a generalized statement of the Distribution of conjunction with respect to disjunction, that is, of '·' over 'v'. This is expressed as

Metatheorem VII.   *If Q is the logical sum of P_1, P_2, . . . , P_n, and S is the logical sum of P_1R, P_2R. . . . , P_nR, then $\vdash QR \equiv S$.*

Proof: We use weak induction on the number of summands P_1, P_2, . . . , P_n.

α) Where $n = 1$, Q is P_1, QR is P_1R, and S is P_1R also. By Th. 7 and DR 14, $\vdash P_1R \equiv P_1R$ which is $\vdash QR \equiv S$.

β) Assume the Metatheorem true for k summands P_1, P_2, . . . P_k. Now let Q be the logical sum or disjunction of P_1, P_2, . . . , P_k, P_{k+1}, and let S be the logical sum of P_1R, P_2R, . . . , P_kR, $P_{k+1}R$. Now we argue that

$\vdash (P_1 \vee P_2 \vee \; . \; . \; . \; \vee P_k)R \equiv P_1R \vee P_2R \; \vee$

$ \qquad\qquad\qquad\qquad\qquad . \; . \; . \; \vee P_kR$ by the β-case assumption

$\vdash P_{k+1}R \equiv P_{k+1}R$ Th. 7 and DR 14

$\vdash (P_1 \vee P_2 \vee \; . \; . \; . \; \vee P_k)R \vee P_{k+1}R \equiv$

$ \qquad (P_1R \vee P_2R \vee \; . \; . \; . \; \vee P_kR) \vee P_{k+1}R$ DR 16, Cor.

$\vdash [(P_1 \vee P_2 \vee \; . \; . \; . \; \vee P_k) \vee P_{k+1}]R \equiv$

$ \qquad (P_1 \vee P_2 \vee \; . \; . \; . \; \vee P_k)R \vee P_{k+1}R$ Th. 30, Cor.

$\vdash [(P_1 \vee P_2 \vee \; . \; . \; . \; \vee P_k) \vee P_{k+1}]R \equiv$

$ \qquad (P_1R \vee P_2R \vee \; . \; . \; . \; \vee P_kR) \vee P_{k+1}R$ MT IV, Cor.

By our convention of *association to the left*, the preceding line can also be written as

$\vdash (P_1 \vee P_2 \vee \; . \; . \; . \; \vee P_k \vee P_{k+1})R \equiv P_1R \vee P_2R \vee \; . \; . \; . \; \vee P_kR \vee P_{k+1}R$

which is $\vdash QR \equiv S$ where Q contains $k + 1$ summands.

Metatheorem VII now follows by weak induction.

To prove that R.S. is deductively complete, we show that all tautologies are provable as theorems in the system. Since all tautologies are expressible as *wffs* of R.S. (by MT I), the deductive completeness of R.S. is expressed as: If S is a tautology then $\vdash S$. A criterion for deciding whether or not any *wff* is a tautology is supplied by the method of truth tables. Any *wff* S has a truth table with as many initial columns in it as there are distinct propositional symbols in S. Where there are n of them, say $P_1, P_2, \ldots, P_n$, the tautology S will have this truth table:

P_1	P_2	$\ldots$	P_n	S
T	T	$\ldots$	T	T
T	T	$\ldots$	F	T
.	.	. . .	.	.
.	.	. . .	.	.
.	.	. . .	.	.
F	F	$\ldots$	T	T
F	F	$\ldots$	F	T

Any such truth table has 2^n rows, each of which represents a different assignment of **T**'s and **F**'s to the P_i's, one row for every possible assignment. That only **T**'s appear in the column under S indicates that every possible assignment of **T**'s and **F**'s to the P_i's must assign a **T** to S.

To show that $\vdash S$ for every such S, we establish the following:

first, that each row of its truth table, that is, each assignment of truth values to the P_i's, can be represented by a *wff* of R.S., the first row by Q_1, the second by $Q_2, \ldots$, and the last or $2^n th$ by Q_{2^n};

second, that if $Q_1, Q_2, \ldots, Q_{2^n}$ are the 2^n *wffs* representing all possible assignments of **T**'s and **F**'s to the P_i's, then $\vdash (Q_1 \vee Q_2 \vee \ldots \vee Q_{2^n})$; and

third, that if a particular assignment of **T**'s and **F**'s to the P_i's assigns a **T** to S, then where Q_j represents that particular assignment, we have $\vdash Q_j \supset S$.

That these will suffice to prove that $\vdash S$ is easily seen. Where the truth table for S has all **T**'s in the column under S, then $\vdash Q_1 \supset S, \vdash Q_2 \supset S,$

. . . , $\vdash Q_{2^n} \supset S$. From these, by $2^n - 1$ uses of DR 10 we have $\vdash (Q_1 \vee Q_2 \vee \ldots \vee Q_{2^n}) \supset S$. And once we have established that $\vdash (Q_1 \vee Q_2 \vee \ldots \vee Q_{2^n})$, we obtain $\vdash S$ by R 1.

Now we proceed to attack the problem in detail. First we must show that each possible assignment of $\mathbf{T}$'s and $\mathbf{F}$'s to the P_i's of a set $(P_1, P_2, \ldots , P_n)$ can be represented by a *wff*. It is convenient to lay down the following:

Definition. A *wff* is said to *represent* a particular assignment of truth values to propositional symbols $P_1, P_2, \ldots , P_n$ if and only if (on the normal interpretation of our operator symbols) that truth value assignment is the only one which makes that *wff* true.

Where $\mathbf{T}$'s are assigned to every P_i, this assignment is represented by the conjunction $P_1 \cdot P_2 \cdot \ldots \cdot P_n$, which we denote by '$Q_1$'. Where $\mathbf{T}$'s are assigned to every P_i except P_n, which is assigned an $\mathbf{F}$, the assignment is represented by the conjunction $P_1 \cdot P_2 \cdot \ldots \cdot P_{n-1} \cdot \sim P_n$, which we denote by '$Q_2$'. Similarly for every other possible assignment corresponding to every row of the truth table, ending with the conjunction $\sim P_1 \cdot \sim P_2 \cdot \ldots \cdot \sim P_n$, which we denote by '$Q_{2^n}$'. In this way any row of any truth table can be represented by a *wff* of R.S., which establishes the *first* result mentioned in the preceding paragraph.

Next we turn our attention to the *second*, which we express as

METATHEOREM VIII. *If $Q_1, Q_2, \ldots , Q_{2^n}$ represent all possible distinct assignments of truth values to the n distinct propositional symbols $P_1, P_2, \ldots , P_n$, then $\vdash (Q_1 \vee Q_2 \vee \ldots \vee Q_{2^n})$.*

Proof: We use weak induction on the number of P_i's.

α) Where $n = 1$, $2^n = 2$, and Q_1 is P_1 and Q_2 is $\sim P_1$. Here we have $\vdash P_1 \vee \sim P_1$ by Th. 7, Cor. which is $\vdash (Q_1 \vee Q_2)$.

β) Assume the Metatheorem true for $P_1, P_2, \ldots , P_k$. Now consider the set $P_1, P_2, \ldots , P_k, P_{k+1}$. Where $Q_1, Q_2, \ldots , Q_{2^k}$ represent all possible distinct assignments of truth values to $P_1, P_2, \ldots , P_k$, we have $\vdash (Q_1 \vee Q_2 \vee \ldots \vee Q_{2^k})$ by the β-case assumption.

Then we continue the argument as follows:

$\vdash P_{k+1} \vee \sim P_{k+1}$ Th. 7, Cor.

$\vdash (Q_1 \vee Q_2 \vee \ldots \vee Q_{2^k})(P_{k+1} \vee \sim P_{k+1})$ DR 14

$\vdash (Q_1 \vee Q_2 \vee \ldots \vee Q_{2^k})(P_{k+1} \vee \sim P_{k+1}) \equiv$
$\qquad (Q_1 \vee Q_2 \vee \ldots \vee Q_{2^k})P_{k+1} \vee$
$\qquad\qquad (Q_1 \vee Q_2 \vee \ldots \vee Q_{2^k})\sim P_{k+1}$ Th. 30

$\vdash (Q_1 \vee Q_2 \vee \ldots \vee Q_{2^k})P_{k+1} \vee$
$\qquad\qquad (Q_1 \vee Q_2\vee \ldots \vee Q_{2^k})\sim P_{k+1}$ MT IV, Cor.

$\vdash (Q_1 \vee Q_2 \vee \ldots \vee Q_{2^k})P_{k+1} \equiv$
$\qquad\qquad (Q_1 P_{k+1} \vee Q_2 P_{k+1} \vee \ldots \vee Q_{2^k}P_{k+1})$ MT VII

$\vdash (Q_1 \vee Q_2 \vee \ldots \vee Q_{2^k})\sim P_{k+1} \equiv$
$\qquad (Q_1 \sim P_{k+1} \vee Q_2 \sim P_{k+1} \vee \ldots \vee Q_{2^k}\sim P_{k+1})$ MT VII

$\vdash (Q_1 P_{k+1} \vee Q_2 P_{k+1} \vee \ldots \vee Q_{2^k}P_{k+1}) \vee (Q_1 \sim P_{k+1} \vee$
$\qquad Q_2 \sim P_{k+1} \vee \ldots \vee Q_{2^k}\sim P_{k+1})$ MT IV, Cor.

$\vdash Q_1 P_{k+1} \vee Q_1 \sim P_{k+1} \vee Q_2 P_{k+1} \vee Q_2 \sim P_{k+1} \vee \ldots \vee$
$\qquad\qquad Q_{2^k}P_{k+1} \vee Q_{2^k}\sim P_{k+1}$ MT VI, Cor.

The preceding expression contains $2^k + 2^k = 2 \cdot 2^k = 2^{k+1}$ summands, each of which represents a different assignment of truth values to P_1, P_2, . . . , P_{k+1}. Each $Q_i P_{k+1}$ and each $Q_i \sim P_{k+1}$ is a different Q_i', where the $2^{k+1} Q_i'$'s represent all possible distinct assignments of truth values to P_1, P_2, . . . , P_{k+1}. Hence $\vdash (Q_1' \vee Q_2' \vee \ldots \vee Q_{2^{k+1}}')$. Metatheorem VIII now follows by weak induction.

We next prove that if the truth value assignment represented by Q_j assigns a **T** to S, then $\vdash Q_j \supset S$. We shall prove this by establishing a slightly more general result, which includes also the case in which the truth value assignment assigns an **F** to S instead. This is

METATHEOREM IX.   *Let Q_j represent any possible assignment of truth values to the n propositional symbols P_1, P_2, . . . , P_n; and let S be any wff which has no components other than $P_i (1 \leq i \leq n)$. If the truth value assignment represented by Q_j assigns a* **T** *to S, then $\vdash Q_j \supset S$; and if the truth value assignment represented by Q_j assigns an* **F** *to S, then $\vdash Q_j \supset \sim S$.*

Proof: We use strong induction on the number of symbols in S, counting each occurrence of $\cdot$, of $\sim$, and of any P_i as a single symbol.

α) Where $n = 1$, S must be a single symbol, and since it is a *wff* it must be a $P_i (1 \leq i \leq n)$.

CASE 1. Q_j assigns a **T** to S, that is, to P_i. Hence P_i rather than $\sim P_i$ must be a factor of Q_j. By MT V, $\vdash Q_j \equiv P_i R$, where R is a conjunction of all the factors of Q_j except P_i. Now we argue

$$\vdash P_i R \supset P_i \quad\quad \text{Ax. 2}$$
$$\vdash Q_j \supset P_i \quad\quad\quad \text{MT IV, Cor.}$$

which is $\vdash Q_j \supset S$.

CASE 2. Q_j assigns an **F** to S, that is, to P_i. Hence $\sim P_i$ must be a factor of Q_j. By MT V, $\vdash Q_j \equiv \sim P_i R$, where R is a conjunction of all the factors of Q_j except $\sim P_i$. Now we argue

$$\vdash \sim P_i R \supset \sim P_i \quad\quad \text{Ax. 2}$$
$$\vdash Q_j \supset \sim P_i \quad\quad\quad \text{MT IV, Cor.}$$

which is $\vdash Q_j \supset \sim S$.

β) Assume the Metatheorem true for any S containing any number $k < n$ symbols. Now consider any S containing $n(>1)$ symbols. The *wff* S must have the structure $S_1 \cdot S_2$ or $\sim S_3$.

CASE 1. S is of the form $S_1 \cdot S_2$.

Subcase A: Q_j assigns a **T** to S. Here Q_j must assign a **T** to S_1 and a **T** to S_2. Since S_1, S_2 contain fewer than n symbols each, we argue as follows:

$$\vdash Q_j \supset S_1 \quad\quad \text{by the } \beta\text{-case assumption}$$
$$\vdash Q_j \supset S_2 \quad\quad \text{by the } \beta\text{-case assumption}$$
$$\vdash Q_j \supset S_1 \cdot S_2 \quad\quad \text{DR 8}$$

which is $\vdash Q_j \supset S$.

Subcase B: Q_j assigns an **F** to S. Here Q_j must assign an **F** to S_1 or an **F** to S_2. If to S_1, then $\vdash Q_j \supset \sim S_1$ by the β-case assumption, and hence by DR 12 $\vdash Q_j \supset \sim(S_1 \cdot S_2)$, which is $\vdash Q_j \supset \sim S$. If to S_2 then $\vdash Q_j \supset \sim S_2$ by the β-case assumption, and hence by DR 13 $\vdash Q_j \supset \sim(S_1 \cdot S_2)$, which is $\vdash Q_j \supset \sim S$.

CASE 2.　S is of the form $\sim S_3$.

Subcase A:　Q_j assigns a **T** to S. Here Q_j must assign an **F** to S_3. Hence by the β-case assumption, $\vdash Q_j \supset \sim S_3$ which is $\vdash Q_j \supset S$.

Subcase B:　Q_j assigns an **F** to S. Here Q_j must assign a **T** to S_3. Hence by the β-case assumption, $\vdash Q_j \supset S_3$. But $\vdash S_3 \supset \sim\sim S_3$ by Th. 4, so by DR 6 we have $\vdash Q_j \supset \sim\sim S_3$, which is $\vdash Q_j \supset \sim S$.

Metatheorem IX now follows by strong induction.

The deductive completeness of the system now follows easily, and may be proved as

METATHEOREM X.　*R.S. is deductively complete (that is, if S is a tautology then $\vdash S$).*

Proof:　If S is a tautology, then every possible assignment of truth values to its constituents $P_1, P_2, \ldots, P_n$ must assign a **T** to S. Hence by MT IX:

$$\vdash Q_1 \supset S$$
$$\vdash Q_2 \supset S$$
$$. \quad . \quad . \quad . \quad .$$
$$\vdash Q_{2^n} \supset S$$

where $Q_1, Q_2, \ldots, Q_{2^n}$ represent all possible assignments of truth values to $P_1, P_2, \ldots, P_n$. Now by $2^n - 1$ uses of DR 10, we have

$$\vdash (Q_1 \text{ v } Q_2 \text{ v } \ldots \text{ v } Q_{2^n}) \supset S$$

and by MT VIII,

$$\vdash (Q_1 \text{ v } Q_2 \text{ v } \ldots \text{ v } Q_{2^n})$$

From these we derive $\vdash S$ by R 1, which completes the proof of Metatheorem X.

The *decision problem* for any deductive system is the problem of stating an effective criterion for deciding whether or not any statement or well formed formula is a theorem of the system. In view of the analyticity and deductive completeness of R.S. (Metatheorems II and X), the method of truth tables constitutes a solution to the decision problem.

Truth tables enable us to decide effectively whether or not any *wff* is a tautology. By MT II, *only* tautologies are theorems, and by MT X, *all* tautologies are theorems. Hence truth tables enable us to decide effectively whether or not any *wff* is a theorem. Moreover, the proofs up to and including that for MT X do not merely assure us that for any tautologous *wff* there exists a demonstration—they prescribe effectively a method of actually constructing its demonstration. The demonstration constructed by following the directions contained in the proof of deductive completeness will in general be longer than one discovered through the exercise of ingenuity and inventiveness. That is to be admitted. But it is significant and important that through the use of the recipe contained in the proofs up to and including that of MT X, a demonstration within the logistic system can be written out for any tautology—*without any need for ingenuity or inventiveness*. That this can be done is guaranteed by our effective solution of the decision problem for the system.[9]

It is clear from the foregoing that any argument whose validity can be established by the use of truth tables can be proved valid in R.S. In Chapter 3 the claim was made that any such argument could be proved valid using the list of nineteen Rules of Inference augmented by the principles of Conditional Proof and Indirect Proof. We are now in a position to substantiate that claim, which is equivalent to the assertion that the method of deduction set forth in Chapter 3 is deductively complete. We can do so by showing that every argument which can be proved valid in R.S. can also be proved valid by the methods of Chapter 3.

Consider any argument $P_1, \ldots, P_n \therefore Q$ that can be proved valid in R.S. To say that it can be proved valid in R.S. is to say that there is a demonstration in R.S. for the derived rule of inference $P_1, \ldots, P_n \vdash Q$. By n uses of the Deduction Theorem, Exportation, and the Substitution Theorem, we have $\vdash P \supset Q$ where P is a conjunction of $P_1, \ldots, P_n$. By the analyticity of R.S., $P \supset Q$ is a truth table

[9] The preceding proof of deductive completeness and solution to the decision problem is an adaptation of Professor E. L. Post's original demonstration which appeared in his 'Introduction to a General Theory of Elementary Propositions', *American Journal of Mathematics*, vol. 43 (1921), pp. 163–185.

tautology, so $P \cdot \sim Q$ is a contradiction. Now there is a formal proof of validity for the argument

(1) $\qquad\qquad P_1, \ldots, P_n, \sim Q \therefore P \cdot \sim Q$

using the methods of Chapter 3 (by iterated uses of the principle of Conjunction). Hence there is a formal proof using the methods of Chapter 3 for the argument

(2) $\qquad\qquad P_1, \ldots, P_n, \sim Q \therefore N$

where N is a disjunctive normal form[10] of the formula $P \cdot \sim Q$, for the equivalences included among the Rules of Inference in Chapter 3 are sufficient to permit deriving the disjunctive normal form of any line in a formal proof.

Because $P \cdot \sim Q$ is a contradiction, N is a disjunction in which every disjunct contains a contradiction as a conjunct. Hence by repeated uses of variants of the formal proof of validity for

$$q \vee [(p \cdot \sim p) \cdot r] \therefore q$$

the formal proof of validity for (2) can be extended to a formal proof of validity for

(3) $\qquad\qquad P_1, \ldots, P_n, \sim Q \therefore N_1$

where N_1 is a single disjunct of N. If N_1 is not itself an explicit contradiction, it is a conjunction containing a contradiction as a conjunct. Hence by Com. and Simp. (and possibly Assoc.) the formal proof of validity for (3) can be extended to provide a derivation of an explicit contradiction from the set of premises $P_1, \ldots, P_n, \sim Q$. And this derivation constitutes an Indirect Proof of validity for the original argument $P_1, \ldots, P_n \therefore Q$. Hence any argument that can be proved valid in R.S. can be proved valid by the methods of Chapter 3, which suffices to show that the method of deduction set forth in Chapter 3 is also a deductively complete system of logic.[11]

---

[10] See Appendix A, pages 325–332.

[11] The preceding proof is adapted from John Thomas Canty's 'Completeness of Copi's Method of Deduction,' *Notre Dame Journal of Formal Logic*, vol. IV (1963), pp. 142–144.

8

ALTERNATIVE
SYSTEMS
AND
NOTATIONS

8.1 ALTERNATIVE SYSTEMS OF LOGIC

There are three different senses in which the phrase 'alternative systems of logic' can be understood. These parallel the three senses of the phrase 'alternative systems of geometry', and can most easily be explained by analogy with the latter. We may speak of Euclidean plane geometry and Euclidean solid geometry as 'alternative systems' in the sense that the first can be studied independently of the second, and they are certainly different in that the second is *more inclusive* than the first. Analogously, we may speak of a Propositional Calculus and a Function Calculus as 'alternative systems of logic' in that the first can be studied independently of the second, and that the second is *more inclusive* than the first—where a Function Calculus contains all the tautologies and rules of the Propositional Calculus *plus* Quantification Axioms, Rules, and Theorems. It is not *this* sense of an alternative system with which we shall be concerned in the present chapter.

A second sense is that in which we can speak of Euclidean geometry and Riemannian (or Lobachevskian) geometry as alternative systems.

248

These are alternative in the sense that, although they may possess some theorems in common, each contains some theorems not included in the other. Parallel to this situation in geometry, there are alternative systems of logic exhibiting the same sort of differences. An ordinary 'two-valued' system of logic, whose formulas—on interpretation—are either *true* or *false*, can be contrasted with 'three-valued' or 'many-valued' systems of logic whose formulas are supposed to take—on interpretation—either three or $n > 3$ different 'truth values'. Alternative systems of logic in this sense have been extensively developed, first by Jan Lukasiewicz in Poland and independently by E. L. Post in this country, more recently by J. B. Rosser and A. R. Turquette.[1] A study of these is beyond the scope of this book. It is not *this* sense of alternative systems with which we shall be concerned in the present chapter.

The third sense in which one can speak of alternative systems of geometry is that in which different axiomatic bases are assumed, but identically the same theorems are derivable from each of them. Thus many different axiom sets for Euclidean geometry have been devised, all of which yield the same theorems. In alternative systems of this sort, different terms are taken as primitive or undefined, and different formulas are assumed as axioms or postulates. What may be a primitive term in one system may be defined by means of other primitives in the other, and what is assumed as an axiom in one may be derived as a theorem from the axioms of the other—where those axioms correspond to theorems of the first. It is *this* sense of alternative systems that will be discussed in the present chapter.

The logical truths whose systematization is under consideration are truth functional tautologies. Any system wholly adequate to their expression and development must be *functionally complete, analytic,* and

---

[1] Cf. J. Lukasiewicz, 'O logice trojwartosciowej', *Ruch Filozoficzny* (Lwow), vol. 5 (1920), pp. 169–171.

E. L. Post, 'Introduction to a General Theory of Elementary Propositions', *American Journal of Mathematics*, vol. 43 (1921), pp. 163–185.

J. B. Rosser, 'On The Many-Valued Logics', *American Journal of Physics*, vol. 9 (1941), pp. 207–212.

J. B. Rosser and A. R. Turquette, 'Axiom Schemes for M-Valued Propositional Calculi', *Journal of Symbolic Logic*, vol. 10 (1945), pp. 61–82, and *Many-valued Logics*, Amsterdam, 1952.

deductively complete, in the senses in which R.S. was proved to possess these properties in Metatheorems I, II, and X of the preceding chapter. Any such system will be called a *Model System of Logic*, and any other axiom system for logic will be a genuine or acceptable alternative to R.S. if and only if it is a Model System. There are many different Model Systems, different in that they start with different primitive or undefined terms, and different in that they assume different formulas as axioms. They are all equivalent, however, first in being able to express—on their normal interpretations—all truth functions, second in including *all* tautologies as theorems, and third in having *only* tautologies as theorems. One such alternative system will be proved to be a *Model System* in the following section.

8.2   THE HILBERT-ACKERMANN SYSTEM

The Hilbert-Ackermann system for the propositional calculus has as its primitive symbols infinitely many single letters with and without subscripts:

$$A \quad A_1 \quad A_2 \quad A_3 \quad \cdots$$
$$B \quad B_1 \quad B_2 \quad B_3 \quad \cdots$$
$$C \quad C_1 \quad C_2 \quad C_3 \quad \cdots$$
$$D \quad D_1 \quad D_2 \quad D_3 \quad \cdots$$

which on their normal interpretations express non-compound propositions, and has in addition to parentheses, the two operator symbols '∼' and 'v' (designated in our metalanguage by '∼' and 'v'), which have as their normal interpretations the operations of negation and weak (or inclusive) disjunction. We continue to use the symbols 'P', 'Q', 'R', 'S', . . . , with and without subscripts, in our metalanguage, to denote well formed formulas of H.A. (the Hilbert-Ackermann system of logic). The notion of a *wff* of H.A. is defined recursively as follows:

Recursive Rule for wffs in H.A.

1. Any single letter of H.A. is a *wff*.
2. If P is a *wff* then $\sim(P)$ is a *wff*.
3. If P and Q are *wffs* then (P) v (Q) is a *wff*.

(No formula of H.A. will be regarded as being a *wff* unless its being so follows from this definition.)

The symbols '$\supset$', '$\cdot$', '$\equiv$', are defined *syntactically* for our meta-language by the following:

$$P \supset Q = \text{df} \sim P \vee Q$$
$$P \cdot Q = \text{df} \sim (\sim P \vee \sim Q)$$
$$PQ = \text{df} P \cdot Q$$
$$P \equiv Q = \text{df} (P \supset Q)(Q \supset P)$$

We shall continue to use the same conventions regarding parentheses which were adopted in the preceding chapter.

Four (patterns of) axioms or postulates are assumed in H.A.

P 1. $(P \vee P) \supset P$
P 2. $P \supset (P \vee Q)$
P 3. $(P \vee Q) \supset (Q \vee P)$
P 4. $(P \supset Q) \supset [(R \vee P) \supset (R \vee Q)]$

Each of these syntactical expressions denotes infinitely many *wffs* of our object language H.A., just as in the metalogical development of R.S.

Finally, a single rule of inference is assumed, which we may state as

R' 1. If P and $P \supset Q$ to infer Q.

It should be realized that R' 1 is different from R 1, because R' 1 legitimizes arguments within H.A. of the form

$$P$$
$$\sim P \vee Q$$
$$Q$$

whereas R 1 legitimizes arguments within R.S. of the form

$$P$$
$$\sim (P \sim Q)$$
$$Q$$

and these are clearly different. We may make the contrast more vivid by writing them as

R 1. From P and $\sim(P{\sim}Q)$ to infer Q.

R′ 1. From P and $\sim P \vee Q$ to infer Q.

By MT IV, Cor., and Th. 29 of R.S., any *wff* in R.S. that follows by R 1 from two other *wffs* must also follow by R′ 1 and conversely. But this cannot be assumed true of H.A. until it is *proved*.

A 'demonstration in H.A.' of the validity of an argument having premises $P_1, P_2, \ldots, P_n$ and conclusion Q is defined to be a sequence of *wffs* $S_1, S_2, \ldots, S_t$ (of H.A.) each of which is either a postulate P 1, P 2, P 3, or P 4 or a $P_i (1 \leq i \leq n)$ or follows from two preceding S's by R′ 1, and such that S_t is Q. That there is such a demonstration in H.A. is written

$$P_1, P_2, \ldots, P_n \mathbin{|_{\overline{\mathrm{HA}}}} Q$$

Similarly, that the formula P is a theorem of H.A. is written

$$\mathbin{|_{\overline{\mathrm{HA}}}} P$$

which asserts that there is a sequence of *wffs* $S_1, S_2, \ldots, S_t$ (of H.A.) each of which is either a postulate P 1, P 2, P 3, or P 4 or follows from two preceding S's by R′ 1, and such that S_t is P.

The functional completeness of H.A. is easily established. (It was Exercise 1 on page 211 in the preceding chapter.) A proof of the analyticity of H.A. is easily given by using truth tables to show that any postulate P 1, P 2, P 3, P 4 is a tautology, and then proving that any *wff* which follows from tautologies by repeated applications of R′ 1 must be tautologous also. The detailed proofs are left as exercises for the reader. There remains only the task of proving H.A. to be deductively complete.

There are two alternative methods by which the deductive completeness of H.A. can be established. The first is that used in proving R.S. to be deductively complete. Involved here would be the development of a considerable number of theorems and derived rules *in* the system, and then the proof of a number of Metatheorems *about* the system, culminating in an analogue of the preceding chapter's Metatheorem X for the Hilbert-Ackermann System. This first method is systematic and elegant, but very lengthy. A shorter method is available. The shorter method of proving H.A. to be deductively complete depends upon the fact that the deductive completeness of R.S. has already been proved. What has been established for R.S. by MT X of the preceding chapter is that any tautological formula S is derivable by one or more applications of R 1 to Ax. 1, Ax. 2, and Ax. 3 of R.S. We wish to prove that H.A. is deductively complete, that is, that any tautological formula S is derivable by one or more applications of R′ 1 to P 1, P 2, P 3, and P 4 of H.A. Now *if* it can be shown that Ax. 1, Ax. 2, and Ax. 3 of R.S. can be derived by repeated applications of R′ 1 to the Hilbert-Ackermann postulates P 1, P 2, P 3, and P 4, and further shown that any *wff* S which is derivable from Ax. 1, Ax. 2, and Ax. 3, by the use of R 1 is also derivable from them by the use of R′ 1, then it will have been shown that any tautological formula S is derivable by repeated applications of R′ 1 to P 1, P 2, P 3, and P 4. The latter, of course, asserts the deductive completeness of H.A. This second, shorter method of proving H.A. to be deductively complete will be adopted here. We begin by establishing Ax. 1, Ax. 2, and Ax. 3 of R.S. as theorems of the Hilbert-Ackermann system. It will be convenient to establish some few derived rules and auxiliary theorems in H.A. first. To this task we now proceed, giving proofs rather than demonstrations in most cases.

THEOREM 1. $|_{\overline{HA}} (Q \supset R) \supset [(P \supset Q) \supset (P \supset R)]$

   Demonstration: $(Q \supset R) \supset [(\sim P \vee Q) \supset (\sim P \vee R)]$ P 4

   $(Q \supset R) \supset [(P \supset Q) \supset (P \supset R)]$ df.

FIRST DERIVED RULE (DR′ 1). $P \supset Q, Q \supset R |_{\overline{HA}} P \supset R$

   Proof: $(Q \supset R) \supset [(P \supset Q) \supset (P \supset R)]$ Th. 1

   $Q \supset R$ premiss

   $(P \supset Q) \supset (P \supset R)$ R′ 1

   $P \supset Q$ premiss

   $P \supset R$ R′ 1

THEOREM 2. $|_{\overline{HA}} P \supset P$

   Proof: $P \supset (P \vee P)$ P 2

   $(P \vee P) \supset P$ P 1

   $P \supset P$ DR′ 1

THEOREM 3. $\vdash_{\overline{HA}} P \vee \sim P$

Proof:	$P \supset P$	Th. 2
	$\sim P \vee P$	df.
	$(\sim P \vee P) \supset (P \vee \sim P)$	P 3
	$P \vee \sim P$	R′ 1

THEOREM 4. $\vdash_{\overline{HA}} P \supset \sim\sim P$

Proof:	$\sim P \vee \sim\sim P$	Th. 3
	$P \supset \sim\sim P$	df.

SECOND DERIVED RULE (DR′ 2). $P \supset Q \vdash_{\overline{HA}} \sim Q \supset \sim P$

Proof:	$P \supset Q$	premiss
	$Q \supset \sim\sim Q$	Th. 4
	$P \supset \sim\sim Q$	DR′ 1
	$\sim P \vee \sim\sim Q$	df.
	$(\sim P \vee \sim\sim Q) \supset (\sim\sim Q \vee \sim P)$	P 3
	$\sim\sim Q \vee \sim P$	R′ 1
	$\sim Q \supset \sim P$	df.

THEOREM 5. $\vdash_{\overline{HA}} P \supset PP$

Proof:	$(\sim P \vee \sim P) \supset \sim P$	P 1
	$\sim\sim P \supset \sim(\sim P \vee \sim P)$	DR′ 2
	$P \supset \sim\sim P$	Th. 4
	$P \supset \sim(\sim P \vee \sim P)$	DR′ 1
	$P \supset PP$	df.

THEOREM 6. $\vdash_{\overline{HA}} \sim\sim P \supset P$

Proof:	$\sim P \supset \sim\sim\sim P$	Th. 4
	$(\sim P \supset \sim\sim\sim P) \supset [(P \vee \sim P) \supset (P \vee \sim\sim\sim P)]$	P 4
	$(P \vee \sim P) \supset [P \vee \sim\sim\sim P]$	R′ 1
	$(P \vee \sim P)$	Th. 3
	$P \vee \sim\sim\sim P$	R′ 1
	$(P \vee \sim\sim\sim P) \supset (\sim\sim\sim P \vee P)$	P 3
	$\sim\sim\sim P \vee P$	R′ 1
	$\sim\sim P \supset P$	df.

THEOREM 7. $\vdash_{\overline{HA}} PQ \supset P$

  Proof: $\sim P \supset (\sim P \vee \sim Q)$ P 2

          $\sim(\sim P \vee \sim Q) \supset \sim\sim P$ DR' 2

          $\sim\sim P \supset P$ Th. 6

          $\sim(\sim P \vee \sim Q) \supset P$ DR' 1

          $PQ \supset P$ df.

THEOREM 8. $\vdash_{\overline{HA}} (P \supset Q) \supset (\sim Q \supset \sim P)$

  Proof: $(Q \supset \sim\sim Q) \supset [(\sim P \vee Q) \supset (\sim P \vee \sim\sim Q)]$ P 4

          $(Q \supset \sim\sim Q)$ Th. 4

          $(\sim P \vee Q) \supset (\sim P \vee \sim\sim Q)$ R' 1

          $(\sim P \vee \sim\sim Q) \supset (\sim\sim Q \vee \sim P)$ P 3

          $(\sim P \vee Q) \supset (\sim\sim Q \vee \sim P)$ DR' 1

          $(P \supset Q) \supset (\sim Q \supset \sim P)$ df.

THEOREM 9. $\vdash_{\overline{HA}} [P \vee (Q \vee R)] \supset [Q \vee (P \vee R)]$

  Proof: $R \supset (R \vee P)$ P 2

          $(R \vee P) \supset (P \vee R)$ P 3

          $R \supset (P \vee R)$ DR' 1

          $[R \supset (P \vee R)] \supset \{(Q \vee R) \supset [Q \vee (P \vee R)]\}$ P 4

          $(Q \vee R) \supset [Q \vee (P \vee R)]$ R' 1

          $\{(Q \vee R) \supset [Q \vee (P \vee R)]\} \supset \{[P \vee (Q \vee R)] \supset$

                                  $\{P \vee [Q \vee (P \vee R)]\}\}$ P 4

          $[P \vee (Q \vee R)] \supset \{P \vee [Q \vee (P \vee R)]\}$ R' 1

          $\{P \vee [Q \vee (P \vee R)]\} \supset \{[Q \vee (P \vee R)] \vee P\}$ P 3

          $[P \vee (Q \vee R)] \supset \{[Q \vee (P \vee R)] \vee P\}$ DR' 1

          $(P \vee R) \supset [(P \vee R) \vee Q]$ P 2

          $[(P \vee R) \vee Q] \supset [Q \vee (P \vee R)]$ P 3

          $(P \vee R) \supset [Q \vee (P \vee R)]$ DR' 1

          $P \supset (P \vee R)$ P 2

          $P \supset [Q \vee (P \vee R)]$ DR' 1

          $\{P \supset [Q \vee (P \vee R)]\} \supset \{\{[Q \vee (P \vee R)] \vee P\} \supset$

                      $\{[Q \vee (P \vee R)] \vee [Q \vee (P \vee R)]\}\}$ P 4

          $\{[Q \vee (P \vee R)] \vee P\} \supset$

                      $\{[Q \vee (P \vee R)] \vee [Q \vee (P \vee R)]\}$ R' 1

          $\{[Q \vee (P \vee R)] \vee [Q \vee (P \vee R)]\} \supset [Q \vee (P \vee R)]$ P 1

          $\{[Q \vee (P \vee R)] \vee P\} \supset [Q \vee (P \vee R)]$ DR' 1

Now from this step and the ninth, we have

$$[P \vee (Q \vee R)] \supset [Q \vee (P \vee R)] \qquad \text{DR}' 1$$

With the establishment of Theorem 9 of the H.A. system, we have proved it equivalent to the *Principia Mathematica*[2] 'calculus of elementary propositions'. The P.M. (*Principia Mathematica*) postulates *1.2, *1.4, *1.6 correspond exactly to P 1, P 3, P 4 of H.A., and in the presence of P 3, P.M.'s *1.3 corresponds to H.A.'s P 2. The additional (fifth) postulate *1.5 of P.M. is identical with Theorem 9 of H.A. That it can be derived as a theorem from the other four postulates shows the association of disjunction to have been an unnecessary assumption. This redundancy of the P.M. postulates was first shown by Paul Bernays.[3]

THEOREM 10. $\mid_{\overline{\text{HA}}} (P \supset Q) \supset [\sim(QR) \supset \sim(RP)]$

Proof:		
$(\sim Q \supset \sim P) \supset [(\sim R \vee \sim Q) \supset (\sim R \vee \sim P)]$		P 4
$(P \supset Q) \supset (\sim Q \supset \sim P)$		Th. 8
$(P \supset Q) \supset [(\sim R \vee \sim Q) \supset (\sim R \vee \sim P)]$		DR' 1
$\sim(P \supset Q) \vee [\sim(\sim R \vee \sim Q) \vee (\sim R \vee \sim P)]$		df.
$\{\sim(P \supset Q) \vee [\sim(\sim R \vee \sim Q) \vee (\sim R \vee \sim P)]\} \supset$		
$\qquad \{\sim(\sim R \vee \sim Q) \vee [\sim(P \supset Q) \vee (\sim R \vee \sim P)]\}$		Th. 9
$\sim(\sim R \vee \sim Q) \vee [\sim(P \supset Q) \vee (\sim R \vee \sim P)]$		R' 1
$(\sim R \vee \sim Q) \supset [\sim(P \supset Q) \vee (\sim R \vee \sim P)]$		df.
$(\sim Q \vee \sim R) \supset (\sim R \vee \sim Q)$		P 3
$(\sim Q \vee \sim R) \supset [\sim(P \supset Q) \vee (\sim R \vee \sim P)]$		DR' 1
$\sim(\sim Q \vee \sim R) \vee [\sim(P \supset Q) \vee (\sim R \vee \sim P)]$		df.
$\{\sim(\sim Q \vee \sim R) \vee [\sim(P \supset Q) \vee (\sim R \vee \sim P)]\} \supset$		
$\qquad \{\sim(P \supset Q) \vee [\sim(\sim Q \vee \sim R) \vee (\sim R \vee \sim P)]\}$		Th. 9
$\sim(P \supset Q) \vee [\sim(\sim Q \vee \sim R) \vee (\sim R \vee \sim P)]$		R' 1
$(P \supset Q) \supset [(\sim Q \vee \sim R) \supset (\sim R \vee \sim P)]$		df.
$[(\sim Q \vee \sim R) \supset (\sim R \vee \sim P)] \supset$		
$\qquad\qquad [\sim(\sim R \vee \sim P) \supset \sim(\sim Q \vee \sim R)]$		Th. 8

[2] By A. N. Whitehead and B. Russell, vol. 1, 1910, vol. 2, 1912, vol. 3, 1913, Cambridge, Eng., Cambridge University Press, second edition, 1925–1927.

[3] P. Bernays, 'Axiomatische Untersuchung des Aussagenkalküls der Principia Mathematica', *Mathematische Zeitschrift*, vol. 25 (1926), pp. 305–320.

$(P \supset Q) \supset [\sim(\sim R \text{ v} \sim P) \supset \sim(\sim Q \text{ v} \sim R)]$ DR′ 1

$(P \supset Q) \supset [(RP) \supset (QR)]$ df.

$[(RP) \supset (QR)] \supset [\sim(QR) \supset \sim(RP)]$ Th. 8

$(P \supset Q) \supset [\sim(QR) \supset \sim(RP)]$ DR′ 1

There is a close analogy between Theorems 5, 7, and 10 of the Hilbert-Ackermann System and Axioms 1, 2, and 3 of R.S. But they are not identical, in spite of their identical *appearance*, because '$P \supset Q$' of R.S. is an abbreviation for '$\sim(P\sim Q)$', while '$P \supset Q$' in the Hilbert-Ackermann System is an abbreviation for '$\sim P \text{ v} Q$'. The possibility of confusion can be eliminated by writing (and then deriving) the three axioms of R.S. in their unabbreviated forms, expressing them entirely by means of the operator symbols '·' and '$\sim$'. So expressed, they are

Ax. 1. $\sim[P \cdot \sim(P \cdot P)]$

Ax. 2. $\sim[(P \cdot Q) \cdot \sim P]$

Ax. 3. $\sim\{\sim(P \cdot \sim Q) \cdot \sim\sim[\sim(Q \cdot R) \cdot \sim\sim(R \cdot P)]\}$

and these will be proved as the next three theorems in H.A.

THEOREM 11. $\mid_{\overline{\text{HA}}} \sim[P \cdot \sim(P \cdot P)]$

Proof: $P \supset (P \cdot P)$ Th. 5

$(P \cdot P) \supset \sim\sim(P \cdot P)$ Th. 4

$P \supset \sim\sim(P \cdot P)$ DR′ 1

$\sim P \text{ v} \sim\sim(P \cdot P)$ df.

$[\sim P \text{ v} \sim\sim(P \cdot P)] \supset \sim\sim[\sim P \text{ v} \sim\sim(P \cdot P)]$ Th. 4

$\sim\sim[\sim P \text{ v} \sim\sim(P \cdot P)]$ R′ 1

$\sim[P \cdot \sim(P \cdot P)]$ df.

THEOREM 12. $\mid_{\overline{\text{HA}}} \sim[(P \cdot Q) \cdot \sim P]$

Proof: $(P \cdot Q) \supset P$ Th. 7

$P \supset \sim\sim P$ Th. 4

$(P \cdot Q) \supset \sim\sim P$ DR′ 1

$\sim(P \cdot Q) \text{ v} \sim\sim P$ df.

$[\sim(P \cdot Q) \text{ v} \sim\sim P] \supset \sim\sim[\sim(P \cdot Q) \text{ v} \sim\sim P]$ Th. 4

$\sim\sim[\sim(P \cdot Q) \text{ v} \sim\sim P]$ R′ 1

$\sim[(P \cdot Q) \cdot \sim P]$ df.

THEOREM 13. $\overline{|_{\text{HA}}} \sim \{\sim(P\cdot\sim Q)\cdot\sim\sim[\sim(Q\cdot R)\cdot\sim\sim(R\cdot P)]\}$

Proof: $(\sim\sim Q \supset Q) \supset [(P \supset \sim\sim Q) \supset (P \supset Q)]$ Th. 1

     $\sim\sim Q \supset Q$ Th. 6

     $(P \supset \sim\sim Q) \supset (P \supset Q)$ R' 1

     $(P \supset Q) \supset [\sim(Q\cdot R) \supset \sim(R\cdot P)]$ Th. 10

     $(P \supset \sim\sim Q) \supset [\sim(Q\cdot R) \supset \sim(R\cdot P)]$ DR' 1

     $[\sim(Q\cdot R) \supset \sim(R\cdot P)] \supset [\sim\sim(R\cdot P) \supset \sim\sim(Q\cdot R)]$ Th. 8

     $(P \supset \sim\sim Q) \supset [\sim\sim(R\cdot P) \supset \sim\sim(Q\cdot R)]$ DR' 1

     $(P \supset \sim\sim Q) \supset [\sim\sim\sim\sim(R\cdot P) \text{ v } \sim\sim(Q\cdot R)]$ df.

     $[\sim\sim\sim(R\cdot P) \text{ v } \sim\sim(Q\cdot R)] \supset$
                    $[\sim\sim(Q\cdot R) \text{ v } \sim\sim\sim(R\cdot P)]$ P 3

     $(P \supset \sim\sim Q) \supset [\sim\sim(Q\cdot R) \text{ v } \sim\sim\sim(R\cdot P)]$ DR' 1

     $(\sim P \text{ v } \sim\sim Q) \supset [\sim\sim(Q\cdot R) \text{ v } \sim\sim\sim(R\cdot P)]$ df.

     $\sim\sim(\sim P \text{ v } \sim\sim Q) \supset (\sim P \text{ v } \sim\sim Q)$ Th. 6

     $\sim\sim(\sim P \text{ v } \sim\sim Q) \supset [\sim\sim(Q\cdot R) \text{ v } \sim\sim\sim(R\cdot P)]$ DR' 1

     $[\sim\sim(Q\cdot R) \text{ v } \sim\sim\sim(R\cdot P)] \supset$
                    $\sim\sim[\sim\sim(Q\cdot R) \text{ v } \sim\sim\sim(R\cdot P)]$ Th. 4

     $\sim\sim(\sim P \text{ v } \sim\sim Q) \supset \sim\sim[\sim\sim(Q\cdot R) \text{ v }$
                         $\sim\sim\sim(R\cdot P)]$ DR' 1

     $\sim\sim[\sim\sim(Q\cdot R) \text{ v } \sim\sim\sim(R\cdot P)] \supset$
                    $\sim\sim\sim\sim[\sim\sim(Q\cdot R) \text{ v } \sim\sim\sim(R\cdot P)]$ Th. 4

     $\sim\sim(\sim P \text{ v } \sim\sim Q) \supset$
                    $\sim\sim\sim\sim[\sim\sim(Q\cdot R) \text{ v } \sim\sim\sim(R\cdot P)]$ DR' 1

     $\sim\sim\sim(\sim P \text{ v } \sim\sim Q) \text{ v }$
                    $\sim\sim\sim\sim[\sim\sim(Q\cdot R) \text{ v } \sim\sim\sim(R\cdot P)]$ df.

     $\{\sim\sim\sim(\sim P \text{ v } \sim\sim Q) \text{ v }$
        $\sim\sim\sim\sim[\sim\sim(Q\cdot R) \text{ v } \sim\sim\sim(R\cdot P)]\} \supset$
                $\sim\sim\{\sim\sim\sim(\sim P \text{ v } \sim\sim Q) \text{ v }$
                $\sim\sim\sim\sim[\sim\sim(Q\cdot R) \text{ v } \sim\sim\sim(R\cdot P)]\}$ Th. 4

     $\sim\sim\{\sim\sim\sim(\sim P \text{ v } \sim\sim Q) \text{ v }$
                $\sim\sim\sim\sim[\sim\sim(Q\cdot R) \text{ v } \sim\sim\sim(R\cdot P)]\}$ R' 1

     $\sim\sim\{\sim\sim(P\cdot\sim Q) \text{ v } \sim\sim\sim\sim[\sim(Q\cdot R)\cdot\sim\sim(R\cdot P)]\}$ df.

     $\sim\{\sim(P\cdot\sim Q)\cdot\sim\sim[\sim(Q\cdot R)\cdot\sim\sim(R\cdot P)]\}$ df.

We have now proved that Axioms 1, 2, and 3 of R.S. can be derived from the Hilbert-Ackermann System's Postulates 1, 2, 3, and 4 by repeated applications of R' 1. In the preceding chapter we proved that every tautology is derivable from Axioms 1, 2, and 3 of R.S. by repeated uses of R 1. If we can show that every *wff* derivable by R 1 is also derivable by R' 1, then we shall have proved that every tautology is derivable from Postulates 1, 2, 3, and 4 of H.A. by repeated uses of R 1. This will complete our proof of the deductive completeness of the Hilbert-Ackermann logistic system.

For any *wff* S to follow by its use, R 1 must be applied to two *wffs* of the structure R and $\sim(R{\cdot}\sim S)$. Thus to show that every *wff* derivable from any other *wffs* by R 1 is *also* derivable from those same *wffs* by R' 1, it will suffice to show that S follows from the *wffs* R and $\sim(R{\cdot}\sim S)$ by R' 1. This will be stated and proved as our

THIRD DERIVED RULE (DR' 3). $R, \sim(R{\cdot}\sim S) \;\big|_{\overline{HA}}\; S.$

Proof: $\sim(R{\cdot}\sim S)$ premiss
  $\sim\sim(\sim R \vee \sim\sim S)$ df.
  $\sim\sim(\sim R \vee \sim\sim S) \supset (\sim R \vee \sim\sim S)$ Th. 6
  $\sim R \vee \sim\sim S$ R' 1
  $R \supset \sim\sim S$ df.
  $\sim\sim S \supset S$ Th. 6
  $R \supset S$ DR' 1
  R premiss
  S R' 1

We have now completed our proof that H.A. is deductively complete. And since it is also functionally complete and analytic, the Hilbert-Ackermann System is a Model System of Logic.

EXERCISES

Prove each of the following to be Model Systems of Logic:

1. The simple system S.S. has as its primitive or undefined symbols, in addition to the propositional symbols $P, Q, R, S, \ldots$, and parentheses, the operator symbols $\sim$ and $\supset$. The axioms of S.S. are

    Ax. 1. $P \supset (Q \supset P)$
    Ax. 2. $[P \supset (Q \supset R)] \supset [(P \supset Q) \supset (P \supset R)]$
    Ax. 3. $(P \supset Q) \supset (\sim Q \supset \sim P)$

Ax. 4. $\sim\sim P \supset P$

Ax. 5. $P \supset \sim\sim P$

Ax. 6. $(P \supset \sim P) \supset \sim(\sim P \supset P)$

The rule of inference for S.S. is R_S 1: From P and $P \supset Q$ to infer Q. The definition of a *wff* of S.S. parallels the recursive definitions used in R.S. and H.A. The definitions of $P_1, P_2, \ldots, P_n \mathbin{\big|_{\overline{S}}} Q$ and of $\mathbin{\big|_{\overline{S}}} Q$ parallel those for R.S. and H.A. The syntactical definitions to be used are

$$P \vee Q = \mathrm{df} \sim P \supset Q$$
$$P \cdot Q = \mathrm{df} \sim (P \supset \sim Q)$$

2. Frege's system F.S. has the same primitive symbols as S.S. and the same rule of inference, the same recursive definition of *wff*, the same syntactical definition of $\vee$ and $\cdot$, but the different axioms:

Ax. 1. $P \supset (Q \supset P)$

Ax. 2. $[P \supset (Q \supset R)] \supset [(P \supset Q) \supset (P \supset R)]$

Ax. 3. $[P \supset (Q \supset R)] \supset [Q \supset (P \supset R)]$

Ax. 4. $(P \supset Q) \supset (\sim Q \supset \sim P)$

Ax. 5. $\sim\sim P \supset P$

Ax. 6. $P \supset \sim\sim P$

The definitions of $P_1, P_2, \ldots, P_n \mathbin{\big|_{\overline{F}}} Q$ and of $\mathbin{\big|_{\overline{F}}} Q$ are as usual.

3. Lukasiewicz's system L.S. is similar to S.S. and F.S. in undefined symbols, rules of inference, recursive definition of *wff*, syntactical definitions of $\vee$ and $\cdot$, but with only three axioms:

Ax. 1. $P \supset (Q \supset P)$

Ax. 2. $[P \supset (Q \supset R)] \supset [(P \supset Q) \supset (P \supset R)]$

Ax. 3. $(\sim P \supset \sim Q) \supset (Q \supset P)$

The definitions of $P_1, P_2, \ldots, P_n \mathbin{\big|_{\overline{L}}} Q$ and of $\mathbin{\big|_{\overline{L}}} Q$ are as usual.

8.3 THE USE OF DOTS AS BRACKETS

It has been remarked that the language of symbolic logic requires punctuation if ambiguity is to be avoided. It shares this characteristic with such natural languages as English, as well as with such other artificial languages as (ordinary) algebra. We have been using three kinds of punctuation marks in our logical language: ordinary parentheses, square brackets, and braces. In the following discussion it will be convenient to use the word 'brackets' to refer indifferently to all of these.

In even moderately complicated formulas it is necessary to use a considerable number of pairs of brackets, which often makes for difficulty in reading the formulas. Any use of paired punctuation marks involves redundancy. Let us consider the formula

$$(P \supset Q) \text{ v } (P \supset \sim Q)$$

in which *some* punctuation is necessary for the avoidance of ambiguity. Brackets are essential to it, but it need not contain *paired* brackets, for the outermost parentheses can be dropped without incurring any ambiguity, leaving

$$P \supset Q) \text{ v } (P \supset \sim Q$$

The same punctuation effect can be obtained by replacing the remaining parentheses by dots, which would give

$$P \supset Q . \text{ v } . P \supset \sim Q$$

There is no danger of confusing the punctuation dot with the conjunction dot because the punctuation dot can occur only adjacently to a connective symbol such as 'v', '$\supset$', or '$\equiv$', whereas the conjunction dot can never do so.

Dots are symmetrical in shape, in contrast to the asymmetry of brackets. Thus '(', '[', '{' are all concave on the right, which indicates that they group or 'operate toward' the right, while ')', ']', '}' are concave on and 'operate toward' the left. The symmetry of the dot notation is compensated for by introducing the convention that punctuation dots always operate *away* from the connective symbol to which they are adjacent.

There is another characteristic that the method of bracketing logical formulas shares with the method of punctuating sentences of natural languages. The latter have punctuation marks of different degrees of strength, the stronger of which 'take precedence over' or 'extend over' the weaker. For example, a period is stronger than a semicolon, and a semicolon is stronger than a comma. Of the three kinds of brackets used for punctuating our logical formulas, the unstated convention has been followed of regarding braces as stronger than square brackets, and square brackets as stronger than parentheses. We have used parentheses to group symbols *within* square brackets, but not conversely, and we have used square brackets to group symbols *within* braces, but not conversely. This usage was illustrated in the statement of Theorem 13 of the Hilbert-Ackermann system:

$$\sim\{\sim(P\cdot\sim Q)\cdot\sim\sim[\sim(QR)\cdot\sim\sim(RP)]\}$$

When this convention is adhered to, it permits the dropping of additional redundant brackets. Thus the formula

$$(P \supset Q) \supset [(R \vee P) \supset (R \vee Q)]$$

remains unambiguous when rewritten as

$$P \supset Q) \supset [R \vee P) \supset (R \vee Q$$

If we use a single dot in place of a parenthesis, and a double dot in place of a square bracket, the preceding formula can be rewritten as

$$P \supset Q \, . \supset : R \vee P \, . \supset . \, R \vee Q$$

where the convention is that two dots bind more strongly or have greater scope than one dot. Using three dots as a punctuation mark which has greater scope than either one or two dots, the seventh formula in the proof of Theorem 9 of H.A.,

$$[P \vee (Q \vee R)] \supset \{P \vee [Q \vee (P \vee R)]\}$$

can be rewritten as

$$P \vee . \, Q \vee R : \supset :. \, P \vee : Q \vee . \, P \vee R$$

In writing the sixth formula of that proof, we were forced to include one pair of braces within another, because we had only three kinds of brackets available. Now the use of dots permits the generation of as many different punctuation marks of different degrees of strength as may be desired, by the simple expedient of adding dots one at a time. The general convention here is that the scope of a group of n dots extends over that of any number of groups of less than n dots, and that the scope of a group of n dots extends to but not beyond the nearest group of n or more dots. The sixth formula of the proof of Theorem 9 of H.A.,

$$\{(Q \vee R) \supset [Q \vee (P \vee R)]\} \supset \{[P \vee (Q \vee R)] \supset \{P \vee [Q \vee (P \vee R)]\}\}$$

can be written as

$$Q \vee R . \supset : Q \vee . P \vee R :. \supset :: P \vee . Q \vee R : \supset :. P \vee : Q \vee . P \vee R$$

For the sake of symmetry and greater ease of reading, one frequently adds dots which are not strictly necessary for the avoidance of ambiguity. Thus the formula

$$P \supset . Q \supset P$$

is frequently written

$$P . \supset . Q \supset P$$

The preceding lengthy formula may be more easily read when rewritten according to this convention as

$$Q \vee R : \supset : Q. \vee . P \vee R :: \supset :: P. \vee . Q \vee R :. \supset :. P : \vee : Q . \vee . P \vee R$$

Now what should be done in case two bracketed expressions are connected by the conjunction symbol, as in the formula

$$(P \supset Q) \cdot (Q \supset P)$$

Applying the technique already described, we should emerge with the awkward expression

$$P \supset Q . \cdot . Q \supset P$$

To avoid this awkwardness, it is customary to let the conjunction dot itself do the bracketing, writing the formula simply as

$$P \supset Q.Q \supset P$$

Here the single dot is to be thought of as operating in *both* directions, left and right. This convention is satisfactory, as can be seen by observing that the different formulas

1. $P \supset [(Q.Q) \supset P]$
2. $[P \supset (Q.Q)] \supset P$
3. $[(P \supset Q).Q] \supset P$
4. $P \supset [Q.(Q \supset P)]$

can be written in distinguishable and unambiguous fashion as

1′. $P \supset :. Q.Q : \supset P$
2′. $P \supset : Q.Q :. \supset P$
3′. $P \supset Q.Q : \supset P$
4′. $P \supset : Q.Q \supset P$

The use of dots as brackets has the advantage of economy, and the further advantage of providing an infinite number of different punctuation marks of different degrees of strength, where the strength or scope of each may be determined by the simple expedient of counting its constituent dots.[4]

8.4   A PARENTHESIS-FREE NOTATION

A logical notation that dispenses with brackets entirely has been devised by the Polish logician, J. Lukasiewicz, and has been extensively used by logicians of the Polish School. Corresponding to the four most commonly used operator symbols

$$\sim \quad \supset \quad \cdot \quad v$$

are the four symbols

$$N \quad C \quad K \quad A$$

In writing their formulas they use lower case letters 'p', 'q', 'r', 's', . . . instead of the capital letters 'P', 'Q', 'R', 'S', . . . Instead of the connective symbols 'C', 'K', 'A' being written *between* the formulas they connect, they are placed directly to the left of the two formulas to be joined. Thus

$$\sim P \text{ is written } Np$$
$$P \supset Q \text{ is written } Cpq$$
$$P \cdot Q \text{ is written } Kpq$$
$$P v Q \text{ is written } Apq$$

[4] A more extended discussion of this topic will be found in *Symbolic Logic*, by C. I Lewis and C. H. Langford, New York, 1932, Appendix I, pp. 486–489. For more technical discussions, the reader is referred to 'On The Use of Dots as Brackets in Logical Expressions', by H. B. Curry, in *The Journal of Symbolic Logic*, vol. 2 (1937), pp. 26–28 and 'The Use of Dots as Brackets in Church's System', by A. M. Turing, *Ibid.*, vol. 7 (1942), pp. 146–156.

That this notation is unambiguous can be seen by comparing the following formulas:

$$P \supset (Q \supset R) \text{ is written } CpCqr$$
$$(P \supset Q) \supset R \text{ is written } CCpqr$$
$$P \supset (Q \cdot R) \text{ is written } CpKqr$$
$$(P \supset Q) \cdot R \text{ is written } KCpqr$$
$$(P \vee Q) \supset (R \cdot S) \text{ is written } CApqKrs$$

The axioms of R.S. translate into the Polish notation as

Ax. 1. *CpKpp*

Ax. 2. *CKpqp*

Ax. 3. *CCpqCNKqrNKrp*

And the three postulates of Lukasiewicz's own system are written in his notation as

P 1. *CpCqp*

P 2. *CCpCqrCCpqCpr*

P 3. *CCNqNpCpq*

The Polish notation has the obvious advantage of dispensing with all special punctuation marks, for the *order* in which its symbols are written suffices to make any formula unambiguous. And its use is becoming more widespread, especially in connection with computer work.[5]

EXERCISES

★1. Translate the postulates of H.A. into the Polish notation.

2. Translate the postulates of F.S. into the Polish notation.

8.5   THE STROKE AND DAGGER OPERATORS

Any of the following pairs of operators provide a functionally complete logic: $\sim$ and $\cdot$, $\sim$ and v, $\sim$ and $\supset$, or $\supset$ and $+$. We can construct a functionally complete system of logic containing just a single operator, and we can do it in either of two ways.

---

[5] Cf. *Truth-function Evaluation Using the Polish Notation*, by Arthur W. Burks, Don W. Warren, and Jesse Wright, Ann Arbor, Michigan, Engineering Research Institute of the University of Michigan.

The first of these ways is by adopting as the single primitive operator the so-called 'stroke function'. This operator symbol, called 'alternative denial' by Quine,[6] operates on or connects two formulas and is written '$P|Q$'. Its standard interpretation is that of denying that both of the formulas P and Q are true, which is the same as affirming that at least one is false. It is defined by the truth table

P	Q	$P|Q$
T	T	F
T	F	T
F	T	T
F	F	T

The other operators, $\sim$, $\cdot$, v, and $\supset$ can all be defined in terms of the stroke function. That the following definitions preserve the standard interpretations of the symbols being defined is easily verified by the method of truth tables:

$$\sim P = \text{df} \quad P|P$$
$$P.Q = \text{df} \quad P|Q.|.P|Q$$
$$P \text{ v } Q = \text{df} \quad P|P.|.Q|Q$$
$$P \supset Q = \text{df} \quad P.|.Q|Q$$

The other operator which suffices for a functionally complete logic is that of 'joint denial', symbolized by a dagger with its point down. Written '$P{\downarrow}Q$', its standard interpretation is that of denying that either of the formulas P or Q is true, which is the same as affirming that they are both false. It is defined by the truth table

P	Q	$P{\downarrow}Q$
T	T	F
T	F	F
F	T	F
F	F	T

[6] Cf. pp. 48–49 of *Mathematical Logic*, by W. V. O. Quine, Cambridge, Mass., Harvard University Press, 1947. The stroke function is frequently referred to as the 'Sheffer stroke function' after Professor H. M. Sheffer, although it was first discovered by C. S. Peirce.

The other operators can all be defined in terms of the dagger function alone. That the following definitions preserve the standard interpretations of the symbols being defined is easily verified by the method of truth tables:

$$\sim P = df \quad P{\downarrow}P$$
$$P.Q = df \quad P{\downarrow}P.{\downarrow}.Q{\downarrow}Q$$
$$P \vee Q = df \quad P{\downarrow}Q.{\downarrow}.P{\downarrow}Q$$
$$P \supset Q = df \quad P{\downarrow}P.{\downarrow}.Q{:}{\downarrow}{:}P{\downarrow}P.{\downarrow}.Q$$

Thus we see that functionally complete systems of logic based on only one operator can be constructed in terms either of the stroke or the dagger. It is interesting to note the parallelism between the definition of the stroke function in terms of the dagger and the definition of the dagger function in terms of the stroke. These are

$$P{\downarrow}Q = df \quad P|P.|.Q|Q{:}|{:}P|P.|.Q|Q$$
$$P|Q = df \quad P{\downarrow}P.{\downarrow}.Q{\downarrow}Q{:}{\downarrow}{:}P{\downarrow}P.{\downarrow}.Q{\downarrow}Q$$

as may easily be verified.

EXERCISES

1. Express Ax. 1 of R.S. in terms of the stroke function.
★2. Express Ax. 1 of R.S. in terms of the dagger function.
3. Express P 1 of H.A. in terms of the dagger function.
4. Express Ax. 3 of R.S. in terms of the stroke function.
5. Express Ax. 1 of L.S. in terms of the dagger function.
★6. Express Ax. 2 of R.S. in terms of the stroke function.
7. Express Ax. 5 of F.S. in terms of the stroke function.
★8. Express Ax. 5 of S.S. in terms of the dagger function.
9. Express Ax. 1 of F.S. in terms of the stroke function.
10. Express P 2 of H.A. in terms of the dagger function.

8.6 THE NICOD SYSTEM

Thus far in the text and exercises, a number of alternative Model Systems of Logic have been set forth. Each of them is based on two primitive operator symbols, and the number of their axioms or postulates ranges from three (for R.S. and L.S.) to six (for S.S. and F.S.). A system that is more economical both in primitive operators and postulates is due to J. G. P. Nicod.[7] The Nicod System can be set forth as follows.

The primitive symbols are infinitely many propositional symbols P, Q, R, S, T, with and without subscripts, parentheses (or dots), and the single operator symbol '$|$'. The recursive rule for well formed formulas in N may be stated as:

1. Any single letter of N is a *wff*.
2. If P and Q are *wffs*, then $(P)|(Q)$ is a *wff*.

(No formula of N will be regarded as being a *wff* unless its being so follows from this definition.)

It should be noted that even the recursive rule for well formed formulas is simpler in the Nicod System, needing only two rather than three clauses. We have here the first fruit of using only one operator symbol.

The single axiom required (or rather, the single pattern for infinitely many axioms of the object logic) is stated in our metalanguage, in which we use dots for brackets, as

$$\text{Ax. } P.|.Q|R:|::T.|.T|T:.|:.S|Q:|:P|S.|.P|S$$

The single rule of inference required may be stated as

RULE.   From P and $P.|.R|Q$ to infer Q.

The definitions of 'valid argument in N' and of 'theorem of N', that is, of

$$P_1, P_2, \ldots, P_n|_{\overline{\text{N}}} Q \qquad \text{and} \qquad |_{\overline{\text{N}}} P$$

are strictly analogous to those given for '$|_{\overline{\text{RS}}}$', '$|_{\overline{\text{HA}}}$', '$|_{\overline{\text{S}}}$', '$|_{\overline{\text{F}}}$', and '$|_{\overline{\text{L}}}$'.

Although more economical in the respects indicated, the Nicod System can scarcely be said to be *simpler* than such systems as R.S., H.A., F.S. and L.S. There is only one axiom for N, but it is more com-

[7] 'A Reduction in the Number of the Primitive Propositions of Logic', by J. G. P. Nicod, *Proceedings of the Cambridge Philosophical Society*, vol. 19 (1916), pp. 32–40. Cf. also

A Treatise of Formal Logic, by J. Jørgensen, London, 1931, vol. 2, pp. 149–172.

'A Note on Nicod's Postulate', by W. V. Quine, *Mind*, n.s. vol. 41 (1932), pp. 345–350.

'Remark on Nicod's Reduction of *Principia Mathematica*', by B. A. Bernstein, *The Journal of Symbolic Logic*, vol. 2 (1937), pp. 165–166.

'Axiomatization of Propositional Calculus with Sheffer Functors', by Thomas W. Scharle, *Notre Dame Journal of Formal Logic*, vol. VI (1965), pp. 209–217.

plicated than any axiom or postulate of any of the other systems. Not only is it longer, but it involves five distinct propositional symbols, '*P*', '*Q*', '*R*', '*S*', and '*T*', whereas the entire set of axioms for any of the other systems can be stated in terms of only three distinct propositional symbols. The situation is similar with respect to the rules of inference of the several systems. The Nicod Rule is not *Modus Ponens*, but a more powerful instrument for deduction. *Modus Ponens*, which may be stated as

From *P* and *P*.|.*Q*|*Q* to infer *Q*

is simply a special case of the Nicod Rule, in which '*R*' and '*Q*' denote identically the same well formed formula of the object language. Nicod's Rule as well as his axiom is more complicated than those required in less economical systems of logic.

That the Nicod System is functionally complete has already been indicated in our discussion of the stroke function in Section 8.5. The analyticity of N is simply enough shown by establishing via truth tables that the Axiom is tautologous, and that the Rule can lead only to tautologies from tautologies. The deductive completeness of N remains to be proved to complete the proof that the Nicod System is a Model Logic. When this is attempted we find that for all the economy of its single axiom and the greater deductive strength of its Rule, it is very difficult indeed to derive theorems in the Nicod System. Nevertheless it is interesting from the point of view of seeing how far one can go in the direction of reducing the number of postulates and still have a deductively complete system of logic.

We shall develop seventeen theorems of the Nicod System, and one derived rule. The last four theorems will be the four axioms of the Hilbert-Ackermann System, and the derived rule will be the Hilbert-Ackermann System's rule R′ 1. Of course these must be stated in their unabbreviated form, and then expressed in the Nicod System's notation. The Hilbert-Ackermann axioms, expressed in terms of that system's primitive symbols $\sim$ and v are

1. $\sim(P \text{ v } P) \text{ v } P$
2. $\sim P \text{ v } (P \text{ v } Q)$
3. $\sim(P \text{ v } Q) \text{ v } (Q \text{ v } P)$
4. $\sim(\sim P \text{ v } Q) \text{ v } [\sim(R \text{ v } P) \text{ v } (R \text{ v } Q)]$

The Hilbert-Ackermann rule, similarly unabbreviated, is

$$\text{From } P \text{ and } {\sim}P \text{ v } Q \text{ to infer } Q$$

These, expressed in the Nicod System's notation, in which '${\sim}P$' is written '$P|P$', and 'P v Q' is written '$P|P.|.Q|Q$', are

1. $P|P.|.P|P:|:P|P.|.P|P:.|:.P|P.|.P|P:|:P|P.|.P|P::|::P|P.$
2. $P|P.|.P|P:.|:.P|P.|.Q|Q:|:P|P.|.Q|Q.$
3. $P|P.|.Q|Q:|:P|P.|.Q|Q:.|:.P|P.|.Q|Q:|:P|P.|.Q|Q:::|:::Q|Q.|.P|P:|:Q|Q.|.$ $P|P.$
4. $P|P.|.P|P:|:Q|Q:.|:.P|P.|.P|P:|:Q|Q::|::P|P.|.P|P:|:Q|Q:.|:.P|P.|.$ $P|P:|:Q|Q:::|:::R|R.|.P|P:|:R|R.|.P|P:.|:.R|R.|.P|P:|:R|R.|.P|P::|::$ $R|R.|.Q|Q:|:R|R.|.Q|Q:.|:.R|R.|.P|P:|:R|R.|.P|P:.|:.R|R.|.P|P:|:R|$ $R.|.P|P::|::R|R.|.Q|Q:|:R|R.|.Q|Q.$

R′ 1. From P and $P|P.|.P|P:|:Q|Q$ to infer Q.

Our development of the Nicod System will be entirely in terms of the stroke function. Since the formulas of the proofs are of almost intolerable length, they will be *described* rather than written out. Our descriptions, however, will be sufficiently complete to permit the reader to write them out for himself.

THEOREM 1. $\vdash_{\overline{N}} Q:.|:.T.|.T|T:|:S::.|:::.S:|:T.|.T|T:.|:.Q::|:::S:|:T.|$ $T|T:.|:.Q.$

Proof: Step 1 is the Nicod Axiom with T in place of P, of Q, and of R. Step 2 is the Nicod Axiom with $T.|.T|T$ in place of P and of Q, and with $S|T:|:T|S.|.T|S$ in place of R. Step 3 is the result of applying the Nicod Rule to steps 1 and 2. Step 4 is the Nicod Axiom with $S:|:T.|.T|T$ in place of P, with $T.|.T|T:|:S$ in place of Q and of R, and with Q in place of S. Step 5 is the result of applying the Nicod Rule to Steps 3 and 4.

THEOREM 2. $\vdash_{\overline{N}} T.|.T|T$

Proof: Step 1 is Theorem 1 with $T.|.T|T$ in place of Q, and with $S|T:|:T|S.|.T|S$ in place of S. Step 2 is the Nicod Axiom with $T.|.T|$ $T::|::T.|.T|T:.|:.S|T:|:T|S.|.T|S$ in place of P, with $S|T:|:T|S.|.T|S:.|$ $:.T.|.T|T::|::T.|.T|T$ in place of Q and of R, and with $S|T:::|:::S|T:$ $|:T|S.|.T|S:.|:.T.|.T|T|T::|:::S::.|:::.S|T:|:T|S.|.T|S:.|:.T.|.T|T|T::|::S::::|$

$::.T.|.T|T$ in place of S. Step 3 is the result of applying the Nicod Rule to steps 1 and 2. Step 4 is the Nicod Axiom with $S|T:|:T|S.|.T|$ $S:.|:.T.|.T|T$ in place of P, with T in place of Q, and with $T|T$ in place of R. Step 5 is Theorem 1 with $S|T:|:T|S.|.T|S:.|:.T.|.T|T::|$ $::T.|.T|T$ in place of Q and with $S|T:::|:::S|T:|:T|S.|.T|S:.|:.T.|.T|T:::$ $|::S:.|::.S|T:|:T|S.|.T|S:.|:.T.|.T|T::|:::S$ in place of S. Step 6 is the result of applying the Nicod Rule to steps 4 and 5. Step 7 is the result of applying the Nicod Rule to steps 3 and 6. Step 8 is the Nicod Axiom with T in place of P, of Q, and of R. Step 9 is the result of applying the Nicod Rule to steps 7 and 8.

THEOREM 3. $|_{\overline{\text{N}}}\ S|P:|:P|S.|.P|S$

Proof: Step 1 is the Nicod Axiom with P in place of Q and of R. Step 2 is Theorem 2 with P in place of T. Step 3 is the result of applying the Nicod Rule to steps 1 and 2.

THEOREM 4. $|_{\overline{\text{N}}}\ P|P.|.P$

Proof: Step 1 is Theorem 3 with $P|P$ in place of P and with P in place of S. Step 2 is Theorem 2 with P in place of T. Step 3 is the result of applying the Nicod Rule to steps 1 and 2.

THEOREM 5. $|_{\overline{\text{N}}}\ P|P:|:S|P.|.S|P$

Proof: Step 1 is Theorem 3 with $P|S$ in place of S and with $S|P.|.S|P$ in place of P. Step 2 is Theorem 3 with P in place of S and S in place of P. Step 3 is the result of applying the Nicod Rule to steps 1 and 2. Step 4 is the Nicod Axiom with $S|P.|.S|P$ in place of P, with P in place of Q, with S in place of R, and with $P|P$ in place of S. Step 5 is the result of applying the Nicod Rule to steps 3 and 4. Step 6 is Theorem 4. Step 7 is the result of applying the Nicod Rule to steps 5 and 6. Step 8 is Theorem 3 with $S|P.|.S|P$ in place of S, and with $P|P$ in place of P. Step 9 is the result of applying the Nicod Rule to steps 7 and 8.

THEOREM 6. $|_{\overline{\text{N}}}\ P.|.Q|R::|:::S|Q:|:P|S.|.P|S:.|:..S|Q:|:P|S.|.P|S$

Proof: Step 1 is the Nicod Axiom with $S|Q:|:P|S.|.P|S:.|:..S|Q:|:$ $P|S.|.P|S$ in place of P, with $T.|.T|T:.|:..S|Q:|:P|S.|.P|S$ in place of Q and of R, and with $P.|.Q|R$ in place of S. Step 2 is Theorem 5 with $S|Q:|:P|S.|.P|S$ in place of P, and with $T.|.T|T$ in place of S. Step 3 is the result of applying the Nicod Rule to steps 1 and 2. Step 4 is the

Nicod Axiom. Step 5 is the result of applying the Nicod Rule to steps 3 and 4. Step 6 is Theorem 3 with $S|Q:|:P|S.|.P|S:.|:.S|Q:|:P|S.|.P|S$ in place of S, and with $P.|.Q|R$ in place of P. Step 7 is the result of applying the Nicod Rule to steps 5 and 6.

THEOREM 7. $|_{\overline{N}}\ Q|S.|.U:|:Q|S.|.U:.|:.S|Q.|.U$

Proof: Step 1 is Theorem 6 with $Q|S$ in place of P, with $S|Q$ in place of Q and of R, and with U in place of S. Step 2 is Theorem 3 with Q in place of S and with S in place of P. Step 3 is the result of applying the Nicod Rule to steps 1 and 2. Step 4 is Theorem 3 with $U.|.S|Q$ in place of S and with $Q|S.|.U:|:Q|S.|.U$ in place of P. Step 5 is the result of applying the Nicod Rule to steps 3 and 4. Step 6 is Theorem 6 with $S|Q.|.U$ in place of P, with $U.|.S|Q$ in place of Q and of R, and with $Q|S.|.U:|:Q|S.|.U$ in place of S. Step 7 is Theorem 3 with $S|Q$ in place of S and with U in place of P. Step 8 is the result of applying the Nicod Rule to steps 6 and 7. Step 9 is the result of applying the Nicod Rule to steps 5 and 8. Step 10 is Theorem 3 with $S|Q.|.U$ in place of S, and with $Q|S.|.U:|:Q|S.|.U$ in place of P. Step 11 is the result of applying the Nicod Rule to steps 9 and 10.

THEOREM 8. $|_{\overline{N}}\ P.|.Q|R::|:::Q|S:|:P|S.|.P|S:.|:.Q|S:|:P|S.|.P|S$

Proof: Step 1 is Theorem 6 with $P.|.Q|R$ in place of P, with $S|Q:|$ $:P|S.|.P|S$ in place of Q and of R, and with $Q|S:|:P|S.|.P|S:.|:.Q|S:|:$ $P|S.|.P|S$ in place of S. Step 2 is Theorem 6. Step 3 is the result of applying the Nicod Rule to steps 1 and 2. Step 4 is Theorem 7 with $P|S.|.P|S$ in place of U. Step 5 is the result of applying the Nicod Rule to steps 3 and 4.

THEOREM 9. $|_{\overline{N}}\ S:.|:.P.|.S|S:|:P.|.S|S$

Proof: Step 1 is Theorem 3 with $S|S.|.P$ in place of S, and with $P.|.S|S:|:P.|.S|S$ in place of P. Step 2 is Theorem 1 with $S|S$ in place of S. Step 3 is the result of applying the Nicod Rule to steps 1 and 2. Step 4 is the Nicod Axiom with $P.|.S|S:|:P.|.S|S$ in place of P, with $S|S$ in place of Q, and with P in place of R. Step 5 is the result of applying the Nicod Rule to steps 3 and 4. Step 6 is Theorem 2 with S in place of T. Step 7 is the result of applying the Nicod Rule to steps 5 and 6. Step 8 is Theorem 3 with $P.|.S|S:|:P.|.S|S$ in place of S, and with S in place of P. Step 9 is the result of applying the Nicod Rule to steps 7 and 8.

THEOREM 10. $\vert_{\overline{N}}\ Q\vert Q\text{:}\vert\text{:}Q\vert S.\vert.Q\vert S$

Proof: Step 1 is Theorem 8 with $Q\vert Q$ in place of P, with $S\vert Q$ in place of Q and of R, and with $Q\vert S.\vert.Q\vert S$ in place of S. Step 2 is Theorem 5 with Q in place of P. Step 3 is the result of applying the Nicod Rule to steps 1 and 2. Step 4 is Theorem 3 with Q in place of P. Step 5 is the result of applying the Nicod Rule to steps 3 and 4.

THEOREM 11. $\vert_{\overline{N}}\ Q\text{:.}\vert\text{:.}Q\vert P.\vert.P\text{:}\vert\text{:}Q\vert P.\vert.P$

Proof: Step 1 is Theorem 8 with Q in place of R and with P in place of S. Step 2 is Theorem 9 with Q in place of S. Step 3 is Theorem 8 with Q in place of P, with $P.\vert.Q\vert Q$ in place of Q and of R, and with $Q\vert P\text{:}\vert\text{:}$ $P\vert P.\vert.P\vert P\text{:.}\vert\text{:.}Q\vert P\text{:}\vert\text{:}P\vert P.\vert.P\vert P$ in place of S. Step 4 is the result of applying the Nicod Rule to steps 2 and 3. Step 5 is the result of applying the Nicod Rule to steps 1 and 4. Step 6 is Theorem 9 with $P\vert P.\vert.P$ in place of S and with Q in place of P. Step 7 is Theorem 4. Step 8 is the result of applying the Nicod Rule to steps 6 and 7. Step 9 is Theorem 8 with $Q\vert P$ in place of P, with $P\vert P$ in place of Q and of R, and with P in place of S. Step 10 is Theorem 8 with Q in place of P, with $Q\vert P\text{:}\vert\text{:}P\vert P.\vert.P\vert P$ in place of Q and of R, and with $P\vert P.\vert.P\text{:.}\vert\text{:.}Q\vert P.\vert.P\text{:}\vert\text{:}Q\vert P.\vert.P\text{::}\vert\text{::}P\vert P.\vert.P\text{:.}\vert$ $\text{:.}Q\vert P.\vert.P\text{:}\vert\text{:}Q\vert P.\vert.P$ in place of S. Step 11 is the result of applying the Nicod Rule to steps 5 and 10. Step 12 is the result of applying the Nicod Rule to steps 9 and 11. Step 13 is Theorem 8 with Q in place of P, with $P\vert P.\vert.P$ in place of Q and of R, and with $Q\vert P.\vert.P\text{:}\vert\text{:}Q\vert P.\vert.P$ in place of S. Step 14 is the result of applying the Nicod Rule to steps 8 and 13. Step 15 is Theorem 8 with Q in place of P, with $P\vert P.\vert.P\text{:.}\vert\text{:.}Q\vert P.\vert.P\text{:}\vert\text{:}Q\vert P.\vert.P$ in place of Q and of R, and with $Q\text{:.}\vert\text{:.}Q\vert P.\vert.P\text{:}\vert\text{:}Q\vert P.\vert.P\text{::}\vert\text{::}Q\text{:.}\vert\text{:.}Q\vert P.\vert.$ $P\text{:}\vert\text{:}Q\vert P.\vert.P$ in place of S. Step 16 is the result of applying the Nicod Rule to steps 12 and 15. Step 17 is the result of applying the Nicod Rule to steps 14 and 16. Step 18 is Theorem 10 with $Q\vert P.\vert.P\text{:}\vert\text{:}Q\vert P.\vert.P$ in place of S. Step 19 is Theorem 3 with $Q\vert Q$ in place of S, and with $Q\text{:.}\vert\text{:.}$ $Q\vert P.\vert.P\text{:}\vert\text{:}Q\vert P.\vert.P\text{::}\vert\text{::}Q\text{:.}\vert\text{:.}Q\vert P.\vert.P\text{:}\vert\text{:}Q\vert P.\vert.P$ in place of P. Step 20 is the result of applying the Nicod Rule to steps 18 and 19. Step 21 is Theorem 8 with $Q\text{:.}\vert\text{:.}Q\vert P.\vert.P\text{:}\vert\text{:}Q\vert P.\vert.P\text{::}\vert\text{::}Q\text{:.}\vert\text{:.}Q\vert P.\vert.P\text{:}\vert\text{:}Q\vert P.\vert.P$ in place of P and of S, and with Q in place of R. Step 22 is the result of applying the

Nicod Rule to steps 20 and 21. Step 23 is the result of applying the Nicod Rule to steps 17 and 22. Step 24 is Theorem 4 with $Q{:}.|{:}.Q|P.|.$ $P{:}|{:}Q|P.|.P{::}|{::}Q{:}.|{:}.Q|P.|.P{:}|{:}Q|P.|.P$ in place of P. Step 25 is the result of applying the Nicod Rule to steps 23 and 24.

THEOREM 12. $|_\overline{N}\ P{:}|{:}Q|R.|.Q|R{::}|{::}Q{:}|{:}P|R.|.P|R{:}.|{:}.Q{:}|{:}P|R.|.P|R$

Proof: Step 1 is Theorem 8 with Q in place of P, with $Q|R.|.R$ in place of Q and of R, and with $P|R.|.P|R$ in place of S. Step 2 is Theorem 11 with R in place of P. Step 3 is the result of applying the Nicod Rule to steps 1 and 2. Step 4 is Theorem 8 with $P{:}|{:}Q|R.|.Q|R$ in place of P, with $Q|R.|.R{:}|{:}P|R.|.P|R$ in place of Q and of R, and with $Q{:}|{:}P|R.|.$ $P|R{:}.|{:}.Q{:}|{:}P|R.|.P|R$ in place of S. Step 5 is Theorem 8 with $Q|R$ in place of Q and of R, and with R in place of S. Step 6 is the result of applying the Nicod Rule to steps 4 and 5. Step 7 is the result of applying the Nicod Rule to steps 3 and 6.

THEOREM 13. $|_\overline{N}\ P.|.Q|Q{::}.|{::}.R|R.|.P|P{:}.|{:}.R|R.|.Q|Q{:}|{:}R|R.|.Q|Q{::}|{::}R$ $|R.|.P|P{:}.|{:}.R|R.|.Q|Q{:}|{:}R|R.|.Q|Q$

Proof: Step 1 is Theorem 12 with $R|R.|.P|P$ in place of P, with $P.|.Q|Q$ in place of Q, and with $R|R.|.Q|Q{:}|{:}R|R.|.Q|Q$ in place of R. Step 2 is Theorem 8 with $R|R$ in place of P, with P in place of Q and of R, and with $Q|Q$ in place of S. Step 3 is the result of applying the Nicod Rule to steps 1 and 2.

THEOREM 14. $|_\overline{N}\ P|P.|.P|P{:}|{:}P|P.|.P|P{:}.|{:}.P|P.|.P|P{:}|{:}P|P.|.P|P{::}|{::}P|P$ (Ax. 1 of H.A.)

Proof: Step 1 is Theorem 4 with $P|P.|.P|P{:}|{:}P|P.|.P|P$ in place of P. Step 2 is Theorem 4 with $P|P$ in place of P. Step 3 is Theorem 8 with $P|P.|.P|P{:}|{:}P|P.|.P|P{:}.|{:}.P|P.|.P|P{:}|{:}P|P.|.P|P$ in place of P, with $P|P.|.$ $P|P$ in place of Q and of R, and with $P|P$ in place of S. Step 4 is the result of applying the Nicod Rule to steps 1 and 3. Step 5 is the result of applying the Nicod Rule to steps 2 and 4.

THEOREM 15. $|_\overline{N}\ P|P.|.P|P{:}.|{:}.P|P.|.Q|Q{:}|{:}P|P.|.Q|Q$ (Ax. 2 of H.A.)

Proof: Step 1 is Theorem 10 with $P|P$ in place of Q, and with $Q|Q$ in place of S.

THEOREM 16. $|_\overline{N}\ P|P.|.Q|Q{:}|{:}P|P.|.Q|Q{:}.|{:}.P|P.|.Q|Q{:}|{:}P|P.|.Q|Q{::}|{::}Q|$ $Q.|.P|P{:}|{:}Q|Q.|.P|P$ (Ax. 3 of H.A.)

Proof: Step 1 is Theorem 3 with $P|P$ in place of S, and with $Q|Q$ in place of P. Step 2 is Theorem 4 with $P|P.|.Q|Q:|:P|P.|.Q|Q$ in place of P. Step 3 is Theorem 8 with $P|P.|.Q|Q:|:P|P.|.Q|Q:.|:.P|P.|.Q|Q:|:$ $P|P.|.Q|Q$ in place of P, with $P|P.|.Q|Q$ in place of Q and of R, and with $Q|Q.|.P|P:|:Q|Q.|.P|P$ in place of S. Step 4 is the result of applying the Nicod Rule to steps 2 and 3. Step 5 is the result of applying the Nicod Rule to steps 1 and 4.

THEOREM 17. $\overline{\text{N}}$ $P|P.|.P|P:|:Q|Q:.|:.P|P.|.P|P:|:Q|Q::|::P|P.|.P|P:|:$ $Q|Q:.|:.P|P.|.P|P:|:Q|Q:::|:::R|R.|.P|P:|:R|R.|.P|P:.|:.R|R.|.P|P:|:R|R.|.$ $P|P:.|:.R|R.|.Q|Q:|:R|R.|.Q|Q:.|:.R|R.|.P|P:|:R|R.|.P|P:.|:.R|R.|.P|P:|:$ $R|R.|.P|P::|::R|R.|.Q|Q:|:R|R.|.Q|Q$ (Ax. 4 of H.A.)

Proof: Step 1 is Theorem 4 with $P|P.|.P|P:|:Q|Q:.|:.P|P.|.P|P:|:Q|Q$ in place of P. Step 2 is Theorem 9 with P for S and $P|P$ for P. Step 3 is Theorem 8 with $P|P.|.P|P$ in place of Q and of R, and with $Q|Q$ in place of S. Step 4 is the result of applying the Nicod Rule to steps 2 and 3. Step 5 is Theorem 8 with $P|P.|.P|P:|:Q|Q:.|:.P|P.|.P|P:|:Q|Q::|::P|P.|.$ $P|P:|:Q|Q:.|:.P|P.|.P|P:|:Q|Q$ in place of P, with $P|P.|.P|P:|:Q|Q$ in place of Q and of R, and with $P.|.Q|Q:|:P.|.Q|Q$ in place of S. Step 6 is the result of applying the Nicod Rule to steps 1 and 5. Step 7 is the result of applying the Nicod Rule to steps 4 and 6. Step 8 is Theorem 13. Step 9 is Theorem 4 with $R|R.|.P|P:|:R|R.|.P|P$ in place of P. Step 10 is Theorem 8 with $R|R.|.P|P:|:R|R.|.P|P:.|:.R|R.|.P|P:|:R|R.|.P|P$ in place of P, with $R|R.|.P|P$ in place of Q and of R, and with $R|R.|.Q|Q:|:$ $R|R.|.Q|Q$ in place of S. Step 11 is the result of applying the Nicod Rule to steps 9 and 10. Step 12 is Theorem 8 with $P.|.Q|Q$ in place of P, with $R|R.|.P|P:.|:.R|R.|.Q|Q:|:R|R.|.Q|Q$ in place of Q and of R, and with $R|R.|.P|P:|:R|R.|.P|P:.|:.R|R.|.P|P:|:R|R.|.P|P::|::R|R.|.Q|Q:|:R|R.|.$ $Q|Q::.|::.R|R.|.P|P:|:R|R.|.P|P:.|:.R|R.|.P|P:|:R|R.|.P|P::|::R|R.|.Q|Q$ $:|:R|R.|.Q|Q$ in place of S. Step 13 is the result of applying the Nicod Rule to steps 8 and 12. Step 14 is the result of applying the Nicod Rule to steps 11 and 13. Step 15 is Theorem 8 with $P|P.|.P|P:|:Q|Q:.|:.P|P.|.$ $P|P:|:Q|Q::|::P|P.|.P|P:|:Q|Q:.|:.P|P.|.P|P:|:Q|Q$ in place of P, with $P.|.Q|Q$ in place of Q and of R, and with $R|R.|.P|P:|:R|R.|.P|P:.|:.R|R.|.$ $P|P:|:R|R.|.P|P::|::R|R.|.Q|Q:|:R|R.|.Q|Q::.|::.R|R.|.P|P:|:R|R.|.P|P:.|$ $:.R|R.|.P|P:|:R|R.|.P|P::|::R|R.|.Q|Q:|:R|R.|.Q|Q$ in place of S. Step 16 is the result of applying the Nicod Rule to steps 7 and 15. Step 17 is the result of applying the Nicod Rule to steps 14 and 16.

DR 1. $P, P|P.|.P|P:|:Q|Q \quad |_{\overline{N}} Q$ (R' 1 of H.A.)

Proof: Step 1 is Theorem 9 with P in place of S, and with $P|P$ in place of P. Step 2 is the premiss P. Step 3 is the result of applying the Nicod Rule to steps 1 and 2. Step 4 is the premiss $P|P.|.P|P:|:Q|Q$. Step 5 is the result of applying the Nicod Rule to steps 3 and 4.

Deriving all tautologies from a single axiom (axiom form) by a single rule in terms of a single operator is thus seen to be possible. But it is a tedious business. As Dr. Samuel Johnson is said to have remarked about a woman preaching, it is '. . . like a dog's walking on his hind legs. It is not done well; but you are surprised to find it done at all.'

9

A
FIRST-ORDER
FUNCTION
CALCULUS

9.1 THE NEW LOGISTIC SYSTEM RS₁

In Chapter 4 and the first four sections of Chapter 5 we *used* logical principles governing the quantification of individual variables to prove the validity of arguments and to demonstrate logical truths. An axiomatic development of those principles is called a 'first-order function calculus', or, alternatively, a 'lower' or 'restricted' function calculus.[1] In this chapter we construct such a logistic system, develop some of its theorems, and prove that it has such (desirable) properties as consistency and completeness—of a sort. Again our metalanguage will be ordinary English plus some elementary arithmetic, and some special symbols that will be introduced and defined as needed. Our object language or object logic is the new system RS_1 which will now be described.

The logistic system RS_1 contains infinitely many primitive symbols, of the following categories.

---

[1] Also a 'first-order', 'lower', or 'restricted' *predicate* calculus.

1. Infinitely many capital letters from the first part of the alphabet, with and without subscripts:

$$A, B, C, A_1, B_1, C_1, A_2, B_2, C_2, \ldots$$

These will be referred to as *propositional constants*, and on the system's intended interpretation will express noncompound propositions.

2. Infinitely many capital letters from the middle part of the alphabet, with and without subscripts:

$$P, Q, R, P_1, Q_1, R_1, P_2, Q_2, R_2, \ldots$$

These will be referred to as *propositional variables*, and on the system's intended interpretation will be statement variables of the kind discussed in Section 2.3 of Chapter 2. Symbols of the first two categories will be referred to as *propositional symbols*.

3. Infinitely many capital letters from the first part of the alphabet, with and without subscripts, having right-hand superscripts '1', '2', '3'. . . .

$$A^1, B^1, C^1, A_1^1, B_1^1, C_1^1, A_2^1, B_2^1, C_2^1, \ldots$$
$$A^2, B^2, C^2, A_1^2, B_1^2, C_1^2, A_2^2, B_2^2, C_2^2, \ldots$$
$$A^3, B^3, C^3, A_1^3, B_1^3, C_1^3, A_2^3, B_2^3, C_2^3, \ldots$$

. . . .

. . . .

These will be referred to as *predicate constants*, and on the system's intended interpretation each of them will designate a particular property or dyadic relation or triadic relation . . . or n-adic relation according as its right superscript is '1' or '2' or '3' or . . . or 'n'.

4. Infinitely many capital letters from the middle part of the alphabet, with and without subscripts, having right-hand superscripts '1', '2', '3', . . .

$$P^1, Q^1, R^1, P_1^1, Q_1^1, R_1^1, P_2^1, Q_2^1, R_2^1, \ldots$$
$$P^2, Q^2, R^2, P_1^2, Q_1^2, R_1^2, P_2^2, Q_2^2, R_2^2, \ldots$$
$$P^3, Q^3, R^3, P_1^3, Q_1^3, R_1^3, P_2^3, Q_2^3, R_2^3, \ldots$$

. . . .

. . . .

These will be referred to as *predicate variables*, and on the system's intended interpretation will be symbols for which names of particular properties, dyadic relations, etc., can be substituted. Symbols of the third and fourth categories will be referred to as *predicate symbols*.

5. Infinitely many lower case letters from the first part of the alphabet, with and without subscripts:

$$a, \; b, \; c, \; a_1, \; b_1, \; c_1, \; a_2, \; b_2, \; c_2, \; \cdot \; \cdot \; \cdot$$

These will be referred to as *individual constants*, and on the system's intended interpretation will be proper names of individuals.

6. Infinitely many lower case letters from the latter part of the alphabet, with and without subscripts:

$$x, \; y, \; z, \; x_1, \; y_1, \; z_1, \; x_2, \; y_2, \; z_2, \; \cdot \; \cdot \; \cdot$$

These will be referred to as *individual variables*, and on the system's intended interpretation will be individual variables of the kind discussed in Chapter 4. Symbols of the fifth and sixth categories will be referred to as *individual symbols*.

7. Just four additional symbols complete the list of primitive symbols of RS₁; these are the tilde, the dot, and left- and right-hand parentheses:

$$\sim, \; \cdot \; , \; (, \;)$$

In addition to the primitive symbols we introduce some defined symbols into our object language RS₁. Before doing so, however, we must indicate the use of certain special symbols of our metalanguage. As in Chapter 7, we introduce the special symbols '$\sim$', '$\cdot$', '$($', and '$)$' to denote the symbols '$\sim$', '$\cdot$', '$($', and '$)$' of the object language, and we shall also use square brackets and braces to denote the object language's parentheses when that is conducive to easier reading. Capital letters, with and without subscripts, will be used in the metalanguage as syntactical variables, that is, as symbols for which designations of any symbols or sequences of symbols of the object language can be substituted. And lower case letters, with and without subscripts, will be used as syntactical individual variables, that is, symbols for which designations of individual symbols of the object language can be substituted. Finally, we adopt the convention that the juxtaposition of two symbols of the object language will be denoted in the metalanguage by the juxtaposition of their names. Thus in any context where 'F' denotes 'A^1' and 'x' denotes 'x', '$F(x)$' will denote '$A^1(x)$'. We shall also find it convenient to insert commas into any sequence of symbols of the metalanguage which designate individual symbols of the object language. Thus where 'F' denotes 'B^3' and 'x_1', 'x_2', and 'x_3' denote 'a_1', 'a_2', and 'a_3', respectively, we shall use '$F(x_1, x_2, x_3)$' to denote '$B^3(a_1a_2a_3)$'.

We introduce the symbols 'v', '$\supset$', '$\equiv$', and '$\exists$' into the object language *by definition*, and shall denote them in the metalanguage by the symbols 'v', '$\supset$', '$\equiv$', and '$\exists$'. The new symbols of the object language are introduced as definitional abbreviations:

Df. $P \vee Q$ is defined to be an abbreviation of $\sim(\sim P \cdot \sim Q)$.
Df. $P \supset Q$ is defined to be an abbreviation of $\sim(P \cdot \sim Q)$.
Df. $P \equiv Q$ is defined to be an abbreviation of $(P \supset Q) \cdot (Q \supset P)$.
Df. $(\exists x)P$ is defined to be an abbreviation of $\sim(x)\sim P$.

We shall feel free to drop parentheses (in the metalanguage), retaining only so many as may be required to avoid ambiguity, or to make for greater ease of interpretation. We shall also, on occasion, write '$P \cdot Q$' as 'PQ'. Although we shall not always take advantage of the following convention by dropping unnecessary parentheses, we set up the following *order of precedence* among the symbols (of our metalanguage), each symbol having precedence over any that lies in a column to its right:

$$\equiv \quad \supset \quad v \quad \cdot \quad \sim$$

$\quad\quad$ (x) where not immediately preceded by a predicate symbol
$\quad\quad$ $(\exists x)$

This convention dictates that an expression such as

$$P \equiv (x)Q \vee \sim RS \supset (\exists x)T \cdot U$$

is understood to denote the same formulas of the object language that are denoted by

$$\{P\} \equiv \{\{[(x)Q] \vee [(\sim R) \cdot (S)]\} \supset \{[(\exists x)T] \cdot [U]\}\}$$

We define *formula of* RS₁ as any finite sequence of symbols of RS₁. Among these are included such sequences as

$$) \sim) ($$
$$(x)(A^1(x))$$
$$((\exists y)(B^2(xy))) \supset (C^1(a))$$
$$(\exists \text{ v} \sim \equiv$$
$$Q^3(ab)$$

of which we shall want to include only the second and third as *well formed*, that is, as meaningful on the system's intended or normal interpretation.

Now we define *well formed formula of* RS₁ by the following recursive rules:

$\alpha)$ 1. If F is a propositional symbol then F is a *wff*.

     2. If F is an n-adic predicate symbol (where $n = 1, 2, 3, \ldots$) then $F(x_1, x_2, \ldots, x_n)$ is a *wff*.

$\beta)$ 1. If F is a *wff* then $\sim(F)$ is a *wff*.

     2. If F is a *wff* and G is a *wff* then $(F) \cdot (G)$ is a *wff*.

     3. If F is a *wff* and x is an individual variable then $(x)(F)$ is a *wff*.

No formula of RS₁ is a *wff* unless its being so follows from these rules, or from these rules together with the definitions of the defined symbols which were stated above.

Now that we have an effective criterion for *wff*, we shall restrict our discussion in the remainder of this chapter to *wff*s, which alone interest us.

It is convenient at this point to introduce and define some additional special terms. (There is no loss of generality in phrasing our definitions in terms of undefined symbols only, for defined symbols are always eliminable.)

Df.   If x is an individual variable, then (x), when not immediately preceded by a predicate symbol, is the *universal quantifier* of x (or on x).

Df.   If Q is a *wff* that is a component of a *wff* P then Q is a *well formed part* of P.

Df.   An occurrence of a variable x in a *wff* P will be called a *bound* occurrence of x in P if it is in a well formed part of P of the form $(x)Q$.

Df.   An occurrence of a variable x in a *wff* P will be called a *free occurrence* if it is not bound.

We assume infinitely many postulates for our object logic. Every *wff* of any of the five following patterns is a postulate:

P 1. $P \supset (P \cdot P)$

P 2. $(P \cdot Q) \supset P$

P 3. $(P \supset Q) \supset [\sim(Q \cdot R) \supset \sim(R \cdot P)]$

P 4. $(x)(P \supset Q) \supset [P \supset (x)Q]$, where x is any individual variable, P is any *wff* containing no free occurrences of x, and Q is any *wff*.

P 5. $(x)P \supset Q$, where x is any individual variable, y is any individual variable or constant, P is any *wff*, Q is the result of replacing each free occurrence of x in P by y, and if y is a variable then it must occur free in Q at all places where x occurs free in P (that is, no bound occurrence of y in Q is the result of replacing a free occurrence of x in P by y).

The restrictions on P 4 and P 5 serve to prevent the inclusion of such manifest falsehoods (on the intended interpretation, of course) as

$$(x)[(x = 1) \supset (x + x = 2)] \supset [(x = 1) \supset (x)(x + x = 2)]$$

which has a true antecedent and a false consequent, but which is *not* an instance of P 4 since x occurs free in $(x = 1)$. Also prevented is such a patent falsehood as

$$(x)[(\exists y)(y \neq x)] \supset [(\exists y)(y \neq y)]$$

which is *not* an instance of P 5 since there is a bound occurrence of the variable y in $(\exists y)(y \neq y)$ which is the result of replacing a free occurrence of the variable x in $(\exists y)(y \neq x)$ by y.

We assume *two* rules of inference for RS_1:

R 1. From P and $P \supset Q$ to infer Q.

R 2. From P to infer $(x)P$.

Next we define 'demonstration' for RS_1. Formally,

$$P_1, P_2, \ldots, P_n \vdash Q$$

asserts that there is a finite sequence of *wffs* S_1, S_2, . . . , S_t such that for every $S_j (1 \leq j \leq t)$ either:

   a) S_j is one of the Postulates P 1–P 5; or

   b) S_j is one of the premises $P_i (1 \leq i \leq n)$; or

   c) S_j is the result of applying R 1 to two earlier S's of the sequence, say S_i and S_k where $i < j$ and $k < j$; or

   d) S_j is the result of applying R 2 to an earlier S_i of the sequence, so that S_j is $(x)S_i$ where $i < j$;

and S_t is Q.

Informally, we regard P_1, P_2, . . . , $P_n \vdash Q$ as asserting that Q is validly inferred from P_1, P_2, . . . , P_n in RS₁.

Next we define 'theorem of RS₁' as any *wff* Q such that $\vdash Q$. It should be noted that '$\vdash$' is a special symbol of our metalanguage, and does not occur in RS₁ itself.

We can now establish the *consistency* of RS₁, following the proof given by Hilbert and Ackermann in 1928. We begin by stating the following definitions:

Df.   A *quantifier-free formula* of RS₁ is a *wff* of RS₁ which contains no quantifiers.

Df.   Where F is any *wff* of RS₁ the *associated quantifier-free formula* of F (symbolized F') is the result of crossing out (erasing) all occurrences of quantifiers in F and all parentheses whose presence was required by the occurrence of those quantifiers.

Examples:

   a) where F is itself a quantifier-free formula, $F = F'$.

   b) where F is $((x)((A^1(y)) \supset (B^1(x)))) \supset ((A^1(y)) \supset ((x)(B^1(x))))$
F' is $((A^1(y)) \supset (B^1(x))) \supset ((A^1(y)) \supset (B^1(x)))$

Df.   Where F is any *wff* of RS₁ its *associated propositional formula* (abbreviated to 'a.f.P.' for 'associated formula of the Propositional Calculus', and symbolized F°) is any result of replacing every well formed part of F' which is of the form $P^n(x_1, x_2, . . . , x_n)$ by a propositional symbol—where different well formed parts beginning with different P^n's are replaced by different propositional symbols, but where different well formed parts beginning with the same P^n are replaced by the same propositional symbol regardless of differences among the individual symbols $x_1, x_2, \ldots, x_n$ which follow them.

Example: where F is

$$((x_1)((x_2)(A^2(x_1x_2)))) \supset (((x_1)(B^1(x_1)))\cdot((x_2)(B^1(x_2))))$$

F' is

$$(A^2(x_1x_2)) \supset ((B^1(x_1))\cdot(B^1(x_2)))$$

and F° is any of the formulas

$$(A) \supset ((B)\cdot(B)), \quad (A) \supset ((C)\cdot(C)), \quad (A) \supset ((A_1)\cdot(A_1)), \ldots$$
$$(A_1) \supset ((B)\cdot(B)), \quad (A_1) \supset ((C)\cdot(C)), \quad (A_1) \supset ((A)\cdot(A)), \ldots$$

. . . .

Next we state and prove the following:

LEMMA: If $\vdash F$ then F° is a (truth table) tautology.

Proof. 1. First we show that every postulate of RS_1 has only tautologies for its a.f.P.'s. Any a.f.P. of any instance of P 1 is of the form $P^\circ \supset (P^\circ\cdot P^\circ)$, which is a tautology. Similarly for P 2 and P 3. Every a.f.P. of any instance of P 4 has the form $(P^\circ \supset Q^\circ) \supset (P^\circ \supset Q^\circ)$ which is a tautology. In P 5, since Q differs from P only in the individual symbols they contain, their a.f.P.'s are identical, so that every a.f.P. of any instance of P 5 has the form $P^\circ \supset P^\circ$ which is a tautology.

2. Next we show that any *wff* obtained by applying the rules of RS_1 to *wffs* which have only tautologies for their a.f.P's has itself the property that all its a.f.P.'s are tautologies. By R 2 we derive $(x)P$ from P. But $(x)P$ and P have identically the same a.f.P.'s, so if all of P's are tautologies, all of $(x)P$'s are also. By R 1 we derive Q from P and $P \supset Q$. Let Q° be *any* a.f.P. of Q, and select P° so that $P^\circ \supset Q^\circ$ is an a.f.P. of $P \supset Q$. (It is obvious that this can always be done since there are infinitely many distinct propositional symbols.) Now if all a.f.P.'s of P and $P \supset Q$ are tautologies, P° and $P^\circ \supset Q^\circ$ are, and hence Q° is also—regardless of which a.f.P. of Q we took for Q°.

Since all theorems of RS_1 follow by the rules from the postulates, all theorems of RS₁ have only tautologies as their a.f.P.'s. And this completes our proof of the lemma.

The consistency of RS₁ will be stated as

METATHEOREM I.   *RS₁ is consistent.*

Proof: (Here we use Post's criterion for consistency: a system is consistent if it contains a *wff* which is not a theorem.) The formula '$(A)\cdot(\sim(A))$' is a *wff* of RS₁ which has an a.f.P. (itself) which is not a tautology. Hence by our lemma it is not a theorem of RS₁, so RS₁ is consistent. The consistency of RS₁ also follows from its analyticity, which is remarked (in passing) in Section 9.6.

9.2   DEVELOPMENT OF RS₁

In developing the present system we shall borrow freely from the results obtained in Chapter 7, in which it was established that every tautology can be demonstrated as a theorem in a Propositional Calculus based on P 1, P 2, P 3, and R 1. This is noted in the following theorem and derived rule.

THEOREM O.   *All tautologies are theorems, and if in any tautology T which contains the propositional symbols P_1, P_2, . . . , P_n we replace all occurrences of P_1, P_2, . . . , P_n respectively by any wffs F_1, F_2, . . . , F_n of RS₁, the result is a theorem F of RS₁.*

Proof.   By the completeness of the Propositional Calculus based on P 1, P 2, P 3, and R 1, there is a demonstration in RS₁ for every tautology. If in every step of that demonstration we replace all occurrences of P_1, P_2, . . . , P_n by F_1, F_2, . . . , F_n we obtain a demonstration in RS₁ of F, since making the indicated substitutions in the postulates P 1, P 2, P 3 gives us simply other instances of those postulates.

DERIVED RULE O.   All tautologically valid argument forms are demonstrable in RS₁, and if in any tautologically valid derived rule S_1, S_2, . . . , $S_m \vdash T$ which contains the propositional symbols P_1,

$P_2, \ldots, P_n$ we replace all occurrences of $P_1, P_2, \ldots, P_n$ respectively by any *wffs* $F_1, F_2, \ldots, F_n$ of RS$_1$, the result is a demonstrably valid derived rule $G_1, G_2, \ldots, G_m \vdash H$ of RS$_1$.

Proof. Exactly parallels the proof of Theorem O.

In any *proof* in RS$_1$, any step which is justified by Th. O or DR O will be noted simply by ℗ (for 'Propositional Calculus').

At this point we proceed to establish the first few derived rules and theorems of RS$_1$.

DR 1. If P contains no free occurrence of x then $P \supset Q \vdash P \supset (x)Q$.

Demonstration:	S_1: $P \supset Q$	premiss
	S_2: $(x)(P \supset Q)$	R 2
	S_3: $(x)(P \supset Q) \supset [P \supset (x)Q]$	P 4
	S_4: $P \supset (x)Q$	R 1

DR 2. $(x)[F(x) \supset G(x)], (x)F(x) \vdash (x)G(x)$

Demonstration:	S_1: $(x)[F(x) \supset G(x)]$	premiss
	S_2: $(x)[F(x) \supset G(x)] \supset [F(x) \supset G(x)]$	P 5
	S_3: $F(x) \supset G(x)$	R 1
	S_4: $(x)F(x)$	premiss
	S_5: $(x)F(x) \supset F(x)$	P 5
	S_6: $F(x)$	R 1
	S_7: $G(x)$	R 1
	S_8: $(x)G(x)$	R 2

DR 3. $(x)(P \cdot Q) \vdash (x)P \cdot (x)Q$

Proof:	$(x)(P \cdot Q)$	premiss
	$(x)(P \cdot Q) \supset P \cdot Q$	P 5
	$P \cdot Q$	R 1
	P	℗
	$(x)P$	R 2
	Q	℗
	$(x)Q$	R 2
	$(x)P \cdot (x)Q$	℗

DR 4. $(x)(P \equiv Q) \vdash (x)P \equiv (x)Q$

   Proof: $(x)(P \equiv Q)$ premiss

            $(x)(P \equiv Q) \supset (P \equiv Q)$ P 5

            $P \equiv Q$ R 1

            $P \supset Q$ Ⓟ

            $(x)P \supset P$ P 5

            $(x)P \supset Q$ Ⓟ

            $(x)P \supset (x)Q$ DR 1

            $Q \supset P$ Ⓟ

            $(x)Q \supset Q$ P 5

            $(x)Q \supset P$ Ⓟ

            $(x)Q \supset (x)P$ DR 1

            $[(x)P \supset (x)Q] \cdot [(x)Q \supset (x)P]$ Ⓟ

            $(x)P \equiv (x)Q$ df.

T$_H$. 1. $\vdash (x)(P \cdot Q) \equiv (x)P \cdot (x)Q$

   Proof: First we establish A: $\vdash (x)(P \cdot Q) \supset (x)P \cdot (x)Q$

                      $\vdash (x)(P \cdot Q) \supset P \cdot Q$ P 5

                      $\vdash P \cdot Q \supset P$ P 2

                      $\vdash (x)(P \cdot Q) \supset P$ Ⓟ

                      $\vdash (x)(P \cdot Q) \supset (x)P$ DR 1

By steps similar to the above we obtain:

                      $\vdash (x)(P \cdot Q) \supset (x)Q$

                      $\vdash (x)(P \cdot Q) \supset (x)P \cdot (x)Q$ Ⓟ

Next we establish B: $\vdash (x)P \cdot (x)Q \supset (x)(P \cdot Q)$

                      $\vdash (x)P \supset P$ P 5

                      $\vdash (x)Q \supset Q$ P 5

                      $\vdash (x)P \cdot (x)Q \supset P \cdot Q$ Ⓟ

                      $\vdash (x)P \cdot (x)Q \supset (x)(P \cdot Q)$ DR 1

Now from A and B,

                      $\vdash [(x)(P \cdot Q) \supset (x)P \cdot (x)Q] \cdot$

                                  $[(x)P \cdot (x)Q \supset (x)(P \cdot Q)]$ Ⓟ

                      $\vdash (x)(P \cdot Q) \equiv (x)P \cdot (x)Q$ df.

TH. 2. $\vdash (x)(P \supset Q) \supset [(x)P \supset (x)Q]$

Proof.

$\vdash [(x)(P \supset Q)\cdot(x)P] \supset (x)(P \supset Q)$ — P 2

$\vdash [(x)(P \supset Q)\cdot(x)P] \supset (x)P$ — ℗

$\vdash (x)(P \supset Q) \supset (P \supset Q)$ — P 5

$\vdash (x)P \supset P$ — P 5

$\vdash [(x)(P \supset Q)\cdot(x)P] \supset [(P \supset Q)\cdot P]$ — ℗

$\vdash [(P \supset Q)\cdot P] \supset Q$ — ℗

$\vdash [(x)(P \supset Q)\cdot(x)P] \supset Q$ — ℗

$\vdash [(x)(P \supset Q)\cdot(x)P] \supset (x)Q$ — DR 1

$\vdash (x)(P \supset Q) \supset [(x)P \supset (x)Q]$ — ℗

Next we state and prove the Deduction Theorem for RS_1, which corresponds to the strengthened method of Conditional Proof used in Chapters 4 and 5.

METATHEOREM II. (*The Deduction Theorem—D.T.*) *If there is a demonstration that* $P_1, P_2, \ldots, P_{n-1}, P_n \vdash Q$ *in which no variable occurring free in* P_n *is ever quantified by* R 2, *then there is a demonstration that* $P_1, P_2, \ldots, P_{n-1} \vdash P_n \supset Q$ *in which exactly those variables are quantified by* R 2 *which were quantified by* R 2 *in the original demonstration.*

Proof. We assume that there is a sequence of *wffs* $S_1, S_2, \ldots, S_t$ such that every $S_j (1 \leq j \leq t)$ is (a) one of the Postulates P 1–P 5, or (b) one of the P_i's $(1 \leq i \leq n)$, or (c) results from applying R 1 to two earlier S's of the sequence, or (d) results from applying R 2 to an earlier S; and S_t is Q. Now consider the sequence of *wffs*: $P_n \supset S_1, P_n \supset S_2, \ldots, P_n \supset S_t$. If we can 'fill in' *wffs* before each $P_n \supset S_j$ in such a way that the resulting total sequence is a demonstration from $P_1, P_2, \ldots, P_{n-1}$, so each line of the resulting total sequence is either (a) one of the Postulates P 1–P 5, or (b) one of the P_i's $(1 \leq i \leq n - 1)$, or (c) results from applying R 1 to two earlier lines of the sequence, or (d) results from applying R 2 to an earlier line of the sequence, then since the last line $P_n \supset S_t$ is $P_n \supset Q$ we shall have a demonstration that $P_1, P_2, \ldots, P_{n-1} \vdash P_n \supset Q$.

The proof proceeds by weak induction on the number of lines (t) in the original demonstration.

α) In case $t = 1$ we have only the formula $P_n \supset S_1$ to consider. We wish to show that $P_1, P_2, \ldots, P_{n-1} \vdash P_n \supset S_1$. By assumption, S_1 is either a Postulate P 1–P 5 or a $P_i(1 \leq i \leq n)$.

CASE 1. S_1 is a Postulate. Here we fill in with the demonstration of $S_1 \supset (P_n \supset S_1)$ and S_1 itself. From these we have $P_n \supset S_1$ by R 1, so the total sequence up to and including $P_n \supset S_1$ is a demonstration that $\vdash P_n \supset S_1$ and hence that $P_1, P_2, \ldots, P_{n-1} \vdash P_n \supset S_1$.

CASE 2. S_1 is a $P_i(1 \leq i < n)$. Here we fill in with the demonstration of $S_1 \supset (P_n \supset S_1)$ and S_1 itself, from which we have $P_n \supset S_1$ by R 1 . Here the total sequence is a demonstration that $S_1 \vdash P_n \supset S_1$, and since S_1 is a $P_i(1 \leq i \leq n - 1)$ it is a demonstration that $P_1, P_2, \ldots, P_{n-1} \vdash P_n \supset S_1$.

CASE 3. S_1 is P_n. Here we fill in with the demonstration of $S_1 \supset S_1$, which is a demonstration that $\vdash P_n \supset S_1$, and hence that $P_1, P_2, \ldots, P_{n-1} \vdash P_n \supset S_1$.

β) Now suppose we have filled in for all lines $P_n \supset S_1$, $P_n \supset S_2$, $\ldots$, up to and including $P_n \supset S_{k-1}$, so we have a sequence of *wffs* which is a demonstration that $P_1, P_2, \ldots, P_{n-1} \vdash P_n \supset S_{k-1}$. Under this assumption we show how to fill in to include $P_n \supset S_k$ in the sequence, which will then be a demonstration that $P_1, P_2, \ldots, P_{n-1} \vdash P_n \supset S_k$. By assumption, S_k is either a postulate, a $P_i(1 \leq i \leq n)$, resulted in the original demonstration from applying R 1 to two earlier S's, or resulted in the original demonstration from applying R 2 to an earlier S.

CASE 1. S_k is a Postulate. Fill in as in the α-case.

CASE 2. S_k is a $P_i(1 \leq i \leq n)$. Fill in as in the α-case.

CASE 3. S_k results from applying R 1 to two previous S's, say S_i and S_j where S_j is $S_i \supset S_k$. By the β-case assumption, since $i < k$, $j < k$ we already have $P_n \supset S_i$ and $P_n \supset S_j$, which is $P_n \supset (S_i \supset S_k)$. Here we insert the demonstration of $[P_n \supset (S_i \supset S_k)] \supset [(P_n \supset S_i) \supset (P_n \supset S_k)]$ (a tautology), and $P_n \supset S_k$ follows by two applications of R 1.

CASE 4. S_k results from applying R 2 to an earlier S, say S_j where $j < k$. By the β-case assumption we already have $P_n \supset S_j$. S_k is $(x)S_j$ where x, by our original assumption, is not free in P_n. Hence by R 2, $(x)(P_n \supset S_j)$, and by P 4, $(x)(P_n \supset S_j) \supset (P_n \supset (x)S_j)$. Now R 1 will give $P_n \supset (x)S_j$ which is $P_n \supset S_k$.

From α, β by weak induction we can thus fill in for *any* number of steps S_j of the original demonstration. Moreover, no variable is quantified in the 'filled in' sequence which was not quantified in the original sequence. This proves Metatheorem II (D.T.).

MT II. COROLLARY: *The D.T. as stated above holds for any system of logic which has only rules R 1 and R 2 and which contains demonstrations for*

$$P \supset P, \; P \supset (Q \supset P), \; [P \supset (Q \supset R)] \supset [(P \supset Q) \supset (P \supset R)], \text{ and}$$
$$(x)(P \supset Q) \supset (P \supset (x)Q) \text{ where no free } x\text{'s occur in } P.$$

Proof: Obvious.

We can illustrate the *use* of the D.T. by using it to prove DR 5:

DR 5. $(x)[F(x) \supset G(x)] \vdash (x)F(x) \supset (x)G(x)$
  Proof: $(x)[F(x) \supset G(x)], \; (x)F(x) \vdash (x)G(x)$ DR 2
  $(x)[F(x) \supset G(x)] \vdash (x)F(x) \supset (x)G(x)$ D.T.

Some additional theorems which can be established quite easily using the Deduction Theorem are

TH. 3. $\vdash (x)(P \equiv Q) \supset [(x)P \equiv (x)Q]$
★TH. 4. $\vdash (x)(P \supset Q) \supset [(\exists x)P \supset (\exists x)Q]$

Their proofs will be left as exercises for the reader. We now proceed to some theorems which state equivalences. Since $(\exists x)$ was introduced as an abbreviation for $\sim(x)\sim$, the next theorem,

TH. 5. $\vdash (\exists x)P \equiv \sim(x)\sim P$

follows immediately from $\vdash \sim(x)\sim P \equiv \sim(x)\sim P$ (Ⓟ) by definition.

The following theorems, however, require proofs which are simple but not quite so simple as that of Th. 5.

TH. 6. $\vdash (x)P \equiv \sim(\exists x)\sim P$

TH. 7. $\vdash \sim(x)P \equiv (\exists x)\sim P$

TH. 8. $\vdash \sim(\exists x)P \equiv (x)\sim P$

The proofs of these will also be left as exercises.

The next theorem provides for the permutation of universal quantifiers:

TH. 9. $\vdash (x)(y)P \equiv (y)(x)P$

Proof:	$\vdash (y)P \supset P$	P 5
	$\vdash (x)[(y)P \supset P]$	R 2
	$\vdash (x)(y)P \supset (x)P$	DR 5
	$\vdash (x)(y)P \supset (y)(x)P$	DR 1

We obtain $\vdash (y)(x)P \supset (x)(y)P$ in the same fashion, and then have

$$\vdash (x)(y)P \equiv (y)(x)P \qquad \text{by } \circledP$$

Another theorem which can be proved quite simply is

TH. 10. $\vdash [(x)P \lor (x)Q] \supset (x)(P \lor Q)$

Proof:	$\vdash (x)P \supset P$	P 5
	$\vdash (x)Q \supset Q$	P 5
	$\vdash [(x)P \lor (x)Q] \supset (P \lor Q)$	$\circledP$
	$\vdash [(x)P \lor (x)Q] \supset (x)(P \lor Q)$	DR 1

Having derived a number of equivalences as theorems, it will be convenient to establish a substitution rule which will permit the interchange of equivalent formulas in any context. This will be proved as the next Metatheorem.

METATHEOREM III.   (*The Substitution Theorem—S.T.*) *Let* $P_1, P_2, \ldots,$ P_n, *be any wffs, let A be any wff that does not occur in any* P_i, *and let W be any wff which contains no symbols other than the* P_i's $(1 \leq i \leq n)$, A, $\cdot$, $\sim$, (x), *and parentheses.*[2] *Let* W^* *be the result of replacing any number of occurrences of A in W by B. Then* $A \equiv B \vdash W \equiv W^*$.

---

[2] The last restriction does not limit the generality of the Metatheorem since all occurrences of the defined symbols $\lor$, $\supset$, $\equiv$, and $\exists$ can be replaced by undefined symbols.

Proof: We use strong induction on the number of symbols in W, counting each occurrence of $P_i(1 \leq i \leq n)$, A, B, $\sim$, $\cdot$, (x), as a single symbol.

α) In case W contains a single symbol, W is either a P_i or A.

CASE 1. W is P_i. Here W^* is P_i, and since $\vdash P_i \equiv P_i$, we have $\vdash W \equiv W^*$, whence $A \equiv B \vdash W \equiv W^*$.

CASE 2. W is A. Here W^* is either A or B.
Subcase A: W^* is A. Since $\vdash A \equiv A$ we have $\vdash W \equiv W^*$, whence $A \equiv B \vdash W \equiv W^*$.
Subcase B: W^* is B. Since $A \equiv B \vdash A \equiv B$ we have $A \equiv B \vdash W \equiv W^*$.

β) Now suppose the Metatheorem true for any *wff* W which contains k or fewer symbols, and consider a *wff* W which has $k + 1$ symbols. W must have the structure $\sim L$, $(x)L$, or $M \cdot N$.

CASE 1. W is $\sim L$. L must have just k symbols, so by the β-case assumption $A \equiv B \vdash L \equiv L^*$. But $(L \equiv L^*) \supset (\sim L \equiv \sim L^*)$ is provable, so $A \equiv B \vdash \sim L \equiv \sim L^*$ which is $A \equiv B \vdash W \equiv W^*$.

CASE 2. W is $(x)L$. Again L has just k symbols, so by the β-case assumption $A \equiv B \vdash L \equiv L^*$. Hence by R 2 we have $A \equiv B \vdash (x)$ $(L \equiv L^*)$, and by DR 4 we have $(x)(L \equiv L^*) \vdash (x)L \equiv (x)L^*$, whence $A \equiv B \vdash W \equiv W^*$.

CASE 3. W is $M \cdot N$. Since M and N each has fewer than k symbols, by the β-case assumption $A \equiv B \vdash M \equiv M^*$ and $A \equiv B \vdash N \equiv N^*$. Since $\vdash [(M \equiv M^*) \cdot (N \equiv N^*)] \supset [M \cdot N \equiv M^* \cdot N^*]$, and $M^* \cdot N^*$ is W^*, we have $A \equiv B \vdash W \equiv W^*$.

This completes the induction and finishes the proof.

MT III. COROLLARY: *If W and W^* are as in* MT III, *then* $A \equiv B$, $W \vdash W^*$. The proof is quite obvious.

9.3 DUALITY

We begin our discussion of duality with a quite complicated definition:

Df. Let W be any *wff* which contains no occurrences of $\supset$ or $\equiv$ (any *wff* can be made into such a W by rewriting every well formed part of the form $P \supset Q$ as $\sim P \mathbin{v} Q$ and every well formed part of the form $P \equiv Q$ as $(\sim P \mathbin{v} Q) \cdot (\sim Q \mathbin{v} P)$). Where $P_1, \ldots, P_n$ are propositional symbols or composed of predicate symbols followed by the appropriate number of individual symbols, W will be constructed out of $P_1, P_2, \ldots, P_n, \cdot, \sim, \mathbin{v}, (x), (\exists x)$ exclusively. Then the *dual* of W (written W^Δ) is formed by

replacing every occurrence of P_i in W by $\sim P_i$,[3]

"	"	"	" $\sim P_i$ " " "	P_i,
"	"	"	" (x) " " "	$(\exists x)$,
"	"	"	" $(\exists x)$ " " "	(x),
"	"	"	" . " " "	$\mathbin{v}$,
"	"	"	" $\mathbin{v}$ " " "	.

Examples (where P, Q, R, S are P_i's):

1. W: $P \cdot Q$
   W^Δ: $\sim P \mathbin{v} \sim Q$
2. W: $(x)(P \mathbin{v} Q)$
   W^Δ: $(\exists x)(\sim P \cdot \sim Q)$
3. W: $(y)(\exists z)[P \mathbin{v} (\sim Q \mathbin{v} R \cdot S)]$
   W^Δ: $(\exists y)(z)[\sim P \cdot Q \cdot (\sim R \mathbin{v} \sim S)]$

There are several immediate consequences of our definition: First, where W is any *wff* which contains no part of the form $\sim\sim P_i$:

1. $W = W^{\Delta\Delta}$

Where W and U are any *wffs* whatever:

2. $(W \cdot U)^\Delta = W^\Delta \mathbin{v} U^\Delta$
3. $(W \mathbin{v} U)^\Delta = W^\Delta \cdot U^\Delta$

---

[3] Except those occurrences of P_i in well formed parts of the form $\sim P_i$.

4. $((x)W)^\Delta = (\exists x)W^\Delta$

5. $((\exists x)W)^\Delta = (x)W^\Delta$

6. $(\sim W)^\Delta$ $\begin{cases} \text{a. If } W \text{ is a } P_i \text{ then } (\sim W)^\Delta \text{ is } P_i. \\ \text{b. If } W \text{ contains at least two symbols then } (\sim W)^\Delta = \\ \quad \sim(W^\Delta). \end{cases}$

We can now establish a general duality result.

METATHEOREM IV.   (*Duality Theorem*) *If* W^Δ *is the dual of* W *then* $\vdash \sim W \equiv W^\Delta$.

Proof: We use strong induction on the structure of W (i.e., the number of symbols it contains, counting each P_i as a single symbol).

α) If W contains just one symbol, W is a P_i. Here W^Δ is $\sim P_i$, and since $\vdash \sim P_i \equiv \sim P_i$ by ℗, we have $\vdash \sim W \equiv W^\Delta$.

β) Assume the Metatheorem true for any W containing k or fewer symbols. Now consider any W containing $k + 1$ symbols.

    CASE 1. W is $\sim R$.

       Subcase A: R contains more than one symbol. Then $(\sim R)^\Delta$ is $\sim R^\Delta$. By the β-case assumption, $\vdash \sim R \equiv R^\Delta$, hence by ℗ $\vdash \sim\sim R \equiv \sim R^\Delta$, which is $\vdash \sim W \equiv W^\Delta$.

       Subcase B: R contains just one symbol, i.e., R is a P_i. Then W is $\sim P_i$ and W^Δ is P_i. By ℗ $\vdash \sim\sim P_i \equiv P_i$, whence $\vdash \sim W \equiv W^\Delta$.

    CASE 2. W is $(x)R$. By β we have $\vdash \sim R \equiv R^\Delta$. We also have, by S.T., $\vdash \sim(x)R \equiv \sim(x)\sim\sim R$, so, by S.T., $\vdash \sim(x)R \equiv \sim(x)\sim R^\Delta$ which (by definition) is $\vdash \sim(x)R \equiv (\exists x)R^\Delta$ or $\vdash \sim W \equiv W^\Delta$.

    CASE 3. W is $(\exists x)R$. By β, $\vdash \sim R \equiv R^\Delta$. We also have (Theorem 8) $\vdash \sim(\exists x)R \equiv (x)\sim R$. By S.T. we have $\vdash \sim(\exists x)R \equiv (x)R^\Delta$ which is $\vdash \sim W \equiv W^\Delta$.

    CASE 4. W is $A \cdot B$. By β, $\vdash \sim A \equiv A^\Delta$ and $\vdash \sim B \equiv B^\Delta$. By ℗, $\vdash \sim(A \cdot B) \equiv \sim A \vee \sim B$, so by S.T., $\vdash \sim(A \cdot B) \equiv A^\Delta \vee B^\Delta$ which is $\vdash \sim W \equiv W^\Delta$.

    CASE 5. W is $A \vee B$. By β, $\vdash \sim A \equiv A^\Delta$ and $\vdash \sim B \equiv B^\Delta$. By ℗, $\vdash \sim(A \vee B) \equiv \sim A \cdot \sim B$, so by S.T., $\vdash \sim(A \vee B) \equiv A^\Delta \cdot B^\Delta$ which is $\vdash \sim W \equiv W^\Delta$.

MT IV. COROLLARY: $\vdash (W \equiv U) \supset (W^\Delta \equiv U^\Delta)$
The proof of the corollary is obvious.

Duality has many uses. The traditional 'Square of Opposition'[4] which displays I and O propositions as the negations of E and A propositions, respectively, is clearly a special case of the duality result established above:

The familiar theorems of De Morgan are also special cases of the duality theorem. And the general duality theorem permits us to formulate negations with ease. For example, the proposition

There is a course which all students take.

may be symbolized as

$$(\exists x)\{C^1(x)\cdot(y)[S^1(y) \supset T^2(y,x)]\}$$

and may have its implication sign deleted to become

$$(\exists x)\{C^1(x)\cdot(y)[\sim S^1(y) \lor T^2(y,x)]\}$$

The dual (and hence the negation) of this formula is

$$(x)\{\sim C^1(x) \lor (\exists y)[S^1(y)\cdot\sim T^2(y,x)]\}$$

which is most 'naturally' written with the implication sign as

$$(x)\{C^1(x) \supset (\exists y)[S^1(y)\cdot\sim T^2(y,x)]\}$$

and is the symbolic translation of the English sentence

For every course there is some student who doesn't take it.

Having established the Substitution and Duality results, some additional theorems are very easily proved.

[4] Discussed in Chapter 4, pp. 76–77.

TH. 11. $\vdash (\exists x)(P \vee Q) \equiv (\exists x)P \vee (\exists x)Q$

    Proof: $\vdash (x)(\sim P \cdot \sim Q) \equiv (x)\sim P \cdot (x)\sim Q$ Th. 1

        $\vdash (\exists x)(P \vee Q) \equiv (\exists x)P \vee (\exists x)Q$ Duality Theorem Cor.

                                       and R 1

The proofs of the next two theorems are equally simple, and may be left as exercises.

TH. 12. $\vdash (\exists x)(\exists y)P \equiv (\exists y)(\exists x)P$

★TH. 13. $\vdash (\exists x)(P \cdot Q) \supset (\exists x)P \cdot (\exists x)Q$

Now that we have the Substitution Theorem, it is desirable to augment our supply of equivalences. For the next ten theorems (Th. 14 through Th. 23) and the next derived rule (DR 6) we make the blanket assumption that *there are no free occurrences* of x in Q. We shall give proofs of some of these next results, and leave others as exercises for the reader:

TH. 14. $\vdash (x)Q \equiv Q$

    Proof: $\vdash (x)Q \supset Q$ P 5

        $\vdash Q \supset Q$ ⓟ

        $\vdash Q \supset (x)Q$ DR 1

        $\vdash (x)Q \equiv Q$ ⓟ

TH. 15. $\vdash (\exists x)Q \equiv Q$

TH. 16. $\vdash (x)(P \cdot Q) \equiv (x)P \cdot Q$

    Proof: $\vdash (x)(P \cdot Q) \equiv (x)P \cdot (x)Q$ Th. 1

        $\vdash (x)Q \equiv Q$ Th. 14

        $\vdash (x)(P \cdot Q) \equiv (x)P \cdot Q$ S.T.

TH. 17. $\vdash (\exists x)(P \vee Q) \equiv (\exists x)P \vee Q$

    Proof: $\vdash (x)(\sim P \cdot \sim Q) \equiv (x)\sim P \cdot \sim Q$ Th. 16

        $\vdash (\exists x)(P \vee Q) \equiv (\exists x)P \vee Q$ Duality Theorem Cor.

                                         and R 1

TH. 18. $\vdash (\exists x)(P \supset Q) \equiv (x)P \supset Q$

TH. 19. $\vdash (\exists x)(Q \supset P) \equiv Q \supset (\exists x)P$

TH. 20. $\vdash (x)(Q \supset P) \equiv Q \supset (x)P$

★TH. 21. $\vdash (x)(P \supset Q) \equiv (\exists x)P \supset Q$

TH. 22. $\vdash (x)(P \vee Q) \equiv (x)P \vee Q$

TH. 23. $\vdash (\exists x)(P \cdot Q) \equiv (\exists x)P \cdot Q$

★DR 6. $P \supset Q \vdash (\exists x)P \supset Q$

The next theorem requires no such restriction on free occurrences of variables in the formulas it contains:

TH. 24. $\vdash (\exists x)(y)P \supset (y)(\exists x)P$

    Proof: $\vdash (x)\sim P \supset \sim P$ P 5

            $\vdash \sim\sim P \supset \sim(x)\sim P$ ℗

            $\vdash P \supset \sim(x)\sim P$ ℗

            $\vdash P \supset (\exists x)P$ df.

            $\vdash (y)P \supset P$ P 5

            $\vdash (y)P \supset (\exists x)P$ ℗

            $\vdash (y)P \supset (y)(\exists x)P$ DR 1

            $\vdash (\exists x)(y)P \supset (y)(\exists x)P$ DR 6

For the next two theorems we make the general assumptions that x and y are any two individual variables, and $F(x)$ and $F(y)$ are exactly alike except that x is free in $F(x)$ at all and only those places that y is free in $F(y)$:

TH. 25. $\vdash (x)F(x) \equiv (y)F(y)$

    Proof: $\vdash (x)F(x) \supset F(y)$ P 5

            $\vdash (x)F(x) \supset (y)F(y)$ DR 1

We obtain $\vdash (y)F(y) \supset (x)F(x)$ the same way, and then have

            $\vdash (x)F(x) \equiv (y)F(y)$ by ℗

TH. 26. $\vdash (\exists x)F(x) \equiv (\exists y)F(y)$

    Proof: $\vdash (x)\sim F(x) \equiv (y)\sim F(y)$ Th. 25

            $\vdash \sim(x)\sim F(x) \equiv \sim(y)\sim F(y)$ ℗

            $\vdash (\exists x)F(x) \equiv (\exists y)F(y)$ df.

Theorems 25 and 26, together with the Substitution Theorem, permit the 'interchange of bound variables'—subject to the restrictions mentioned in the statement of the theorems.

We end the present group of theorems with

TH. 27. If P and Q are as in P 5, then $\vdash Q \supset (\exists x)P$.

    Proof: $\vdash (x)\sim P \supset \sim Q$ P 5

            $\vdash \sim\sim Q \supset \sim(x)\sim P$ ℗

            $\vdash Q \supset \sim(x)\sim P$ ℗

            $\vdash Q \supset (\exists x)P$ df.

9.4   RS₁ AND THE 'NATURAL DEDUCTION' TECHNIQUES

We wish now to show that RS_1 *is* an axiomatization of the logic we *used* in validating inferences by our list of nineteen Rules of Inference, the strengthened method of Conditional Proof, and the Quantification Rules set forth in Chapter 4. That RS_1 contains all the nineteen Rules of Inference has been shown by our completeness proof for the system of logic based on P 1, P 2, P 3, and R 1, and our discussion in connection with Th. 0 and DR 0. In a sense, the Deduction Theorem for RS_1 corresponds to the strengthened method of Conditional Proof.

In the presence of R 1, P 5 corresponds to **UI**. The restrictions on **UI** are exactly the same as the restrictions on P 5. We may establish **UI** as a derived rule of RS_1:

DR 7.   If P and Q are as in P 5 then $(x)P \vdash Q$.

     Proof: $(x)P \vdash (x)P$ premiss

                    $(x)P \vdash (x)P \supset Q$ P 5

                    $(x)P \vdash Q$ R 1

Again in the presence of R 1, **EG** follows directly from P 5. The restrictions on **EG** are exactly the same as those on P 5. We may establish **EG** as a derived rule of RS_1:

DR 8.   If P and Q are as in P 5 then $Q \vdash (\exists x)P$.

     Proof: $Q \vdash Q$ premiss

                    $Q \vdash Q \supset (\exists x)P$ Th. 27

                    $Q \vdash (\exists x)P$ R 1

The rule **UG** corresponds roughly to R 2, although it seems from one point of view weaker than R 2, and from another point of view stronger. The second restriction on **UG** prevents its use to infer $(\mu)\Phi\mu$ from $\Phi\nu$ where ν is a variable that occurs free in an assumption within whose scope $\Phi\nu$ lies. But there is no such restriction on R 2. That restriction on **UG**, however, serves only to limit its application in conjunction with the rule of Conditional Proof. In RS_1 the same limitation is imposed by placing the restriction on the rule of Conditional Proof itself, in our statement of the Deduction Theorem—which does not permit going from $P \vdash Q$ to $\vdash P \supset Q$ if R 2 is used on a variable occurring free in P. Hence in the context of RS_1 the second restriction on **UG** applies to

R 2 although it is stated for the Deduction Theorem rather than for R 2 itself. So **UG** is not really weaker (more restricted) than R 2.

UG seems stronger than R 2 in that it permits a change of variable in its application, which R 2 does not. But in the presence of the rest of the system RS₁, **UG** is easily proved as a derived rule, combining the power of R 2 and Th. 25. The general convention governing $\Phi\mu$ and $\Phi\nu$ in Chapter 4, and the first restriction on **UG** (that ν does not occur free in $(\mu)\Phi\mu$), are together equivalent to the conditions stated for Th. 25, that $\Phi\mu$ and $\Phi\nu$ are exactly alike except that μ is free in $\Phi\mu$ at all and only those places that ν is free in $\Phi\nu$. We have $F(x) \vdash (x)F(x)$ directly by R 2, and hence by Th. 25 we have

DR 9.   If $F(x)$ and $F(y)$ are exactly alike except that x is free in $F(x)$ at all and only those places that y is free in $F(y)$, then $F(x) \vdash (y)F(y)$.

We can do everything in RS₁ by DR 9 that we could do earlier by **UG**.

In Th. 0 and DR 0, and in DR 7, DR 8, DR 9, and the Deduction Theorem, the system RS₁ is seen to comprise all of the deductive strength available in our nineteen Rules of Inference, Quantification Rules **UI**, **EG**, **UG**, and the strengthened principle of Conditional Proof.

Instead of attempting to formulate a derived rule in RS₁ corresponding to **EI**, we prove a Metatheorem that legitimizes any use of **EI** in a proof subject to the restrictions involved in its statement.

METATHEOREM V. (The legitimacy of **EI**—perhaps better, the eliminability or avoidability of **EI**.)

If there is a sequence of wffs which constitutes a demonstration that P_1, P_2, . . . , $P_n \vdash Q$ except that some wffs follow from preceding ones by **EI** *(here construed simply as the rule that if R can be derived in a given context from $F(y)$ then it can be derived in that context from $(\exists x)F(x)$) such that:*

1. *there are m uses of* **EI** *of which the i-th use is to infer R_i from $(\exists x_i)F(x_i)$ on the basis of its having been derived from $F_i(y_i)$, where the free x_i's in $F_i(x_i)$ correspond exactly to the free y_i's in $F_i(y_i)$, and*

2. *no y_i occurs free either in any premiss P_j, or in any wff of the sequence that precedes $F_i(y_i)$, or in the wff R_i derived by means of $F_i(y_i)$;*

then there is a genuine demonstration that P_1, P_2, . . . , $P_n \vdash Q$ *which makes no use of* **EI**. *And in the latter (genuine) demonstration there are no uses of* R 2 *to quantify variables free in* P_1, P_2, . . . , P_n *which were not quantified by* R 2 *in the original sequence or 'quasi-demonstration'.*

Proof:[5]   In any such quasi-demonstration every *wff* $F_i(y_i)$ is preceded by a *wff* $(\exists x_i)F_i(x_i)$ and followed by a *wff* R_i. Except for the *m formulas* $F_1(y_1)$, $F_2(y_2)$, . . . , $F_m(y_m)$ every *wff* of the indicated sequence is either an axiom or a P_j or follows from preceding *wffs* by R 1 or R 2. Suppose there are exactly *t* uses of R 2 of which the *q*-th use is to infer S_{k_q} $(= (x_{j_q})S_{j_q})$ from S_{j_q}.

We define S'_{k_q} to be (x_{j_1}) . . . $(x_{j_{q-1}})(x_{j_{q+1}})$ . . . $(x_{j_t})S_{k_q}$, which is (x_{j_1}) . . . $(x_{j_{q-1}})(x_{j_{q+1}})$ . . . $(x_{j_t})(x_{j_q})S_{j_q}$. Since $S'_{k_q} \vdash S_{k_q}$ by $t - 1$ uses of P 5 and R 1, it is obvious from the existence of the original quasi-demonstration that there exists a genuine demonstration that

(1) P_1, P_2, . . . , P_n, S'_{k_1}, S'_{k_2}, . . . , S'_{k_t}, $F_1(y_1)$, $F_2(y_2)$, . . . ,
$$F_m(y_m) \vdash Q$$

which involves no use of either **EI** or R 2. (Where $F_i(y_i)$ occurred without justification in the quasi-demonstration, here it is a premiss; and where S_{k_q} was inferred by R 2, here it is inferred from the premiss S'_{k_q} by $t - 1$ uses of P 5 and R 1.)

Since no use is made of R 2 in the demonstration that (1), we can use the Deduction Theorem to obtain

(1') P_1, P_2, . . . , P_n, S'_{k_1}, S'_{k_2}, . . . , S'_{k_t}, $F_1(y_1)$, $F_2(y_2)$, . . . ,
$$F_{m-1}(y_{m-1}) \vdash F_m(y_m) \supset Q$$

Now by successive uses of R 2, Theorems 21 and 26, and the Substitution Theorem, we obtain from those same premisses first

$$\vdash (y_m)[F_m(y_m) \supset Q]$$

then

$$\vdash (\exists y_m)F_m(y_m) \supset Q$$

and finally

$$\vdash (\exists x_m)F_m(x_m) \supset Q$$

[5] The statement and proof of Metatheorem V are adapted from 'Another Variant of Natural Deduction,' *The Journal of Symbolic Logic*, vol. 21 (1956), No. 1, pp. 52–55.

Since $F_m(y_m)$ is preceded by $(\exists x_m)F_m(x_m)$ original the in quasi-demonstration, we have also

$$\vdash (\exists x_m)F_m(x_m)$$

and finally by R 1

$$\vdash Q$$

Thus we have a demonstration that

(2) $P_1, P_2, \ldots, P_n, S'_{k_1}, S'_{k_2}, \ldots, S'_{k_t}, F_1(y_1), F_2(y_2), \ldots,$
$$F_{m-1}(y_{m-1}) \vdash Q$$

in which R 2 is not used to quantity any variable free in any of the premisses $S'_{k_1}, S'_{k_2}, \ldots, S'_{k_t}, F_1(y_1), F_2(y_2), \ldots, F_{m-1}(y_{m-1})$. The foregoing argument can be used m times to obtain a demonstration that

(m) $P_1, P_2, \ldots, P_n, S'_{k_1}, S'_{k_2}, \ldots, S'_{k_t} \vdash Q$

in which R 2 is not used to quantify any variable free in any of the premisses $S'_{k_1}, S'_{k_2}, \ldots, S'_{k_t}$. Hence we can use the Deduction Theorem again to obtain

$$P_1, P_2, \ldots, P_n, S'_{k_1}, S'_{k_2}, \ldots, S'_{k_{t-1}} \vdash S'_{k_t} \supset Q$$

Since S_{j_t} preceded S_{k_t} in the original quasi-demonstration, we obtain also from those same premisses

$$\vdash S_{j_t}$$

Now by t uses of R 2 we obtain

$$\vdash S'_{k_t}$$

and finally by R 1

$$\vdash Q$$

Thus we have a demonstration that

(m+1) $P_1, P_2, \ldots, P_n, S'_{k_1}, S'_{k_2}, \ldots, S'_{k_{t-1}} \vdash Q$

in which R 2 is not used to quantify any variable free in any of the premisses $S'_{k_1}, S'_{k_2}, \ldots, S'_{k_{t-1}}$. The foregoing argument can be used t times to obtain a genuine demonstration that

(m+t) $P_1, P_2, \ldots, P_n \vdash Q$

in which there are no uses of R 2 to quantify variables free in $P_1, P_2,$

. . . , P_n which were not quantified by R 2 in the original quasi-demonstration. This completes our proof of Metatheorem V.

The preceding discussion suffices to show that our first-order function calculus RS_1 *is* an axiomatization of the logic *used* in Chapter 4 and the first three sections of Chapter 5. That it contains no *more* than was used there can be shown by giving demonstrations (in the earlier sense of 'demonstration') of the postulates of RS_1.

The question naturally arises as to *how much* logic is contained in RS_1. We shall present a proof that RS_1 is deductively complete in the sense that all logically true propositions involving quantification of individual variables only are provable as theorems within it. This sense will be specified more precisely in Section 9.6. Before proving the completeness of our first-order function calculus, however, we shall develop some notions and Metatheorems concerning the subject of 'Normal Forms.'

9.5   NORMAL FORMS

We begin by defining the notion of 'prenex normal form'. A *wff* is in *prenex normal form* if and only if it has the structure $(Qx_1)(Qx_2)$ . . . $(Qx_n)G$ where $x_1, x_2, \ldots, x_n$ are distinct individual variables, (Qx_i) is either $(\exists x_i)$ or (x_i), and G is a quantifier-free *wff* containing at least one occurrence of each of the x_i's. Some samples of formulas of RS_1 which are in prenex normal form are

$$(x)(A^1(x))$$
$$(\exists x)((B^1(x)) \supset (C^2(xy)))$$
$$(y)((\exists z)(\sim (A^3(xyz))))$$

We now define the term 'scope' as follows: If $(Qx)B$ is a well formed part (i.e., a *wff* which is a part) of a *wff* A then the scope of that particular occurrence of (Qx) in A is the particular occurrence of B which immediately follows (Qx).[6] And we define the phrase 'initially placed' in this way: A quantifier is initially placed in a *wff* F if it either stands at the beginning of F or is preceded (except for parentheses) only by other quantifiers, and its scope extends to the end of F. It should be

---

[6] This definition provides a more precise formulation of the notion of scope which was discussed informally in Section 4.4, Cf. pp. 100ff.

clear that an equivalent definition of 'prenex normal form' can be stated as: A *wff* is in *prenex normal form* if and only if all its quantifiers are initially placed, no two quantifiers are on the same variable, and every variable occurring in a quantifier occurs also at least once within the *scope* of that quantifier.

We can now state and prove our next Metatheorem.

METATHEOREM VI.　*Given any wff F of RS_1, a formula P in prenex normal form can be found such that $\vdash F \equiv P$.*

Proof:　If F is in prenex normal form, P is F and $\vdash F \equiv P$ by ⓟ. If F is not in prenex normal form, it must either: (a) contain a quantifier which is not initially placed, or (b) contain two quantifiers on the same variable, or (c) contain a variable which occurs *only* in a quantifier.

CASE 1.　All quantifiers in F are initially placed.

Subcase 1.*i*.　At least two quantifiers are on the same variable. Here F is of the form

$$(Qx_1)(Qx_2) \ldots (Qx_i) \ldots (Qx_i) \ldots (Qx_n)G$$

If we denote all of F which immediately follows the first (Qx_i) by A, then x_i does not occur free in A, and by Th. 14 or Th. 15, $\vdash (Qx_i)A \equiv A$. Hence by the Substitution Theorem the first of any initially placed quantifiers on the same variable can be simply dropped out to yield an equivalent formula. So if all quantifiers of F are initially placed, then there is an equivalent formula all of whose quantifiers are initially placed and which has at most one quantifier on any variable.

Subcase 1.*ii*.　There is a variable in F which occurs only in a quantifier. Here we have F of the form

$$(Qx_1) \ldots (Qx_i) \ldots (Qx_n)G$$

where x_i does not occur free in G. If we denote all of F which immediately follows (Qx_i) by A, then x_i does not occur free in A and by Th. 14 or Th. 15, $\vdash (Qx_i)A \equiv A$. Hence by the Substitution Theorem any initially placed quantifier on a variable which has no occurrence outside of that quantifier may simply be dropped out to yield an equivalent formula. So if all quantifiers of F are initially placed then there is an equivalent formula all of whose quantifiers are initially placed and which contains no variables whose only occurrences are in quantifiers.

CASE 2. Some quantifiers in F are not initially placed. In this case it is convenient to write F in unabbreviated form, so the only propositional calculus symbols in it are $\cdot$ and $\sim$. Next we consider a *wff* G such that no two quantifiers in G are on the same variable, no variable in G has both free and bound occurrences, and $\vdash F \equiv G$. If F is such a *wff*, let F be G; otherwise G is obtained from F by interchanging bound variables according to Theorems 25 and 26 and the Substitution Theorem.

Apart from parentheses, each symbol other than a quantifier that occurs to the left of a given quantifier (Qx_j) in a *wff* G can be counted as a "reason" why (Qx_j) is not initially placed in G, and each symbol that occurs to the right of (Qx_j) in G and does not lie within its scope can also be counted as a "reason" why (Qx_j) is not initially placed in G. It is obvious that any quantifier (Qx_j) occurring in a *wff* G is initially placed in G if and only if there are no "reasons" why it is not initially placed in G.

Given any such *wff* G in which the quantifier on x_j is not initially placed and all quantifiers in G preceding the quantifier on x_j are initially placed in G, we can construct a *wff* G_1 such that: every initially placed quantifier in G is initially placed in G_1 also, $\vdash G \equiv G_1$, and there are fewer "reasons" why the quantifier on x_j is not initially placed in G_1 than there were "reasons" why the quantifier on x_j was not initially placed in G. The construction of G_1 proceeds as follows.

If (Qx_j) is the first quantifier in G that is not initially placed in G, then it can occur in only one of the following wf parts of G: $((Qx_j)(A))\cdot(B)$ or $(B)\cdot((Qx_j)(A))$ or $\sim((Qx_j)(A))$.

In the first case, since x_j has no occurrence in B, we replace the wf part $((Qx_j(A))\cdot(B)$ by $(Qx_j)((A)\cdot(B))$, using Theorem 16 or Theorem 23 and the Substitution Theorem, to obtain the *wff* G_1.

In the second case, we first use Ⓟ and the Substitution Theorem to replace the wf part $(B)\cdot((Qx_j)(A))$ by $((Qx_j)(A))\cdot(B)$, and then replace that as in the preceding case by $(Qx_j)((A)\cdot(B))$ to obtain the *wff* G_1.

In the third case we obtain the *wff* G_1 using Theorem 7 or Theorem 8 and the Substitution Theorem to replace the wf part $\sim((Qx_j)(A))$ by $(Q^*x_j)(\sim(A))$, where (Q^*x_j) is either (x_j) or $(\exists x_j)$ according as (Qx_j) is $(\exists x_j)$ or (x_j).

If the quantifier on x_j is not initially placed in G_1, we repeat the construction just described to obtain G_2, in which there are still fewer "reasons" why the quantifier on x_j is not initially placed. Since each *wff* contains only finitely many symbols, in any *wff* there can be only finitely many "reasons" why any quantifier in it is not initially placed. Hence the construction described need be iterated only finitely many times to produce a *wff* G_k in which the quantifier on x_j is initially placed.

A new series of such constructions can be used for each quantifier that is not initially placed in the original *wff* F, until finally a *wff* G_K is obtained in which all quantifiers are initially placed and such that $\vdash F \equiv G_K$. And to G_K there is an equivalent *wff* in prenex normal form by Case 1.

We define two new terms at this point: In any *wff* in prenex normal form

$$(Qx_1)(Qx_2) \ . \ . \ . \ (Qx_n)G$$

the group of quantifiers $(Qx_1)(Qx_2) \ . \ . \ . \ (Qx_n)$ is the *prefix* and the quantifier-free formula G is the *matrix*.

EXERCISES

Find a prenex normal form for

1. $(x)(\exists y)(\exists x)(y)[(z)G(z) \cdot F(x) \supset (\exists z)H(z) \cdot F(z)]$
★2. $[(x)G(x) \text{ v } H(y)] \equiv [(y)(z)F(y,z)]$
3. $(x)[F(x) \supset G(x)] \supset [(x)F(x) \supset (x)G(x)]$
★4. $(y)(\exists x)F(x,y) \supset (\exists x)(y)F(x,y)$
5. $(x_1)(\exists x_2)(x_3)(\exists x_4)(x_5)[P^6(x_1, \ . \ . \ . \ , x_6) \supset (z_1)(\exists x)(\exists z)H(x_1,z)]$

A *wff* in prenex normal form may contain free variables. We wish to be able, without any loss in generality, to confine our attention to *wffs* containing no free variables. These will be referred to as *closed wffs* (abbreviated *cwffs*). To legitimize our concentrating on *cwffs*, we state and prove the following:

METATHEOREM VII.   *For any wff F a cwff G may be found in prenex normal form such that* $\vdash F$ *if and only if* $\vdash G$.

Proof: By Metatheorem VI we can always find the prenex normal form P for any *wff* F such that $\vdash F \equiv P$.

CASE 1.   If P is a *cwff* then G is the same as P, and because $\vdash F \equiv G$, $\vdash F$ if and only if $\vdash G$.

CASE 2.   If P contains n free variables $x_1, x_2, \ldots, x_n$, then G is the *cwff* $(x_1)(x_2) \ldots (x_n)P$. For if $\vdash F$ then $\vdash P$, and by R 2, $\vdash (x_n)P$, and by n uses of R 2 we have $\vdash G$. And if $\vdash G$, that is, $\vdash (x_1)(x_2) \ldots (x_n)P$, then since $\vdash (x_1)(x_2) \ldots (x_n)P \supset (x_2) \ldots (x_n)P$ by P 5, R 1 gives $\vdash (x_2) \ldots (x_n)P$, and by n uses of P 5 and R 1, we have $\vdash P$, and hence $\vdash F$.

We prove now a further result which gives for any *wff* a still more specialized normal form *wff* that is a theorem if and only if the original *wff* is a theorem.

METATHEOREM VIII.   *For any wff F a cwff R may be found which is in prenex normal form and begins with an existential quantifier, such that* $\vdash F$ *if and only if* $\vdash R$.

Proof: By Metatheorem VII, for any *wff* F there is a *cwff* G in prenex normal form such that $\vdash F$ if and only if $\vdash G$. Let $D(t)$ be a function of one variable t such that neither D nor t occurs in G. Then by Ⓟ, $\vdash G \equiv \{G \cdot [D(t) \supset D(t)]\}$.
Hence

$\vdash G \supset \{G \cdot [D(t) \supset D(t)]\}$	by Ⓟ
$\vdash (\exists t)\{G \supset \{G \cdot [D(t) \supset D(t)]\}\}$	by DR 8, (**EG**)
$\vdash G \supset (\exists t)\{G \cdot [D(t) \supset D(t)]\}$	by Th. 19 and S.T.

We also have

$\vdash \{G \cdot [D(t) \supset D(t)]\} \supset G$	P 2
$\vdash (t)\{\{G \cdot [D(t) \supset D(t)]\} \supset G\}$	R 2
$\vdash (\exists t)\{G \cdot (D(t) \supset D(t))\} \supset G$	Th. 21 and S.T.

Hence

$$\vdash (\exists t)\{G\cdot[D(t) \supset D(t)]\} \equiv G \qquad\qquad \text{by} \quad \textcircled{P}$$

Now the prenex normal form of $(\exists t)\{G\cdot[D(t) \supset D(t)]\}$ is the formula *of type R* that was desired, for it is closed, is in prenex normal form, begins with an existential quantifier, and $\vdash F$ if and only if $\vdash R$. Where G is $(Qx_1)(Qx_2) \ldots (Qx_n)G'$, then

$$\vdash (\exists t)\{G\cdot[D(t) \supset D(t)]\} \text{ or}$$
$$\vdash (\exists t)\{[(Qx_1)(Qx_2) \ldots (Qx_n)G']\cdot\sim[D(t)\cdot\sim D(t)]\}$$

has as its prenex normal form

$$\vdash (\exists t)(Qx_1)(Qx_2) \ldots (Qx_n)\{G'\cdot\sim[D(t)\cdot\sim D(t)]\}$$

by repeated uses of Th. 16 or Th. 23 and the Substitution Theorem.

By definition, any *cwff* in prenex normal form which begins with an existential quantifier will be said to be *of type R*.

EXERCISES

For each of the following *wffs* construct a formula *of type R* that is a theorem if and only if the given *wff* is a theorem:

★1. $(x)(y)(z)\{[H(x) \vee H(y)] \vee H(z)\}$
 2. $F(x_1, x_2, \ldots, x_n) \supset G(z)$
★3. $(\exists x)G(x,y) \vee F(z)$
 4. $(\exists z)F(z,z) \supset (x)G(x,y)$
 5. $(x)F(x,y) \supset G(z)$

Next we present three new definitions, of which the third defines the 'Skolem normal form', which is a still more specialized type of well formed formula, about which we shall establish a further Metatheorem.

Df. The *rank of an occurrence of an existential quantifier* in a formula *of type R* is the number of universal quantifiers which precede that existential quantifier in the prefix.

Df.   The *rank of a formula of type R* is the greatest of the ranks of the occurrences of the existential quantifiers of its prefix.

Df.   A *wff F* is in *Skolem normal form* if and only if it is *of type R* and of rank 0.

METATHEOREM IX.   *Given any wff F we can find a formula F_0 in Skolem normal form such that $\vdash F$ if and only if $\vdash F_0$.*

Proof: For any *wff F* we can construct a formula *of type R*, call it F_1, such that $\vdash F$ if and only if $\vdash F_1$. (If F is already *of type R* then $F = F_1$.) If F_1 is of rank 0, then it is in the desired Skolem normal form. If F_1 is of rank $k > 0$, then we show how to construct a formula *of type R* of rank less than k, call it F_2, such that $\vdash F_1$ if and only if $\vdash F_2$. We thus embark on a process which will yield formulas F_3, F_4, F_5, . . . all *of type R* and of decreasing rank. Ultimately, then, we arrive at a formula F_0 *of type R* and of rank 0, such that $\vdash F$ if and only if $\vdash F_0$.

If F_1 is not in Skolem normal form, then its rank is greater than 0, that is, F_1 has the structure

$$(\exists x_1)(\exists x_2) \; . \; . \; . \; (\exists x_n)(y)(Qz_1)(Qz_2) \; . \; . \; . \; (Qz_m)G$$

where $(Qz_1)(Qz_2)$, . . . , (Qz_m) are quantifiers of which at least one is an existential quantifier. We now introduce the following notations:

1. $B(x_1, x_2, . . . , x_n, y) =\mathrm{df} (Qz_1)(Qz_2) \; . \; . \; . \; (Qz_m)G$. This we shall abbreviate as A.
2. $H(y) =\mathrm{df} H(x_1, x_2, . . . , x_n, y)$ where H is any $(n + 1)$-place predicate variable (with arguments $x_1, x_2, . . . , x_n, y$) such that H does not occur in G.
3. $H(t) =\mathrm{df} H(x_1, x_2, . . . , x_n, t)$ where t is a variable which does not occur in G.
4. $C =\mathrm{df} (\exists x_1)(\exists x_2) \; . \; . \; . \; (\exists x_n)\{(y)[(Qz_1)(Qz_2) \; . \; . \; . \; (Qz_m)G \supset H(y)] \supset (t)H(t)\}$

First we want to show that $\vdash F_1$ if and only if $\vdash C$. The two implications are

(i) If $\vdash F_1$ then $\vdash C$. Here we prove that $\vdash F_1 \supset C$.

$\vdash A \supset \{[A \supset H(y)] \supset H(y)\}$	℗
$\vdash (y)\{A \supset \{[A \supset H(y)] \supset H(y)\}\}$	R 2
$\vdash (y)A \supset (y)\{[A \supset H(y)] \supset H(y)\}$	DR 5
$\vdash (y)A \supset \{(y)[A \supset H(y)] \supset (y)H(y)\}$	Th. 2, ℗
$\vdash (y)A \supset \{(y)[A \supset H(y)] \supset (t)H(t)\}$	Th. 25, Substitution
$\vdash (x_n)\{(y)A \supset \{(y)[A \supset H(y)] \supset (t)H(t)\}\}$	R 2
$\vdash (\exists x_n)(y)A \supset (\exists x_n)\{(y)[A \supset H(y)] \supset (t)H(t)\}$	Th. 4, R 1

. . . .

. . . .

$\vdash (\exists x_1)(\exists x_2) \ \ldots \ (\exists x_n)(y)A \supset (\exists x_1)(\exists x_2) \ \ldots$
$\qquad (\exists x_n)\{(y)[A \supset H(y)] \supset (t)H(t)\}$ by n uses of R 2, Th. 4, R 1

$\vdash F_1 \supset C$ df.

Hence if $\vdash F_1$ then $\vdash C$.

(ii) If $\vdash C$ then $\vdash F_1$. Here we must assume that $\vdash C$ and derive $\vdash F_1$.

$\vdash (\exists x_1) \ \ldots \ (\exists x_n)\{(y)[(Qz_1) \ \ldots \ (Qz_m)G \supset$
$\qquad\qquad\qquad\qquad H(y)] \supset (t)H(t)\}$ C

$\vdash (\exists x_1) \ \ldots \ (\exists x_n)\{(y)[B(x_1, \ \ldots \ , x_n, y) \supset$
$H(x_1, \ \ldots \ , x_n, y)] \supset (t)H(x_1, \ \ldots \ , x_n, t)\}$ df.

$\vdash (\exists x_2) \ \ldots \ (\exists x_n)\{(y)[B(x'_1, \ \ldots \ , x_n, y) \supset$
$H(x'_1, \ \ldots \ , x_n, y)] \supset (t)H(x'_1, \ \ldots \ , x_n, t)\}$ **EI**

. . . .

$\vdash (y)[B(x'_1, \ \ldots \ , x'_n, y) \supset$
$H(x'_1, \ \ldots \ , x'_n, y)] \supset (t)H(x'_1, \ \ldots \ , x'_n, t)$ n uses of **EI**

Now we substitute $B(x'_1, \ \ldots \ , \ x'_n, \ y)$ for the predicate variable
$H(x'_1, \ \ldots \ , \ x'_n, y)$[7]

$\vdash (y)[B(x'_1, \ \ldots \ , x'_n, y) \supset$
$B(x'_1, \ \ldots \ , x'_n, y)] \supset (t)B(x'_1, \ \ldots \ , x'_n, t)$

---

[7] The rule governing such substitution (rule of substitution for functional variables) is difficult and complicated to express. Since this is our only use of it, we shall not state it here. A discussion of alternative formulations can be found in A. Church, *Introduction to Mathematical Logic I*, Princeton, 1956, pp. 193ff., 289f., and 297f.

$\vdash (y)[B(x'_1, \ldots, x'_n, y) \supset$
$\qquad B(x'_1, \ldots, x'_n, y)] \supset (y)B(x'_1, \ldots, x'_n, y)$ Th. 25, Substitution

$\vdash (\exists y)\{[B(x'_1, \ldots, x'_n, y)$
$\qquad\qquad \supset B(x'_1, \ldots, x'_n, y)]$
$\qquad\qquad\qquad \supset (y)B(x'_1, \ldots, x'_n, y)\}$ Th. 18, Substitution

$\vdash [B(x'_1, \ldots, x'_n, y) \supset B(x'_1, \ldots, x'_n, y)]$
$\qquad\qquad\qquad \supset (y)B(x'_1, \ldots, x'_n, y)$ **EI**

$\vdash B(x'_1, \ldots, x'_n, y) \supset B(x'_1, \ldots, x'_n, y)$ ⓟ

$\vdash (y)B(x'_1, \ldots, x'_n, y)$ R 1

$\vdash (\exists x_n)(y)B(x'_1, \ldots, x_n, y)$ DR 8, (**EG**)

$\cdots \cdots \cdots \cdots \cdots \cdots \cdots$

$\vdash (\exists x_1) \ldots (\exists x_n)(y)B(x_1, \ldots, x_n, y)$ n uses of **EG**

$\vdash (\exists x_1) \ldots (\exists x_n)(y)(Qz_1) \ldots (Qz_m)G$ df.

$\vdash F_1$ df.

Hence if $\vdash C$ then $\vdash F_1$.

C is not in prenex normal form. Its prenex normal form is constructed as follows, using the notation Q^* defined as follows:

$$\text{If } (Qz_i) \text{ is } (z_i) \text{ then } (Q^*z_i) \text{ is } (\exists z_i)$$
$$\text{If } (Qz_i) \text{ is } (\exists z_i) \text{ then } (Q^*z_i) \text{ is } (z_i)$$

$$C \equiv (\exists x_1) \ldots (\exists x_n)\{(y)[(Qz_1)(Qz_2) \ldots$$
$$(Qz_m)G \supset H(y)] \supset (t)H(t)\}$$

Since $H(y)$ does not contain any free z_i's,

$$\vdash (Qz_1) \ldots (Qz_m)G \supset H(y) \equiv (Q^*z_1) \ldots (Q^*z_m)[G \supset H(y)]$$

by m uses of Th. 18 or Th. 21. Hence by Substitution,

$$C \equiv (\exists x_1) \ldots (\exists x_n)\{(y)(Q^*z_1) \ldots (Q^*z_m)[G \supset H(y)] \supset (t)H(t)\}$$

Since $(t)H(t)$ does not contain any free z_i's,

$$\vdash \{(y)(Q^*z_1) \ldots (Q^*z_m)[G \supset H(y)] \supset (t)H(t)\} \equiv$$
$$\{(\exists y)(Qz_1) \ldots (Qz_m)[[G \supset H(y)] \supset (t)H(t)]\}$$

by $m + 1$ uses of Th. 18 or Th. 21. Hence by Substitution,

$$C \equiv (\exists x_1) \ldots (\exists x_n)(\exists y)(Qz_1) \ldots (Qz_m)[[G \supset H(y)] \supset (t)H(t)]$$

Since t is not free in $G \supset H(y)$, by Th. 20,

$$\vdash [[G \supset H(y)] \supset (t)H(t)] \equiv (t)[[G \supset H(y)] \supset H(t)],$$

hence by Substitution,

$$C \equiv (\exists x_1) \ \ldots \ (\exists x_n)(\exists y)(Qz_1) \ \ldots \ (Qz_m)(t)[[G \supset H(y)] \supset H(t)]$$

The right-hand formula is the formula F_2 *of type R* such that $\vdash F$ if and only if $\vdash F_2$. Now the rank of F_2 is lower than the rank of F_1, for their prefixes are the same except that F_2 has an additional universal quantifier in the final position, which does not affect the rank, and one of the universal quantifiers $((y))$ which preceded an existential quantifier has been replaced by an existential quantifier, which lowers the rank by one. If F_2 has rank 0 then it is the Skolem normal form of F. If it is not, then the argument can be repeated to obtain a formula F_3 *of type R* of still lower rank. Hence we can ultimately arrive at a formula *of type R* of rank 0, which is the desired Skolem normal form.

EXERCISES

Find a Skolem normal form for
★1. $(\exists x)(y)(\exists z)[F(x,y) \vee G(z)]$
  2. $(x)F(x) \supset [(\exists y)G(y) \supset (z)H(z)]$
★3. $(x)(\exists y)F(x,y)$
  4. $(x)(y)(\exists z)(\exists x)\{[[F(x)\cdot G(y)] \vee H(z)] \supset I(w)\}$
  5. $(\exists x_1)(x_2)(x_3)(\exists x_4)F(x_1, x_2, x_3, x_4)$

9.6 COMPLETENESS OF RS$_1$

We turn now to the problem of proving our first-order function calculus complete. There are several different senses of the term 'complete' which must be distinguished. A very strong kind of completeness is possessed by a system *all* of whose well formed formulas are provable as theorems. But this kind of completeness amounts to inconsistency, and is of course undesirable. Our first Metatheorem, which established the consistency of our system, proved it to lack *this* kind of completeness. A somewhat weaker kind of completeness is possessed by a system each of whose *wffs* is either provable as a theorem or else has its denial provable as a theorem; that is, for every *wff* F either $\vdash F$ or $\vdash \sim F$. This kind of completeness is not desirable either, for on their normal interpretations, each of the following *wffs*

N_1: $(\exists x)F(x) \supset (x)F(x)$

N_2: $(\exists x)(\exists y)\{F(x) \cdot F(y) \cdot [G(x) \equiv \sim G(y)]\} \supset (x)F(x)$

N_3: $(\exists x)(\exists y)(\exists z)\{F(x) \cdot F(y) \cdot F(z) \cdot [G(x) \equiv \sim G(y)] \cdot$
$[H(y) \equiv \sim H(z)] \cdot [I(x) \equiv \sim I(z)]\} \supset (x)F(x)$

. . . .

. . . .

asserts (respectively) that there is at most one individual, that there are at most two individuals, that there are at most three individuals, . . . But if we want our logical system to be applicable to *any* possible non-empty universe *regardless* of the exact number of individuals it contains, there is no N_i such that we want either N_i or $\sim N_i$ to be provable as theorems. A different kind of completeness was proved for the propositional calculus presented in Chapter 7. That logistic system was proved to be complete in the sense that every *wff* which (on its normal interpretation) is a truth table tautology is provable as a theorem in the system. That kind of completeness is admirably suited for a propositional calculus, but it will not do for a functional calculus. A first-order function calculus which did not have the *wff*

$$(\exists x)(y)F(x,y) \supset (y)(\exists x)F(x,y)$$

provable as a theorem within it would be woefully unsatisfactory and 'incomplete', even though the formula in question is *not* a truth table tautology. The reason for regarding as unsatisfactory a logic in which the given expression is a *wff* but not provable is that (on its normal interpretation) the formula expresses a logical truth—where a 'logical truth' is a proposition which is true in (or of) *every possible nonempty universe*. The kind of completeness desired for our first-order function calculus can be expressed loosely by saying that every logical truth which can be expressed in the system is provable as a theorem within it. This notion, however, must be expressed much more precisely before it can be used in any proof of completeness.[8]

[8] The following discussion and proof of completeness is an adaptation to RS_1 of the completeness proof for an alternative first-order function calculus given by Leon

Instead of continuing to speak of 'possible universes' we shall talk about *models*, where a model is any (nonempty) collection of elements each of which is thought of as an *individual*. And instead of speaking of our system of logic as being 'applied' to a 'possible universe', we shall speak of a model as constituting an 'interpretation' of our formal system. This last term will be given a precise meaning presently. With any given set of individuals which may be intended to serve as a *model*, we assume that we are given also the properties which may belong to the individual elements, and the relations (dyadic, triadic, etc.) that may hold between (or among) them. Now we define '*interpretation of a wff S with respect to a given model*' as an assignment of meanings such that

1. To each propositional symbol in S we assign a truth value, either **T** or **F**.

2. To each individual constant, and to each variable with free occurrence in S, we assign an element of the model.

3. To each predicate symbol we assign a property or a dyadic or triadic or n-adic relation according as it is of degree (has right superscript) 1, 2, 3, or n

This notion of interpretation of a *wff* with respect to a given model is incomplete, however, because no mention is made of what to do with the logical symbols $\sim$, $\cdot$, and the quantifier symbol (x). Our intended or *normal* interpretation of a *wff* S with respect to a given model is defined as an interpretation of S with respect to that model, subject to the following conditions:

a. Any well formed part $\sim W$ is assigned the truth value **T** or **F** according as the well formed part W is assigned the truth value **F** or **T**.

b. Any well formed part of the form $X \cdot Y$ is assigned the truth value **T** if and only if both X and Y are assigned the truth value **T**.

Henkin in his article 'The Completeness of the First-Order Functional Calculus', *The Journal of Symbolic Logic*, vol. 14 (1949), pp. 159–166. The respect in which the following is a simplification of the published proof is due to Professor Henkin himself, who communicated it to the present writer in the spring of 1951. It is reproduced here with his kind permission.

The first proof of completeness for a first-order function calculus was published by Kurt Gödel, 'Die Vollstandigkeit der Axiome der logischen Funktionenkalkuls', *Monatshefte für Mathematik und Physik*, vol. 37 (1930), pp. 349–360.

c. Any well formed part $(x)R$ is assigned the truth value **T** if and only if R is assigned the value **T** regardless of which element of the model is assigned to all free occurrences of x in R.

d. Any well formed part $P^n(x_1, x_2, \ldots, x_n)$ is assigned the truth value **T** if and only if the elements of the model assigned to $x_1, x_2, \ldots, x_n$, in that order, stand to each other in the n-adic relation assigned to P^n.

So far we have defined 'interpretation' and 'normal interpretation' only for a *wff* with respect to a given model. An *interpretation of a system with respect to a given model* is an assignment of meanings which provides interpretations for *all wffs* of the system, and a *normal interpretation of a system with respect to a given model* is an assignment of meanings which provides *normal* interpretations for all *wffs* of the system.

There are many interpretations, and even many normal interpretations of a formal system with respect to a given model. On some of these the value **T** may be assigned a *wff* that on another interpretation is assigned the truth value **F**. It is obvious, however, that the postulates of our first-order function calculus will be assigned the truth value **T** on *any* normal interpretation of the system with respect to *any* given model. A particular normal interpretation of a *wff* S with respect to a given model will be said to *satisfy* S with respect to that model if by it S is assigned the truth value **T**. A *wff* S will be said to be *satisfiable with respect to a given model* if there is a normal interpretation of S with respect to that model which assigns the truth value **T** to S. And a *wff* S will be said to be *satisfiable* if there is at least one model and a normal interpretation of S with respect to it which assigns the truth value **T** to S. Another term it is important to introduce in this connection is 'valid'. A *wff* S is *valid with respect to a given model* if every normal interpretation of S with respect to that model assigns the truth value **T** to S. It follows immediately from the definitions that the *wff* S is *valid* with respect to a given model if and only if every normal interpretation of S with respect to that model *satisfies* S. Finally we define the term 'valid' by itself: a *wff* S is *valid* if it is valid with respect to every model. It follows immediately from the definitions that for any *wff* S either S is valid or $\sim S$ is satisfiable.

In the notion of a *model* we have a precise formulation of our informal notion of a possible universe, and *normal interpretation* is what ought to be signified by the looser phrase 'intended application'. Consequently, the *validity* of a *wff* is a precise notion which serves the purpose suggested by the phrase 'logically true'. The completeness we wish to prove for our first-order function calculus RS_1 can now be defined precisely. A first-order function calculus is *complete* if and only if every valid *wff* is provable in it as a theorem.

As for a propositional calculus, so for a first-order function calculus: the converse of completeness is analyticity. An *analytic* first-order function calculus is one all of whose theorems are valid. It is obvious that all the postulates of RS_1 are valid, and that any *wffs* derived from them by R 1 and R 2 are valid also. Clearly RS_1 is analytic. The consistency of RS_1 is a consequence of its analyticity, just as the consistency of R.S. was shown to be a consequence of the analyticity of R.S. in Chapter 7.

In establishing the completeness of RS_1 it will be sufficient to confine our attention to *wffs* containing no free individual variables, for it is easily demonstrated that to every *wff* S which contains free individual variables there corresponds a *wff* S^c (called the *closure* of S) containing no free individual variables, such that $\vdash S$ if and only if $\vdash S^c$, and such that S is valid if and only if S^c is valid. Where S contains exactly n free variables, say $x_1, x_2, \ldots, x_{n-1}, x_n$ (in the order of their occurrence), then S^c will be $(x_1)(x_2) \ldots (x_{n-1})(x_n)S$. Now if $\vdash S$ then $\vdash (x_n)S$ by R 2, and another application of R 2 gives $\vdash (x_{n-1})(x_n)S$; finally we have $\vdash S^c$ by n uses of R 2. Conversely, if $\vdash S^c$, that is, $\vdash (x_1)(x_2) \ldots (x_{n-1})(x_n)S$, then applying R 1 to it and the instance of P 5 which is $(x_1)(x_2) \ldots (x_{n-1})(x_n)S \supset (x_2) \ldots (x_{n-1})(x_n)S$ will give $\vdash (x_2) \ldots (x_{n-1})(x_n)S$; so by n uses of R 1 and P 5 we obtain $\vdash S$. If S is valid, every normal interpretation of S with respect to any model assigns to S the value **T** regardless of which elements of the model its free individual variables $x_1, x_2, \ldots, x_n$ are taken to denote. From this it follows that $(x_n)S$ is valid, and $(x_{n-1})(x_n)S$ is valid, $\ldots$, and finally that S^c is valid. On the other hand, if S^c is valid, $(x_2)(x_3) \ldots (x_n)S$ is assigned the value **T** regardless of which element of the model x_1 is taken to denote, from which it follows that $(x_3) \ldots (x_n)S$ is assigned the value

T regardless of which elements x_1 and x_2 are taken to denote, from which it follows . . . finally that S is assigned the value **T** regardless of which elements of the model the free individual variables $x_1, x_2, . . . ,$ x_n are taken to denote, which means that S is valid. Hence with no real loss in generality we can confine our attention to closed *wffs* (*wffs* containing no free variables), which we shall refer to as *cwffs*.

To prove our system complete it is useful to introduce the notion of a *set* of *cwffs*. We shall use the capital Greek letters *Gamma* and *Lambda*, with and without subscripts, to denote *sets* of *cwffs* of RS$_1$. We shall also make use of braces to represent sets of *cwffs*: for example, the set whose only member is the *cwff* S will be written $\{S\}$, the set whose only two members are the *cwffs* S_1 and S_2 will be written $\{S_1, S_2\}$, and so on. To assert that there is a demonstration of the *wff* Q from the closed well formed premisses $P_1, P_2, . . . , P_n$ we may write *either*

$$P_1, P_2, . . . , P_n \vdash Q$$

or

$$\{P_1, P_2, . . . , P_n\} \vdash Q$$

If Γ is a set of *cwffs* and S is a *cwff* not belonging to Γ, then the new set containing all members of Γ *and* S will be written as $\{\Gamma, S\}$. To assert that there is a demonstration of Q from premisses belonging to $\{\Gamma, S\}$ we may write either

$$\{\Gamma, S\} \vdash Q \quad \text{or} \quad \Gamma, S \vdash Q$$

An alternative statement of the Deduction Theorem makes use of this new notation:

$$\text{If } \Gamma, P \vdash Q \quad \text{then} \quad \Gamma \vdash P \supset Q$$

If there is a demonstration of the *wff* Q from the premisses $P_1, P_2, . . . ,$ P_n, then there is, of course, a demonstration of Q from any set of *cwffs* Γ which contains $\{P_1, P_2, . . . , P_n\}$ as a subset (which will be written $\{P_1, P_2, . . . , P_n\} \subset \Gamma$), no matter what other *cwffs* Γ may contain. The set Γ may even be infinite: there is nothing in our proof of the Deduction Theorem that requires any revision to accommodate this possibility. Of course in any demonstration of Q from an infinite set of premisses only a finite number of them will actually be *used*, for a demonstration is always a *finite* sequence of *wffs*.

We defined a first-order function calculus to be *complete* if and only if every valid *wff* is provable in it as a theorem, and then showed that the first-order function calculus RS₁ is complete if and only if every valid *cwff* is provable in it as a theorem. To say that every valid *cwff* is provable in RS₁ as a theorem is, by transposition, to say that for any *cwff* S, if S is *not* a theorem then S is *not* valid.

In defining the terms 'valid' and 'satisfiable' we remarked that for any *wff* S either S is valid or $\sim S$ is satisfiable. Hence to say that S is not valid is to say that $\sim S$ is satisfiable. And so we can say that RS₁ is complete if and only if for any *cwff* S if S is not a theorem then $\sim S$ is satisfiable. We can establish this result by introducing a property φ such that both

1) If S is a *cwff* that is not a theorem then S has property ϕ; and
2) If S is a *cwff* that has property ϕ then $\sim S$ is satisfiable;

for from 1) and 2) the completeness of RS₁ follows by a Hypothetical Syllogism.

We first define two properties for *sets* of *cwffs*. A set Λ of *cwffs* is *inconsistent* if $\Lambda \vdash \sim P \cdot P$, otherwise Λ is consistent. It is obvious that *any* *wff* can be inferred from an inconsistent set, for where S is any *wff*, $\sim P \cdot P \vdash (\sim P \cdot P) \text{ v } S$ by Ⓟ, which is by definition, the same as $\sim P \cdot P \vdash \sim (\sim P \cdot P) \supset S$. Since $\vdash \sim (\sim P \cdot P)$ by Ⓟ, we have by R 1 that $\sim P \cdot P \vdash S$, whence $\Lambda \vdash S$ where Λ is any inconsistent set of *cwffs* and S is any *wff* whatever. Now the property φ referred to above can be defined as follows: a *cwff* S has property φ if and only if $\{\sim S\}$ is a consistent set.

And we demonstrate 1) above as the following:

LEMMA: If S is a *cwff* that is not a theorem then $\{\sim S\}$ is a consistent set.

Proof: We proceed to show that for any *cwff* S, if $\{\sim S\}$ is *not* a consistent set then S is a theorem. Let S be any *cwff* such that $\{\sim S\}$ is not consistent. If $\{\sim S\}$ is not consistent then it is inconsistent, which means that

$$\sim S \vdash \sim P \cdot P$$

Because S is a *cwff* we can use the Deduction Theorem to obtain

$$\vdash \sim S \supset \sim P{\cdot}P$$

from which

$$\vdash \sim(\sim P{\cdot}P) \supset \sim\sim S$$

follows by ℗. We already have

$$\vdash \sim(\sim P{\cdot}P)$$

by ℗, so by R 1 we obtain

$$\vdash \sim\sim S$$

which by ℗ gives

$$\vdash S$$

which is the desired result.

Instead of demonstrating 2) above, simply, as

If any *cwff* S is such that $\{\sim S\}$ is a consistent set then $\sim S$ is satisfiable,

we prove a somewhat more general result, for the statement of which the term 'simultaneously satisfiable' must be defined. The definition is this: A set Λ of *cwffs* of a formal system is *simultaneously satisfiable* by a given model if and only if there is a normal interpretation of all formulas of Λ with respect to that model which satisfies all the *wffs* of Λ. Now we state and prove

METATHEOREM X. *Any consistent set of cwffs of RS_1 is simultaneously satisfiable.*

Proof: Our proof of the simultaneous satisfiability of any arbitrary consistent set Λ proceeds by constructing a larger set of *cwffs* which includes Λ as a subset, and then proving that this larger set is simultaneously satisfiable. This will of course establish the desired result for Λ.

We begin by considering a set of distinct symbols u_1, u_2, u_3, . . . which are different from any of those contained in RS_1. We denote by '$RS_1{}^*$' the formal system obtained from RS_1 by adding to it the symbols u_1, u_2, u_3, . . . which serve as individual constants. The only difference between RS_1 and $RS_1{}^*$ is that the latter has a larger number of primitive symbols: their rules for *wffs*, postulates, and theorems are identically the same. We assume—for definiteness—that all *cwffs* of RS$_1$* have been ordered in a sequence, so we can refer to them as the first, the second, the third, and so on (there are many alternative ways of accomplishing this, of course).

Starting with any arbitrary consistent set Λ of *cwffs* of RS$_1$, we enlarge it by adding *cwffs* to it one at a time. The first *cwff* to be added is $(\exists x)Q_1 \supset Q_1{}^*$, where $(\exists x)Q_1$ is the first *cwff* of RS$_1$* which begins with an existential quantifier, and $Q_1{}^*$ is the result of replacing all free occurrences of x in Q_1 by u_{i_1}, where u_{i_1} is the first u_i which has no occurrence in Q_1. We may call the resulting set 'Λ_1', where $\Lambda_1 = $ df $\{\Lambda,\ (\exists x)Q_1 \supset Q_1{}^*\}$, and can easily prove it to be consistent. For if Λ_1 were inconsistent, we should have $\Lambda,\ (\exists x)Q_1 \supset Q_1{}^* \vdash \sim P{\cdot}P$, and by the Deduction Theorem, $\Lambda \vdash [(\exists x)Q_1 \supset Q_1{}^*] \supset \sim P{\cdot}P$. Since Λ contains no occurrences of u_{i_1} nor any free individual variables, in the derivation of $[(\exists x)Q_1 \supset Q_1{}^*] \supset \sim P{\cdot}P$ from Λ we could replace all occurrences of u_{i_1} by the free individual variable x to obtain $\Lambda \vdash [(\exists x)Q_1 \supset Q_1] \supset \sim P{\cdot}P$. From that we could successively obtain

$\Lambda \vdash (x)\{[(\exists x)Q_1 \supset Q_1] \supset \sim P{\cdot}P\}$	by R 2
$\Lambda \vdash (\exists x)[(\exists x)Q_1 \supset Q_1] \supset \sim P{\cdot}P$	by Th. 21 and Substitution
$\Lambda \vdash [(\exists x)Q_1 \supset (\exists x)Q_1] \supset \sim P{\cdot}P$	by Th. 19 and Substitution
$\Lambda \vdash [(\exists x)Q_1 \supset (\exists x)Q_1]$	by Ⓟ

and finally $\Lambda \vdash \sim P{\cdot}P$

which is contrary to the assumption that Λ is consistent. Hence Λ_1 is a consistent set.

The next *cwff* to be added is $(\exists x)Q_2 \supset Q_2{}^*$, where $(\exists x)Q_2$ is the second *cwff* of RS$_1$* which begins with an existential quantifier, and $Q_2{}^*$ is the result of replacing all free occurrences of x in Q_2 by u_{i_2}, where u_{i_2} is the first u_i not in either Q_2 or Λ_1. We now define Λ_2 as $\{\Lambda_1,\ (\exists x)Q_2 \supset Q_2{}^*\}$, and it can be proved to be consistent in exactly the same way that Λ_1 was. We continue to add *cwffs* one at a time: to Λ_{j-1} we add $(\exists x)Q_j \supset Q_j{}^*$ where $(\exists x)Q_j$ is the jth *cwff* of RS$_1$* which begins with an existential quantifier, and $Q_j{}^*$ is the result of replacing all free occurrences of x in Q_j by u_{i_j}, where u_{i_j} is the first u_i not present either in Q_j or in Λ_{j-1}. Each Λ_j is consistent, each of them contains Λ as a subset, and each set is contained in all of the later sets of the sequence.

Next we define the set Λ_ω as the sum or union of all sets in the preceding sequence. Any *cwff* of RS₁* is a member of Λ_ω provided that it is a member of any of the sets Λ_i of the sequence. It is clear that $\Lambda \subset \Lambda_\omega$, and easily proved that Λ_ω is consistent. For if Λ_ω were inconsistent, there would be a demonstration of $\sim P \cdot P$ from a finite number of formulas of Λ_ω. Each of these would have to occur in Λ or some Λ_i for the first time and in every Λ_j thereafter, for Λ_ω contains no formulas except those which occur in Λ or Λ_1 or Λ_2 or Λ_3 or . . . , and we have observed that $\Lambda \subset \Lambda_1 \subset \Lambda_2 \subset \Lambda_3 \subset$ . . . Since there can be only a finite number of premises used in any demonstration, there would have to be a first set Λ_i which contains all the premises actually used in the alleged proof that $\Lambda_\omega \vdash \sim P \cdot P$. But that proof, then, would equally well be a proof that $\Lambda_i \vdash \sim P \cdot P$, contrary to the fact that each Λ_i is consistent. Hence Λ_ω is consistent.

Now we proceed to enlarge Λ_ω until we obtain a *maximal* consistent set Γ of *cwffs* of RS₁*. Our method of 'enlarging' Λ_ω is by successively adding to it each *cwff* of RS₁* which is consistent with the formulas of Λ_ω together with those previously added to it. The resulting set Γ will be consistent, since any demonstration that $\Gamma \vdash \sim P \cdot P$ would make use of only a finite number of formulas of Γ, the last of which (in the order of their addition) could *not* have been added if the directions for adding formulas had been followed. From our definition of Γ it follows for any *cwff* of RS₁* which is not in Γ that its addition to Γ would result in an inconsistent set; hence we call Γ a *maximal* consistent set.

It is obvious that Γ contains all the postulates of RS₁* that are closed and the closures of those that are not, and also all theorems of RS₁* that are closed, because if S is a *cwff* such that $\Gamma \vdash S$ then S is contained in Γ. For since Γ is maximal, the addition to it of any *cwff* S not already contained in it results in an inconsistent set, that is, for any *cwff* S not belonging to Γ, we have $\Gamma, S \vdash \sim P \cdot P$. From this, by the Deduction Theorem, we have $\Gamma \vdash S \supset \sim P \cdot P$. Now if we were also to have $\Gamma \vdash S$ then by R 1 we should have $\Gamma \vdash \sim P \cdot P$, contrary to the fact that Γ is consistent. It should also be observed that where S is any *cwff* of RS₁*, either $\Gamma \vdash S$ or $\Gamma \vdash \sim S$. This follows from the fact that every *cwff* S of RS$_1$* either is or is not contained in Γ. If S is in Γ then obviously $\Gamma \vdash S$. While if S is not in Γ then $\Gamma, S \vdash \sim P \cdot P$ and by the Deduction Theorem, $\Gamma \vdash S \supset \sim P \cdot P$. From this, by ⓟ, we have $\Gamma \vdash \sim(\sim P \cdot P) \supset \sim S$, and since we also have by ⓟ that $\Gamma \vdash \sim(\sim P \cdot P)$, by R 1 we have $\Gamma \vdash \sim S$. From the preceding remarks it follows that for any *cwff* S either S belongs to Γ or $\sim S$ belongs to Γ.

To show that the formulas of Γ, and hence certainly those of Λ, are simultaneously satisfiable, we take as our model the set I of all individual constants of RS$_1$*, regarded as *individuals*. These are all the individual constants of RS$_1$, a, b, c, a_1, b_1, c_1, a_2, b_2, c_2, . . . , together with all the symbols u_1, u_2, u_3, u_4, ... Our interpretation of the *cwffs* of Γ consists of the following assignment of meanings:

1. To each propositional symbol of RS$_1$* we assign the truth value **T** if it belongs to Γ; otherwise it is assigned the truth value **F**. This clearly assigns a definite truth value to every propositional symbol which is a component of any *cwff* of Γ.

2. To each individual constant of RS$_1$* (considered as a symbol in an interpreted system) we assign itself (considered as an individual which belongs to the model I). There are no free individual variables in any *wff* of Γ, since these are all *cwffs*; consequently no attention need be paid to them here.

3. To each predicate symbol P^n we assign the n-adic relation (or property, if $n = 1$) among n individuals of I of having their names, properly parenthesized, adjoined in that order to P^n, constitute a *cwff* of Γ.

The interpretation is completed and made normal by adding the conditions

a. Any *cwff* $\sim S$ is assigned the truth value **T** or **F** according as the *cwff* S is assigned the truth value **F** or **T**.

b. Any *cwff* $X \cdot Y$ is assigned the truth value **T** if both X and Y are assigned the truth value **T**; otherwise it is assigned **F**.

c. Any *cwff* $(x)R$ is assigned the truth value **T** if the truth value **T** is assigned to every result of replacing all free occurrences of x in R by an individual constant of RS_1*; otherwise it is assigned **F**.

d. Every *cwff* $P^n(a_1, a_2, \ldots, a_n)$ is assigned the truth value **T** if the elements of the model assigned to $a_1, a_2, \ldots, a_n$, in that order, stand to each other in the *n*-adic relation assigned to P^n, otherwise it is assigned **F**.

We now can prove that all *wffs* of Γ are satisfied on this interpretation. What we shall actually prove is the stronger result that every *cwff* S of RS_1^* is assigned the truth value **T** or **F** according as S belongs or does not belong to Γ. Our proof is by strong induction on the number of symbols in S, counting each propositional symbol, each *cwff* of the form $P^n(a_1, a_2, \ldots, a_n)$, each universal quantifier (x), and each occurrence of $\cdot$ and $\sim$ as a single symbol.

$\alpha)$ In case $n = 1$, S is either a propositional symbol or a *cwff* of the form $P^n(a_1, a_2, \ldots, a_n)$. If S is a propositional symbol, by paragraph 1 of the original assignment of meanings, S is assigned the truth value **T** or **F** according as it is contained or not contained in Γ. If S is the *cwff* $P^n(a_1, a_2, \ldots, a_n)$ then by paragraph 3 and condition *d*, S is assigned the truth value **T** or **F** according as it is contained or not contained in Γ.

$\beta)$ Here we assume that every *cwff* of RS_1^* which contains fewer than k symbols is assigned the truth value **T** or **F** according as it is contained or not contained in Γ. Now we consider any *cwff* S of RS_1^* which contains exactly k symbols. S must be of the form $\sim W$ or $X \cdot Y$ or $(x)R$.

CASE 1. S is $\sim W$. If $\sim W$ is in Γ then since Γ is a maximal consistent set, W is not in Γ. Here, by the β-case assumption, since W contains fewer than k symbols, W is assigned the truth value **F**. By condition *a*, $\sim W$ must be assigned **T**. Hence if S is in Γ it is assigned the truth value **T**. If $\sim W$ is not in Γ then W is in Γ. Here W is assigned **T**, so that $\sim W$ must be assigned **F**. Hence if S is not in Γ it is assigned the truth value **F**.

CASE 2. S is $X \cdot Y$. If $X \cdot Y$ is in Γ then by ℗ $\Gamma \vdash X$ and $\Gamma \vdash Y$, so X and Y are both in Γ. Since each contains fewer than k symbols, by the β-case assumption they are both assigned the truth value **T**, and by condition

b, S is also. If $X \cdot Y$ is not in Γ then not both X and Y can be in Γ (for if they were, then by ℗ $\Gamma \vdash X \cdot Y$ and $X \cdot Y$ would have to be contained in Γ), so not both X and Y are assigned the truth value **T**, and by condition b, S is assigned the truth value **F**.

CASE 3. S is $(x)R$. If $(x)R$ is in Γ then where Q is any result of replacing all free occurrences of x in R by an individual constant, $\vdash (x)R \supset Q$ by P 5, and by R 1, $\Gamma \vdash Q$. Since Γ is a maximal consistent set, every such Q is contained in Γ, and since each of them contains fewer than k symbols, they are all assigned the truth value **T** by the β-case assumption, and by condition c, $(x)R$ is assigned **T** also. Hence if $(x)R$ is in Γ it is assigned the truth value **T**. If $(x)R$ is not in Γ, then $\Gamma \vdash \sim (x)R$, which is, by Th. 7 and the Substitution Theorem, $\Gamma \vdash (\exists x)\sim R$. Since Γ is a maximal consistent set, it must contain $(\exists x)\sim R$. But $(\exists x)\sim R$ is a *cwff* of RS₁* which begins with an existential quantifier, and so the formula $(\exists x)\sim R \supset \sim R^*$ must have been added to some Λ_{j-1} to form Λ_j—where $\sim R^*$ is the result of replacing all free occurrences of x in $\sim R$ by u_{i_j}. Since the *cwff* $(\exists x)\sim R \supset \sim R^*$ belongs to some such Λ_j it must belong to Γ. Hence, by R 1, $\Gamma \vdash \sim R^*$, so that $\sim R^*$ belongs to Γ also. Since Γ is consistent, R^* does *not* belong to Γ, and since it contains fewer than k symbols, by the β-case assumption it is assigned the truth value **F**. Hence by condition c, $(x)R$ is assigned the truth value **F**.

This completes the induction, and proves that all formulas of Γ, and hence all those of Λ, are simultaneously satisfiable. Metatheorem X, together with the discussion which preceded it, completes our proof of

METATHEOREM XI. *RS₁ is complete.*

In the preceding section we showed that RS₁ is logically equivalent to the natural deduction techniques developed in Chapter 4. Hence our proof of Metatheorem XI validates the claim made at the end of Chapter 4 that the natural deduction techniques there developed 'permit the demonstration of all logically true propositions constructed out of truth-functional connectives and the quantifications of individual variables'.

A more complicated logistic system is required for the formalization of the logical principles involved in appraising arguments which concern properties of properties or of relations, or relations among properties and relations, or the notions of *all* or *some* properties or relations. Such logistic systems are generally called *extended function calculi*, and if they are consistent, they are demonstrably incomplete.[9] But these more advanced parts of symbolic logic lie beyond the scope of the present book.

[9] Proved by Kurt Gödel in 'Über formal unentscheidbare Sätze der Principia Mathematica und verwandter Systeme', *Monatshefte für Mathematik und Physik*, vol. 38 (1931), pp. 173–198.

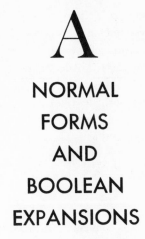

NORMAL
FORMS
AND
BOOLEAN
EXPANSIONS

In this Appendix we develop an alternative method for distinguishing between valid and invalid arguments by distinguishing between tautologous, contradictory, and contingent statement forms. First we observe that given a complicated statement form it is frequently possible to find a simpler one logically equivalent to it, to which the original form may be 'reduced' by means of certain algebraic operations. In treating the logic of compound statements and statement forms from the algebraic point of view, it is convenient to use a different notation for denial or negation. Here we symbolize the negation of an expression by drawing a bar above it. In this notation, the familiar truths of De Morgan are symbolized as $\overline{p \cdot q} \equiv (\bar{p} \vee \bar{q})$ and $\overline{p \vee q} \equiv (\bar{p} \cdot \bar{q})$. All of the statement forms treated here are truth-functional, so their status as tautologous, contradictory, or contingent remains unchanged when any part is replaced by a logically equivalent expression. Thus $p \vee \bar{p}$ is a tautology and remains one when p is replaced in it by $\bar{p}$, since p and $\bar{p}$ are logically equivalent by the principle of Double Negation.

Since $p \cdot (q \cdot r)$ and $(p \cdot q) \cdot r$ are logically equivalent, they may be indifferently written as $p \cdot q \cdot r$. Similarly, both $p \vee (q \vee r)$ and $(p \vee q) \vee r$

may be written as $p \vee q \vee r$. The logical equivalences involved are principles of Association. The convention of dropping these unnecessary parentheses permits us to enunciate generalized statements of De Morgan's Theorems as $\overline{p_1 \cdot p_2 \cdot p_3 \cdot \ldots \cdot p_n} \equiv (\bar{p}_1 \vee \bar{p}_2 \vee \bar{p}_3 \vee \ldots \vee \bar{p}_n)$ and $\overline{p_1 \vee p_2 \vee p_3 \vee \ldots \vee p_n} \equiv (\bar{p}_1 \cdot \bar{p}_2 \cdot \bar{p}_3 \cdot \ldots \cdot \bar{p}_n)$. The two tautologies $[p \cdot (q \vee r)] \equiv [(p \cdot q) \vee (p \cdot r)]$ and $[p \vee (q \cdot r)] \equiv [(p \vee q) \cdot (p \vee r)]$ are principles of Distribution. Generalized principles of Distribution may be expressed as

$$[p \cdot (q_1 \vee q_2 \vee \ldots \vee q_n)] \equiv [(p \cdot q_1) \vee (p \cdot q_2) \vee \ldots \vee (p \cdot q_n)]$$

and

$$[p \vee (q_1 \cdot q_2 \cdot \ldots \cdot q_n)] \equiv [(p \vee q_1) \cdot (p \vee q_2) \cdot \ldots \cdot (p \vee q_n)]$$

It is convenient to have four other principles of logical equivalence available for purposes of algebraic manipulation and transformation. First, the principles of Commutation, expressed as

$$(p \cdot q) \equiv (q \cdot p) \quad \text{and} \quad (p \vee q) \equiv (q \vee p)$$

Second, the principles of Tautology, which, stated as

$$p \equiv (p \vee p) \quad \text{and} \quad p \equiv (p \cdot p)$$

assure us that any statement, wherever it may occur, is replaceable by the disjunction (conjunction) both of whose disjuncts (conjuncts) are the same as the given statement, and vice versa. Third is the principle that any statement p is logically equivalent to the conjunction of itself with any tautology of the form $q \vee \bar{q}$, that is

$$p \equiv [p \cdot (q \vee \bar{q})]$$

Our fourth and final principle is the logical equivalence

$$p \equiv [p \vee (q \cdot \bar{q})]$$

which permits us to interchange p and $p \vee (q \cdot \bar{q})$ wherever either of them occurs.

It is clear that by invoking the defining equivalences

$$(p \supset q) \equiv (\bar{p} \vee q) \quad \text{and} \quad (p \equiv q) \equiv [(p \cdot q) \vee (\bar{p} \cdot \bar{q})]$$

material implications and equivalences can always be eliminated in favor of, or expressed in terms of, conjunctions, disjunctions, and negations. Moreover, by repeated uses of De Morgan's Theorems and Double Negation, any form can be replaced by a logically equivalent one in which no negation symbol applies to a compound part. Thus

$$\overline{\bar{p}\cdot[(\overline{\bar{q}\,\text{v}\,r})\cdot(s\cdot\bar{t})]}$$

is transformed by repeated applications of De Morgan's principles and Double Negation as follows:

$$\bar{p}\,\text{v}\,\overline{[(\overline{\bar{q}\,\text{v}\,r})\cdot(s\cdot\bar{t})]}$$
$$p\,\text{v}\,[(\overline{\overline{\bar{q}\,\text{v}\,r}})\,\text{v}\,(\overline{s\cdot\bar{t}})]$$
$$p\,\text{v}\,[(\bar{q}\,\text{v}\,r)\,\text{v}\,(\bar{s}\,\text{v}\,t)]$$
$$p\,\text{v}\,[(\bar{q}\,\text{v}\,r)\,\text{v}\,(\bar{s}\,\text{v}\,t)]$$

which becomes, by the principle of Association,

$$p\,\text{v}\,\bar{q}\,\text{v}\,r\,\text{v}\,\bar{s}\,\text{v}\,t$$

in which the negation symbol is applied only to the single variables q and s.

The principle of Distribution permits us to change any given form into an equivalent one in which conjunction symbols occur—if at all—only between single variables or their negations, or else into a different equivalent form in which disjunction symbols occur—if at all—only between single variables or their negations. Thus the expression

(1) $(p\,\text{v}\,q)\cdot(r\,\text{v}\,s)$

in which the conjunction symbol occurs between disjunctions, reduces by repeated applications of the principles of Distribution, Commutation, and Association into

(2) $(p\cdot r)\,\text{v}\,(q\cdot r)\,\text{v}\,(p\cdot s)\,\text{v}\,(q\cdot s)$

in which conjunction symbols connect single variables only. And the expression

(3) $(p\cdot q)\,\text{v}\,(r\cdot s)$

in which the disjunction symbol occurs between conjunctions, reduces by repeated applications of the other parts of the principles of Distribution, Commutation, and Association into

(4) $(p \vee r) \cdot (q \vee r) \cdot (p \vee s) \cdot (q \vee s)$

in which disjunction symbols connect single variables only.

Two 'normal forms' can be defined. A statement form is in *conjunctive normal form* when in addition to statement variables it contains no symbols other than those for conjunction, disjunction, and negation; negation symbols apply only to single variables; and no disjunct is a conjunction, i.e., disjunction symbols occur only between single variables or their negations. Thus (1) and (4) above are in *conjunctive normal form*. A statement form is in *disjunctive normal form* when in addition to statement variables it contains no symbols other than those for conjunction, disjunction, and negation; negation symbols apply only to single variables; and no conjunct is a disjunction, i.e., conjunction symbols occur only between single variables or their negations. Thus (2) and (3) above are in *disjunctive normal form*.

Let us examine the moderately complicated form $(p \supset \bar{q}) \supset (p \equiv \bar{q})$ to see what gain in perspicuity is achieved by reducing it to disjunctive normal form. By replacing the material implication symbols by their definitions, the initial expression is reduced first to

$$(\bar{p} \vee \bar{q}) \supset (p \equiv \bar{q})$$

and then to

$$\overline{(\bar{p} \vee \bar{q})} \vee (p \equiv \bar{q})$$

Replacing the material equivalence symbol by its definition, we obtain

$$\overline{(\bar{p} \vee \bar{q})} \vee [(p \cdot \bar{q}) \vee (\bar{p} \cdot \bar{\bar{q}})]$$

Applying De Morgan's principle we obtain

$$(\bar{\bar{p}} \cdot \bar{\bar{q}}) \vee [(p \cdot \bar{q}) \vee (\bar{p} \cdot \bar{\bar{q}})]$$

which by the principles of Double Negation and Association becomes

$$(p \cdot q) \vee (p \cdot \bar{q}) \vee (\bar{p} \cdot q)$$

Although it is already in disjunctive normal form, it can be further simplified by the following transformations. First we apply the principle of Tautology to replace the first disjunct by its 'double', obtaining

$$(p \cdot q) \text{ v } (p \cdot q) \text{ v } (p \cdot \bar{q}) \text{ v } (\bar{p} \cdot q)$$

Then we rearrange the terms by simply commuting or interchanging the second and third disjuncts, to get

$$(p \cdot q) \text{ v } (p \cdot \bar{q}) \text{ v } (p \cdot q) \text{ v } (\bar{p} \cdot q)$$

Using the principle of Distribution on the first pair of disjuncts we obtain

$$[p \cdot (q \text{ v } \bar{q})] \text{ v } (p \cdot q) \text{ v } (\bar{p} \cdot q)$$

and using it and Commutation on the two right-hand disjuncts we get

$$[p \cdot (q \text{ v } \bar{q})] \text{ v } [(p \text{ v } \bar{p}) \cdot q]$$

Now by the principle that the conjunction of any statement p with a tautology of the form $q \text{ v } \bar{q}$ is logically equivalent to the statement itself, we obtain first

$$p \text{ v } [(p \text{ v } \bar{p}) \cdot q]$$

and finally

$$p \text{ v } q$$

which is logically equivalent to, but much simpler than the form with which we began.[1]

The term 'normal form' is sometimes reserved for more specific types of expressions. These more specific types are also called *Boolean Expansions* or *Boolean normal forms*, after the British logician George Boole (1815–1864). A statement form containing the variables p, q, r, . . . is said to be in disjunctive Boolean normal form, or a disjunctive Boolean Expansion, provided that it is in disjunctive normal form,

[1] An application of normal forms to electrical circuits (parallel connections being representable by 'v' and series connections being representable by '·') has been made by Claude E. Shannon, "A Symbolic Analysis of Relay and Switching Circuits", *Transactions of the American Institute of Electrical Engineers*, vol. 57 (1938), pp. 713–723.

An informal account of the above and several other interesting applications can be found in John E. Pfeiffer's article "Symbolic Logic", in *Scientific American*, vol. 183, no. 6 (December 1950). Cf. also "Logic Machines" by Martin Gardner, *ibid.*, vol. 186, no. 3 (March 1952).

every disjunct contains exactly one occurrence of every variable (either the variable or its negation), the variables occur in alphabetical order in each disjunct, and no two disjuncts are the same. The disjunctive Boolean Expansion of $p \vee q$ is formed by first replacing p by $p \cdot (q \vee \bar{q})$ and q by $(p \vee \bar{p}) \cdot q$ to obtain the equivalent expression $p \cdot (q \vee \bar{q}) \vee (p \vee \bar{p}) \cdot q$, then using the Distribution and Association rules to obtain $(p \cdot q) \vee (p \cdot \bar{q}) \vee (p \cdot q) \vee (\bar{p} \cdot q)$, and finally cancelling out any repetitions of the same disjunct by the rules of Commutation and Tautology, which results in $(p \cdot q) \vee (p \cdot \bar{q}) \vee (\bar{p} \cdot q)$. The disjunctive Boolean Expansion of any noncontradictory statement form can be obtained by the same general method.

A statement form containing the variables p, q, r, . . . is said to be in conjunctive Boolean normal form, or a conjunctive Boolean Expansion, provided that it is in conjunctive normal form, every conjunct contains exactly one occurrence of every variable (either the variable or its negation), the variables occur in alphabetical order in each conjunct, and no two conjuncts are the same. The conjunctive Boolean Expansion of $p \cdot q$ is formed by first replacing p by $p \vee (q \cdot \bar{q})$ and q by $(p \cdot \bar{p}) \vee q$ to obtain $[p \vee (q \cdot \bar{q})] \cdot [(p \cdot \bar{p}) \vee q]$, then using the Distribution and Association rules to obtain $(p \vee q) \cdot (p \vee \bar{q}) \cdot (p \vee q) \cdot (\bar{p} \vee q)$, and finally cancelling out any repetition of the same conjunct by the rules of Commutation and Tautology, which results in $(p \vee q) \cdot (p \vee \bar{q}) \cdot (\bar{p} \vee q)$. The conjunctive Boolean Expansion of any nontautologous statement form is easily obtained by the same general method, and can be used for deciding whether the original form is contradictory. Any conjunctive Boolean Expansion containing n variables and 2^n conjuncts is reducible to an explicit contradiction. Thus the conjunctive Boolean Expansion $(p \vee q) \cdot (p \vee \bar{q}) \cdot (\bar{p} \vee q) \cdot (\bar{p} \vee \bar{q})$ is equivalent by the rule of Distribution to $[p \vee (q \cdot \bar{q})] \cdot [\bar{p} \vee (q \cdot \bar{q})]$, which is equivalent to the explicit contradiction $p \cdot \bar{p}$. It is equally obvious that the conjunctive Boolean Expansion of any contradiction will contain 2^n conjuncts if it involves n variables. Hence the general rule is that a statement form containing n variables is contradictory if and only if it has a conjunctive Boolean Expansion which contains 2^n conjuncts.

The negation of a conjunctive Boolean Expansion is reducible by repeated applications of De Morgan's Theorem and Double Negation to a logically equivalent disjunctive Boolean Expansion which contains the same variables and has the same number of disjuncts as the original conjunctive Boolean Expansion has conjuncts. Thus the conjunctive Boolean Expansion $(p \vee q \vee r) \cdot (p \vee q \vee \bar{r}) \cdot (\bar{p} \vee \bar{q} \vee r)$ has its negation $\overline{(p \vee q \vee r) \cdot (p \vee q \vee \bar{r}) \cdot (\bar{p} \vee \bar{q} \vee r)}$ logically equivalent to the disjunctive Boolean Expansion $(\bar{p} \cdot \bar{q} \cdot \bar{r}) \vee (\bar{p} \cdot \bar{q} \cdot r) \vee (p \cdot q \cdot \bar{r})$. Since the negation of a contradiction is a tautology, and a conjunctive Boolean Expansion containing n variables is a contradiction if and only if it contains 2^n conjuncts, it follows that a disjunctive Boolean Expansion containing n variables is a tautology if and only if it contains 2^n disjuncts.

That such a disjunctive Boolean Expansion must be tautologous can perhaps be seen more clearly by the following considerations. In the first place, since we are concerned with truth-functional compounds only, to speak of substituting statements for the statement variables of a form is equivalent to speaking of an assignment of truth values to the variables of that form. Now just as each row of a truth table with n initial or guide columns represents a different assignment of truth values to the n statement variables involved, so each disjunct of the Boolean Expansion represents a different assignment of truth values to the variables they contain. And just as the 2^n rows of a truth table having n initial or guide columns represent all possible assignments of truth values to its variables, so the 2^n disjuncts of a disjunctive Boolean Expansion represent all possible assignments of truth values to its variables. Since the 2^n disjuncts represent all possible assignments of truth values to its variables, at least one of them must be true. And since it asserts only that at least one of its disjuncts is true, any disjunctive Boolean Expansion containing n variables and 2^n disjuncts is tautologous.

It was pointed out in Chapter 2 that a truth-functional argument is valid if and only if its corresponding conditional statement (whose antecedent is the conjunction of the argument's premises and whose consequent is the argument's conclusion) is a tautology. Since counting the number of disjuncts of its disjunctive Boolean Expansion permits us to decide whether or not a given form is a tautology, this provides us with an alternative method of deciding the validity of arguments. Thus the argument form $p \vee q$, $\sim p$ $\therefore$ q is proved valid by constructing the disjunctive Boolean Expansion of its corresponding conditional $[(p \lor q) \cdot \bar{p}] \supset q$, and observing that the number of its disjuncts is 2^2.

Since the negation of a tautology is a contradiction, an argument is valid if and only if the negation of its corresponding conditional is a contradiction. Hence another method of deciding the validity of an argument is to form the conjunctive Boolean Expansion of the negation of its corresponding conditional and count the number of its conjuncts. If it contains n distinct variables and has 2^n conjuncts, then the argument is valid; otherwise it is invalid.

EXERCISES

For each of the following find as simple an equivalent as you can:

1. $p \lor (q \cdot \bar{p})$
★2. $p \lor (p \cdot q)$
3. $q \cdot (p \lor \bar{q})$
4. $p \cdot (p \lor q)$
5. $(p \lor q) \cdot (q \lor r) \cdot (p \lor r) \cdot r$
★6. $(p \cdot q) \lor (q \cdot r) \lor (p \cdot r) \lor r$
7. $p \cdot \{p \supset [q \cdot (q \supset r)]\}$
8. $p \lor \{\bar{p} \supset [q \lor (\bar{q} \supset r)]\}$
9. $(p \lor q) \supset [(p \supset q) \supset (\overline{q \lor \bar{q}})]$
★10. $(p \cdot \bar{q}) \supset [(p \supset q) \supset (\overline{p \cdot \bar{q}})]$
11. $\{p \cdot [(q \cdot r) \lor \bar{p}]\} \lor \{(p \cdot q) \cdot [r \supset (\bar{p} \cdot \bar{r})]\} \lor \{p \cdot [\bar{p} \supset (p \cdot q \cdot \bar{r})]\}$
12. $(p \cdot q) \lor (\bar{p} \cdot \bar{q} \cdot r) \lor (\bar{p} \cdot q) \lor (p \cdot \bar{q} \cdot r) \lor (p \cdot \bar{q}) \lor (p \cdot q \cdot r) \lor (\bar{p} \cdot q \cdot r)$

B

THE
ALGEBRA
OF
CLASSES

The four traditional types of subject-predicate propositions discussed in Section 4.1 of Chapter 4 can be interpreted as assertions about classes. On this interpretation, these categorical propositions (as they have been traditionally called) are understood to affirm or to deny that one class is included in another, either in whole or in part. Thus the *A* proposition 'All humans are mortal' is taken to assert that the whole of the class of humans is contained in the class of mortal beings, and the *I* proposition 'Some humans are mortal' asserts that *part* of the class of humans is contained in the class of mortals. Their respective negations, the *O* and *E* propositions, simply deny these inclusions.

On the class interpretation of categorical propositions both their subject and predicate terms designate classes, where a class is any collection of distinct objects. In treating of classes, we permit, and shall later discuss, a class which contains no members at all. In this appendix we shall use lower case letters of the Greek alphabet to designate classes. Given the classes α, β, γ, . . . certain further classes can be defined in terms of them. Thus we can define the class of all objects which belong *either* to α *or* to β: this class formed by the *addition* of α and β, is called the *sum* or *union* of α and β, and is symbolized as '$\alpha \cup \beta$'. And we can define the class of all objects which belong *both* to α *and* to β: this class, formed by the *multiplication* of α and β, is called the *product* or *intersection* of α and β, and is symbolized sometimes as '$\alpha \cap \beta$', more often simply as '$\alpha\beta$'. Given any class α we can define the *complement* of α, symbolized as '$\bar{\alpha}$', to be the class of all objects which do *not* belong to α.

Many statements about classes can be formulated using the ordinary equals sign: '$\alpha = \beta$' asserts that all members of α, if any, are also members of β, *and* that all members of β, if any, are also members of α. Many of the properties of the sum, product, and complement of classes can be expressed by means of equations. It is clear, for example, that the operations of forming the sum and forming the product of two classes are commutative: symbolically, we have

$$(\alpha \cup \beta) = (\beta \cup \alpha) \quad \text{and} \quad \alpha\beta = \beta\alpha$$

They are also associative:

$$(\alpha \cup \beta) \cup \gamma = \alpha \cup (\beta \cup \gamma) \quad \text{and} \quad (\alpha\beta)\gamma = \alpha(\beta\gamma)$$

Two principles of distribution also hold for class sums and products. Any object which belongs either to α or to both β and γ must belong either to α or to β and must also belong either to α or to γ, and conversely. In other words, for classes, addition is distributive with respect to multiplication, which may be expressed symbolically as

$$\alpha \cup (\beta\gamma) = (\alpha \cup \beta)(\alpha \cup \gamma)$$

Moreover, any object which belongs both to α and to either β or γ must belong either to both α and β or to both α and γ. For classes, then, multiplication is distributive with respect to addition, which is expressed symbolically as

$$\alpha(\beta \cup \gamma) = \alpha\beta \cup \alpha\gamma$$

Two principles which resemble the tautology principle for statements (cf. p. 326) are immediate consequences of the definitions of the sum and the product of classes:

$$\alpha = \alpha \cup \alpha \quad \text{and} \quad \alpha = \alpha\alpha$$

Another immediate consequence of those definitions is the so-called Law of Absorption:

$$\alpha = \alpha \cup \alpha\beta$$

Turning now to the notion of class complement, we observe that since anything belongs to a given class if and only if it does not belong to the class of all things which do not belong to the given class, the complement of the complement of a class is the class itself. We thus have a sort of double negative rule for complementation, which can be expressed in symbols as

$$\alpha = \bar{\bar{\alpha}}$$

An object which does not belong to the sum of two classes belongs to neither of them, and must therefore belong to both of their complements. And an object which does not belong to the product of two classes must belong to the class complement of at least one of them. These two propositions, and their converses, which are also true, can be expressed symbolically as

$$\overline{\alpha \cup \beta} = \bar{\alpha}\bar{\beta} \quad \text{and} \quad \overline{\alpha\beta} = \bar{\alpha} \cup \bar{\beta}$$

which are versions of De Morgan's theorems applying to classes.

Two special classes are the null class, which has no members, and the *universal* class, to which all objects belong. The null class (also called the *empty* class) is symbolized as '0' (sometimes as 'Λ'), and the universal class is symbolized as '1' (sometimes as 'V'). It is clear that the null class is the complement of the universal class:

$$\bar{1} = 0$$

The following two equations are immediate consequences of the preceding definitions:

$$\alpha \cup \bar{\alpha} = 1 \quad \text{and} \quad \alpha\bar{\alpha} = 0$$

Further immediate consequences are these:

$$\alpha \cup 0 = \alpha, \; \alpha 1 = \alpha, \; \alpha 0 = 0, \quad \text{and} \quad \alpha \cup 1 = 1$$

It is easily shown that any class can be designated by infinitely many different *class-expressions*. Thus the class designated by 'α' can also be designated by '$\alpha(\beta \cup \bar{\beta})$' (since $\beta \cup \bar{\beta} = 1$ and $\alpha 1 = \alpha$), and by '$[\alpha(\beta \cup \bar{\beta})](\gamma \cup \bar{\gamma})$', and so on. By this 'Law of Expansion' we can always introduce any class symbol we choose into a given class expression in such a way that the original and the expanded class expressions designate the same class.

By the principle of distribution, the class $\alpha(\beta \cup \bar{\beta})$ is the same as $\alpha\beta \cup \alpha\bar{\beta}$. To aid in describing the form of the latter expression, let us use the phrase 'simple class term' to refer to the class symbols 'α', 'β', 'γ', . . . , in contrast to other class expressions such as sums and products. Now we can describe the expression '$\alpha\beta \cup \alpha\bar{\beta}$' as a sum of distinct products, such that in each product appear only simple class terms or their complements, and such that any simple class term which appears anywhere in the entire expression appears exactly once in every product. Any such expression is said to be a Boolean Expansion or Boolean normal form.[1] By means of the equations presented thus far, any class expression can be transformed into a Boolean Expansion which designates the same class. Thus $\overline{\alpha(\bar{\alpha} \cup \beta)}$ is equal by De Morgan's Theorem to $\bar{\alpha} \cup \overline{(\bar{\alpha} \cup \beta)}$ which is equal, again by De Morgan's Theorem, to $\bar{\alpha} \cup \bar{\bar{\alpha}}\bar{\beta}$, which by double negation is equal to $\bar{\alpha} \cup \alpha\bar{\beta}$, which is equal by Expansion to $\bar{\alpha}(\beta \cup \bar{\beta}) \cup \alpha\bar{\beta}$, which by distribution is equal to the Boolean Expansion $\bar{\alpha}\beta \cup \bar{\alpha}\bar{\beta} \cup \alpha\bar{\beta}$. (Our association principle, $(\alpha \cup \beta) \cup \gamma = \alpha \cup (\beta \cup \gamma)$, permits us to drop parentheses and write either simply as $\alpha \cup \beta \cup \gamma$.)

Any class whatever will divide the universal class into two subdivisions or subclasses which are mutually exclusive and jointly exhaustive. That is, for any class α: $1 = \alpha \cup \bar{\alpha}$ and $\alpha\bar{\alpha} = 0$. Any two classes will divide the universal class into *four* subclasses which are exclusive and exhaustive. Thus for any classes α and β: $1 = \alpha\beta \cup \alpha\bar{\beta} \cup \bar{\alpha}\beta \cup \bar{\alpha}\bar{\beta}$, and the product of any two of those four products is the null class. Similarly, any n classes will divide the universal class into 2^n subclasses which are exclusive and exhaustive. The class expression which symbolizes such a division of the universal class, it should be observed, is a Boolean Expansion. A Boolean Expansion containing n different simple class terms designates the universal class if it is the sum

[1] Compare these with the Boolean Expansions for statements discussed in Appendix A.

of 2^n distinct products (where a mere difference in the order of their terms does not make two products distinct). Boolean Expansions thus provide us with a method for deciding whether or not any class expression designates the universal class regardless of what classes are designated by the simple class terms which it contains. Given any class expression, we need only construct its Boolean Expansion and count the number of products of which it is the sum.

The Boolean Expansions discussed above are often called *disjunctive* Boolean Expansions, to contrast them with *conjunctive* Boolean Expansions. A conjunctive Boolean Expansion is a product of distinct sums of simple class terms or their complements, where any simple class term which occurs anywhere in the expression will occur exactly once in every sum. By De Morgan's Theorem and the other equivalences already mentioned, the complement of any disjunctive Boolean Expansion can be transformed into a conjunctive Boolean Expansion which involves the same simple class terms and which is the product of as many sums as the disjunctive Boolean Expansion is the sum of products. Since the complement of 1 is 0, a conjunctive Boolean Expansion containing n different simple class terms designates the null class if it is the product of 2^n distinct sums. Hence we have a method for deciding whether or not any class expression designates the null class regardless of what classes are designated by the simple class terms which it contains.

The notations introduced thus far permit the symbolization of the A and E subject-predicate propositions. The E proposition: *No α is β*, asserts that the classes α and β have no members in common, which means that their product is null. The E proposition is therefore symbolized as

$$\alpha\beta = 0$$

The A proposition: *All α is β*, asserts that there is nothing which belongs to α but not to β, which means that the product of α and the complement of β is null. The A proposition is therefore symbolized as

$$\alpha\bar{\beta} = 0$$

To symbolize the I and O categorical propositions we must introduce the inequality sign '$\neq$', where '$\alpha \neq \beta$' asserts that either α contains an object which is not a member of β or β contains an object which is not a member of α. The I proposition: *Some α is β*, asserts that there is at least one member of α which is also a member of β, i.e., that the product of α and β is not null. In symbols, the I proposition appears as

$$\alpha\beta \neq 0$$

The O proposition: *Some α is not β*, asserts that there is at least one member of α which is not a member of β, i.e., that the product of α and $\bar{\beta}$ is not null. In symbols, the O proposition is expressed as

$$\alpha\bar{\beta} \neq 0$$

When formulated in our class notation it is completely obvious that the A and O propositions are contradictories, as are the E and I propositions.

Some of the traditional 'immediate inferences' involving categorical propositions are already contained in the notation of the class algebra. Thus every proposition has exactly the same symbolization as its obverse, e.g., '$\alpha\bar{\beta} = 0$' symbolizes both *All α is β* and *No α is non-β*. And conversion, where it is valid, is an immediate consequence of the principle of commutation, e.g., *Some α is β* and *Some β is α* are symbolized by '$\alpha\beta \neq 0$' and '$\beta\alpha \neq 0$', respectively, which are obviously equivalent since $\alpha\beta = \beta\alpha$ by commutation.

When we turn to the 'mediate inferences' of the traditional categorical syllogism, we can divide all categorical syllogisms into two kinds: those which contain only universal propositions (A and E), and those which contain at least one existential proposition (I or O). It is easily shown that all valid syllogisms of the first kind have the form

$$\alpha\bar{\beta} = 0, \ \beta\bar{\gamma} = 0 \ \therefore \ \alpha\bar{\gamma} = 0$$

The validity of this form can be derived within the algebra of classes by appealing to the results already set forth in this appendix. Since $\bar{\gamma}0 = 0$, and $\alpha\bar{\beta} = 0$ is a premiss, we have $\bar{\gamma}(\alpha\bar{\beta}) = 0$, which by association and commutation yields $(\alpha\bar{\gamma})\bar{\beta} = 0$. Now $\alpha0 = 0$, and $\beta\bar{\gamma} = 0$ is a premiss, so we have $\alpha(\beta\bar{\gamma}) = 0$, which by association and commutation yields $(\alpha\bar{\gamma})\beta = 0$. Hence $(\alpha\bar{\gamma})\beta \cup (\alpha\bar{\gamma})\bar{\beta} = 0$, which by distribution yields $(\alpha\bar{\gamma})(\beta \cup \bar{\beta}) = 0$. Since $\beta \cup \bar{\beta} = 1$ and $(\alpha\bar{\gamma})1 = \alpha\bar{\gamma}$ we have $\alpha\bar{\gamma} = 0$, the syllogism's conclusion.

It can also be shown that all valid syllogisms of the second kind have the form

$$\alpha\beta \neq 0, \ \beta\bar{\gamma} = 0 \ \therefore \ \alpha\gamma \neq 0$$

To establish the validity of the form we first observe that since $\alpha0 = 0$, if $\alpha\beta \neq 0$ then $\alpha \neq 0$ and $\beta \neq 0$. Since $\alpha0 = 0$, and $\beta\bar{\gamma} = 0$ as a premiss, $\alpha(\beta\bar{\gamma}) = 0$. By association we have $(\alpha\beta)\bar{\gamma} = 0$. Now $\alpha\beta = (\alpha\beta)1$ and $\gamma\cup\bar{\gamma} = 1$, hence $\alpha\beta = (\alpha\beta)(\gamma\cup\bar{\gamma})$, and by distribution, $\alpha\beta = (\alpha\beta)\gamma\cup(\alpha\beta)\bar{\gamma}$. But $(\alpha\beta)\gamma\cup0 = (\alpha\beta)\gamma$, and we have already shown that $(\alpha\beta)\bar{\gamma} = 0$, hence $\alpha\beta = (\alpha\beta)\gamma$. Since $\alpha\beta \neq 0$ is a premiss, we know that $(\alpha\beta)\gamma \neq 0$. By association and commutation we obtain $(\alpha\gamma)\beta \neq 0$ from which it follows that $\alpha\gamma \neq 0$, which is the syllogism's conclusion. Hence the algebra of classes is adequate not only to validate immediate inferences involving categorical propositions, but is capable of validating categorical syllogisms also.

The symbol '$\subset$' for *class inclusion* is often used in working with the algebra of classes. The expression '$\alpha \subset \beta$' asserts that all members of α, if any, are also members of β, and is used as an alternative symbolization of the *A* proposition: *All α is β*. It can be defined in terms of the symbols already introduced in various ways: either as $\alpha\bar{\beta} = 0$ or as $\alpha\beta = \alpha$ or as $\alpha\cup\beta = \beta$ or as $\bar{\alpha}\cup\beta = 1$, all of which are obviously equivalent. The relation $\subset$ is reflexive and transitive (cf. pages 146–147) and has the (transposition) property that if $\alpha \subset \beta$ then $\bar{\beta} \subset \bar{\alpha}$. The latter is an immediate consequence of double negation and commutation when '$\alpha \subset \beta$' is rewritten as '$\alpha\bar{\beta} = 0$' and '$\bar{\beta} \subset \bar{\alpha}$' is rewritten as '$\bar{\beta}\bar{\bar{\alpha}} = 0$'. Its reflexiveness is obvious when '$\alpha \subset \alpha$' is rewritten as '$\alpha\bar{\alpha} = 0$', and its transitivity has already been established in our algebraic proof of validity for categorical syllogisms containing only universal propositions.

The algebra of classes can be set up as a formal deductive system. Such a system is called a Boolean Algebra, and a vast number of alternative postulate sets for Boolean Algebra have been proposed. One of them can be set forth as follows.

Special undefined primitive symbols:

$$\mathbf{C}, \cap, \cup, -, \alpha, \beta, \gamma, \ \ldots$$

Axioms:

Ax. 1. If α and β are in **C** then $\alpha \cup \beta$ is in **C**.

Ax. 2. If α and β are in **C** then $\alpha \cap \beta$ is in **C**.

Ax. 3. There is an entity 0 in **C** such that $\alpha \cup 0 = \alpha$ for any α in **C**.

Ax. 4. There is an entity 1 in **C** such that $\alpha \cap 1 = \alpha$ for any α in **C**.

Ax. 5. If α and β are in **C** then $\alpha \cup \beta = \beta \cup \alpha$.

Ax. 6. If α and β are in **C** then $\alpha \cap \beta = \beta \cap \alpha$.

Ax. 7. If α, β, γ are in **C** then $\alpha \cup (\beta \cap \gamma) = (\alpha \cup \beta) \cap (\alpha \cup \gamma)$.

Ax. 8. If α, β, γ are in **C** then $\alpha \cap (\beta \cup \gamma) = (\alpha \cap \beta) \cup (\alpha \cap \gamma)$.

Ax. 9. If there are unique entities 0 and 1 satisfying Axioms 3 and 4 then for every α in **C** there is an $-\alpha$ in **C** such that

$$\alpha \cup -\alpha = 1 \quad \text{and} \quad \alpha \cap -\alpha = 0$$

Ax. 10. There is an α in **C** and a β in **C** such that $\alpha \neq \beta$.

The present system[2] is a formal deductive system rather than a logistic system (cf. Chapter 6). On its intended interpretation, of course, **C** is the collection of all classes, 0 and 1 are the null and universal classes, respectively, and the symbols $\cup$, $\cap$, and $-$ represent class addition, multiplication, and complementation, respectively.

The reader who is interested in deducing some theorems from these axioms will find the following fairly easy to derive:

Th. 1. There is at most one entity 0 in **C** such that $\alpha \cup 0 = \alpha$.

★Th. 2. There is at most one entity 1 in **C** such that $\alpha \cap 1 = \alpha$.

Th. 3. $\alpha \cup \alpha = \alpha$.

Th. 4. $\alpha \cap \alpha = \alpha$.

Th. 5. $\alpha \cup 1 = 1$.

Th. 6. $\alpha \cap 0 = 0$.

★Th. 7. $0 \neq 1$.

Th. 8. If $\alpha = -\beta$ then $\beta = -\alpha$.

Th. 9. $\alpha = --\alpha$.

Th. 10. If $\alpha \cap \beta \neq 0$ then $\alpha \neq 0$.

Th. 11. $\alpha = (\alpha \cap \beta) \cup (\alpha \cap -\beta)$.

[2] From E. V. Huntington's 'Sets of Independent Postulates for the Algebra of Logic', *Transactions of the American Mathematical Society*, vol. 5 (1904), p. 288.

★Th. 12. $\alpha \cup (\beta \cup \gamma) = (\alpha \cup \beta) \cup \gamma$.

Th. 13. $\alpha \cap (\beta \cap \gamma) = (\alpha \cap \beta) \cap \gamma$.

Th. 14. $0 = -1$.

Th. 15. $\alpha \cup (\alpha \cap \beta) = \alpha$.

Th. 16. $\alpha \neq -\alpha$.

Th. 17. $-(\alpha \cap \beta) = -\alpha \cup -\beta$.

Th. 18. $-(\alpha \cup \beta) = -\alpha \cap -\beta$.

Th. 19. If $\alpha \cap -\beta = 0$ and $\beta \cap -\gamma = 0$, then $\alpha \cap -\gamma = 0$.

★Th. 20. If $\alpha \cap \beta \neq 0$ and $\beta \cap -\gamma = 0$, then $\alpha \cap \gamma \neq 0$.

The methods of proof proceed largely by the substitution of equals for equals. For example, Th. 1 is proved by considering any entities 0_1 and 0_2 in **C** such that $\alpha \cup 0_1 = \alpha$ and $\alpha \cup 0_2 = \alpha$. Since α is any member of **C**, we have both $0_1 \cup 0_2 = 0_1$ and $0_2 \cup 0_1 = 0_2$. Since $0_1 \cup 0_2 = 0_2 \cup 0_1$ by Ax. 5, we obtain by substitution first $0_1 \cup 0_2 = 0_2$ and then $0_1 = 0_2$, which establishes the theorem.

The whole of the algebra of classes can be derived within a first-order function calculus. To every property corresponds the class of all individuals which exemplify that property. The expression '$\hat{x}(Fx)$' is commonly used to symbolize the class of all individuals having the property F. More generally, where $\Phi\mu$ is any propositional function containing no free variables other than μ, $\hat{\mu}(\Phi\mu)$ is the class of all individuals which satisfy that propositional function. The various symbols for classes used in the class algebra can be defined as follows, where α, β, γ, . . . are the classes $\hat{x}(Ax)$, $\hat{x}(Bx)$, $\hat{x}(Cx)$, . . . :

$$\bar{\alpha} = \text{df } \hat{x}(\sim Ax)$$
$$\alpha \cap \beta = \text{df } \hat{x}(Ax \cdot Bx)$$
$$\alpha \cup \beta = \text{df } \hat{x}(Ax \text{ v } Bx)$$
$$0 = \text{df } \hat{x}(Ax \cdot \sim Ax)$$
$$1 = \text{df } \hat{x}(Ax \text{ v } \sim Ax)$$

Class inclusion, equality, and inequality may be defined as follows:

$$\alpha \subset \beta = \text{df } (x)(Ax \supset Bx)$$
$$\alpha = \beta = \text{df } (x)(Ax \equiv Bx)$$
$$\alpha \neq \beta = \text{df} \sim (x)(Ax \equiv Bx)$$

Using these definitions we can express all of the formulas of Boolean Algebra in the notation of propositional functions and quantifiers. When that is done it is easily shown that all of the axioms and hence all of the theorems of Boolean Algebra become provable theorems of out first-order function calculus.

Since a Boolean Algebra is a formal deductive system in its own right, it is susceptible of various interpretations. One of them, of course, is the algebra of classes. But we can give our Boolean Algebra a propositional rather than a class interpretation. Suppose we interpret 'C' as the collection of all propositions, and 'α', 'β', 'γ', . . . as symbolizing propositions, and interpret '$\cap$', '$\cup$', and '$-$' as symbolizing conjunction, (weak) disjunction, and negation. Then if we further interpret the equals sign as symbolizing material equivalence, all axioms and theorems of the Boolean Algebra become logically true propositions of the propositional calculus. Hence we can say that the propositional calculus is a Boolean Algebra.

From a somewhat different point of view, we can regard a part of the algebra of classes as an alternative interpretation of the propositional calculus. All formulas of a propositional calculus can be expressed in terms of '$\sim$', '$\cdot$', and 'v', with '$p \supset q$' defined as '$\sim p$ v q' and '$p \equiv q$' defined as '$p \cdot q$ v $\sim p \cdot \sim q$'. We can interpret the propositional symbols 'p', 'q', 'r', . . . as denoting the classes α, β, γ, . . . ; and where 'p' denotes α, we shall understand '$\sim p$' to denote $\bar{\alpha}$, the complement of α. Where 'p' and 'q' denote α and β, then '$p \cdot q$' will be understood to denote the product $\alpha\beta$, and 'p v q' will denote the sum $\alpha \cup \beta$.

On the interpretation sketched in the preceding paragraph every truth table tautology of the propositional calculus designates the universal class. This can easily be established as follows. It was proved in Chapter 7 that all (and only) truth table tautologies can be derived as theorems by repeated application of R 1 to the three axioms of R.S. Each of those axioms designates the universal class: Axiom 1, '$P \supset (P \cdot P)$', which can be expressed as '$\sim p$ v $(p \cdot p)$', denotes $\bar{\alpha} \cup \alpha\alpha$ or $\bar{\alpha} \cup \alpha$, which is the universal class 1. Axiom 2, '$(P \cdot Q) \supset P$', expressed as '$\sim(p \cdot q)$ v p', denotes $\overline{\alpha\beta} \cup \alpha$, which by De Morgan's Theorem is $(\bar{\alpha} \cup \bar{\beta}) \cup \alpha$, which by commutation and association is equal to $(\alpha \cup \bar{\alpha}) \cup \bar{\beta}$, which is $1 \cup \bar{\beta}$ and equal to 1. Axiom 3, '$(P \supset Q) \supset [\sim(Q \cdot R) \supset$

$\sim(R \cdot P)]'$, expressed as '$\sim(\sim p \text{ v } q) \text{ v } [\sim\sim(q \cdot r) \text{ v } \sim(r \cdot p)]'$, denotes $\overline{\overline{\alpha \cup \beta}} \cup \overline{\overline{\beta \gamma}} \cup \overline{\gamma \alpha}$, which is equal by De Morgan's Theorem and double negation to $\alpha\beta \cup \beta\gamma \cup \bar{\gamma} \cup \bar{\alpha}$. The latter is equal, by the Law of Expansion, to $\alpha\bar{\beta}(\gamma \cup \bar{\gamma}) \cup \beta\gamma(\alpha \cup \bar{\alpha}) \cup \bar{\gamma}(\alpha \cup \bar{\alpha})(\beta \cup \bar{\beta}) \cup \bar{\alpha}(\beta \cup \bar{\beta})(\gamma \cup \bar{\gamma})$, which by repeated uses of distribution is equal to $\alpha\bar{\beta}\gamma \cup \alpha\beta\bar{\gamma} \cup \beta\gamma\alpha \cup \beta\gamma\bar{\alpha} \cup \bar{\gamma}\alpha\beta \cup \bar{\gamma}\alpha\bar{\beta} \cup \bar{\gamma}\bar{\alpha}\beta \cup \bar{\gamma}\bar{\alpha}\bar{\beta} \cup \bar{\alpha}\beta\gamma \cup \bar{\alpha}\beta\bar{\gamma} \cup \bar{\alpha}\bar{\beta}\gamma \cup \bar{\alpha}\bar{\beta}\bar{\gamma}$. If we now use commutation to rearrange the terms of the latter expression, and combine equal terms by the principle that $\alpha \cup \alpha = \alpha$, we obtain $\alpha\beta\gamma \cup \alpha\beta\bar{\gamma} \cup \alpha\bar{\beta}\gamma \cup \alpha\bar{\beta}\bar{\gamma} \cup \bar{\alpha}\beta\gamma \cup \bar{\alpha}\beta\bar{\gamma} \cup \bar{\alpha}\bar{\beta}\gamma \cup \bar{\alpha}\bar{\beta}\bar{\gamma}$, a (disjunctive) Boolean Expansion involving 3 simple class terms. Since it is the sum of 2^3 distinct products it designates the universal class.

Next we show that any formula of the propositional calculus must designate the universal class if it 'follows' by R 1 from two formulas each of which designates the universal class. R 1 permits us to pass to Q from P and $P \supset Q$ (or $\sim P \text{ v } Q$). Now suppose that 'P' denotes α and that 'Q' denotes β, so that '$\sim P \text{ v } Q$' denotes $\bar{\alpha} \cup \beta$. Under the assumption that $\alpha = 1$ and $\bar{\alpha} \cup \beta = 1$ it is easily demonstrated that $\beta = 1$. For since $1 \cap 1 = 1$, $\alpha(\bar{\alpha} \cup \beta) = 1$. By distribution, $\alpha\bar{\alpha} \cup \alpha\beta = 1$, and since $\alpha\bar{\alpha} = 0$, it follows that $\alpha\beta = 1$. But $\alpha\beta = 1$ implies both that $\alpha = 1$ *and* that $\beta = 1$, the latter being the desired conclusion.

Therefore every provable theorem of R.S. designates the universal class.

Next we wish to prove that if Π is a class expression such that $\Pi = 1$ is logically true, then Π is designated by a theorem of R.S. We know that $\Pi = 1$ if and only if its Boolean Expansion Σ involves n simple class terms and is the sum of 2^n distinct products. But any Boolean Expansion involving the simple class terms α, β, γ, . . . will be denoted by a disjunctive Boolean normal form formula (cf. pages 323–325ff.) which involves the statement variables p, q, r, . . . where 'p' denotes α, 'q' denotes β, 'r' denotes γ, etc., and the latter will be the disjunction of as many conjunctions as the former is the sum of products. Hence if Σ is a Boolean Expansion in n simple class terms which is the sum of 2^n products, then it is denoted by the Boolean normal form S which contains n statement variables and is the disjunction of 2^n conjunctions. The latter is therefore a tautology, and hence a provable theorem of R.S. Moreover, the class algebra principles by which Π is expanded into Σ all have their analogues in tautology-preserving transformations in the propositional calculus, so that if $\Pi = \Sigma$ and 'P' denotes Π and 'S' denotes Σ, then if 'S' is a tautology, 'P' is a tautology also, and therefore a theorem of R.S.

It is shown in this way that a class algebra equation of the form $\Pi = 1$ is logically true if and only if the *wff* 'P' which designates Π is a theorem of the propositional calculus. Since every equation of the class algebra is equivalent to an equation of the forms $\Pi = 1$ ($\Gamma = \Lambda$ is equivalent to $\Gamma \subset \Lambda$ and $\Lambda \subset \Gamma$, which are equivalent to $\bar{\Gamma} \cup \Lambda = 1$ and $\bar{\Lambda} \cup \Gamma = 1$, whose combined expression is $(\bar{\Gamma} \cup \Lambda)(\bar{\Lambda} \cup \Gamma) = 1$), it follows that to every logically true equation of the class algebra corresponds a provable theorem of the propositional calculus.

Similarly, logically true inequations of the class algebra correspond to *wffs* of R.S. which are *not* provable as theorems. In the first place, any inequation $\Gamma \neq \Lambda$ is equivalent to an inequation of the form $\Pi \neq 1$, namely $(\bar{\Gamma} \cup \Lambda)(\bar{\Lambda} \cup \Gamma) \neq 1$. And if it is logically true that $\Pi \neq 1$, then it is not logically true that $\Pi = 1$, from which it follows that the *wff* which designates Π is not a provable theorem in R.S. Since we have an effective criterion for distinguishing between theorems and nontheorems of R.S., we have therein an effective criterion for distinguishing between logically true equations and inequations of the class algebra.

The preceding discussion should suffice to indicate the intimacy of the connection between the algebra of classes and the propositional calculus.

C

THE
RAMIFIED
THEORY
OF
TYPES

The *simple* theory of types, which was expounded briefly on pages 173–174, suffices to eliminate such logical paradoxes as that of the alleged property *impredicable*. But there is another kind of paradox or contradiction which is not prevented by the simple theory of types. One example of this other kind is the paradox of the liar, which was discussed on page 197. These two kinds of paradoxes were first explicitly distinguished by F. P. Ramsey in 1926.[1] Since then those of the first kind have been known as 'logical paradoxes', the second kind either as 'epistemological paradoxes' or, more usually, as 'semantical paradoxes'.

A singularly clear example of a semantical paradox is due to Kurt Grelling.[2] The Grelling paradox can be stated informally as follows. Some words designate properties which are exemplified by the words

---

[1] 'The Foundations of Mathematics' by F. P. Ramsey, in *Proceedings of the London Mathematical Society*, second series, vol. XXV (1926), pp. 338–384. Reprinted in *The Foundations of Mathematics* (London and New York, 1931), pp. 1–61.

[2] 'Bemerkungen zu den Paradoxien von Russell und Burali-Forti' by K. Grelling and L. Nelson, in *Abhandlung der Fries'schen Schule*, n.s. vol. II (1907–1908), pp. 300–324.

themselves, e.g., 'English' is an English word, and 'short' is a short word. Other words designate properties which are not exemplified by the words themselves, e.g., 'French' is not a French word, and 'long' is not a long word. We shall use the word 'heterological' to designate the property possessed by words which designate properties *not* exemplified by themselves. Thus the words 'French' and 'long' are both heterological. The contradiction now arises when we ask whether or not the word 'heterological' is heterological. If it is heterological, then it designates a property which it does not exemplify, and since it designates heterological, it is not heterological. But if it is not heterological, then the property which it designates *is* exemplified by itself, so that it *is* heterological. Here is the contradiction made explicit: if it is then it isn't, and if it isn't then it is.

A somewhat more formal derivation of the Grelling paradox, patterned after Ramsey's version of it,[3] is the following. Where 'Des' designates the name relation, so that 's designates ϕ' is symbolized as 'sDesϕ', we begin with the definition

$$\text{Het(s)} = \text{df} \ (\exists\phi){:}\text{sDes}\phi{\cdot}\text{sDes}\psi \equiv_\psi \psi = \phi{\cdot}{\sim}\phi(s)[4]$$

CASE 1.

(1) Het('Het') $\supset$:$(\exists\phi)$:'Het'Des$\phi{\cdot}$'Het'Des$\psi \equiv_\psi \psi = \phi{\cdot}{\sim}\phi$('Het')

(2) $\supset$:'Het'Des$\phi{\cdot}$'Het'Des$\psi \equiv_\psi \psi = \phi{\cdot}{\sim}\phi$('Het')

(3) $\supset$:'Het'Des$\phi{\cdot}$'Het'DesHet $\equiv$ Het $= \phi{\cdot}{\sim}\phi$('Het')

(4) $\supset$:'Het'DesHet $\equiv$ Het $= \phi{\cdot}{\sim}\phi$('Het')

(5) $\supset$:Het $= \phi{\cdot}{\sim}\phi$('Het')

(6) $\supset$:${\sim}$Het('Het')

CASE 2.

(1) ${\sim}$Het('Het') $\supset$:$(\phi){\sim}$['Het'Des$\phi{\cdot}$'Het'Des$\psi \equiv_\psi$

$\psi = \phi{\cdot}{\sim}\phi$('Het')]

(2) $\supset$:'Het'DesHet $\supset {\sim}$['Het'Des$\psi \equiv_\psi$

$\psi = $ Het${\cdot}{\sim}$Het('Het')]

---

[3] *Op. cit.*, p. 358 and pp. 369–372; reprint p. 27 and pp. 42–46.

[4] Where writing the *psi* as a subscript to the equivalence symbol serves to abbreviate the universal quantification of the equivalence with respect to *psi*, so that 'sDes $\psi \equiv_\psi \psi = \phi$' is an abbreviation for '(ψ)[sDes$\psi \equiv \psi = \phi$]'.

(3) $\supset$:'Het'Des$\psi \equiv_\psi \psi$ = Het$\cdot \supset \cdot$Het('Het')

(4) $\supset$:'Het'Des$\psi \equiv_\psi \psi$ = Het (assuming 'Het'

univocal)

(5) $\supset$:Het('Het')

Hence

$$Het('Het') \equiv \sim Het('Het')$$

which is a contradiction.

The derivation of the preceding contradiction did not violate any restrictions imposed by the simple theory of logical types, so the adoption of that theory does not suffice to prevent such contradictions. Contradictions of this second kind can be eliminated, however, by the adoption of a more complicated version of the theory of logical types, known as the 'ramified' (or 'branching') theory of logical types. Now according to the simple theory of logical types, all entities are divided into different logical types, of which the lowest contains all individuals, the next lowest consists of all properties of individuals (designated by functions of individuals), the next, of all properties of properties of individuals (designated by functions of functions of individuals), and so on. There are also hierarchies of relations among individuals and properties, and of properties of relations, but they need not be considered here. Where we use lower case letters to denote individuals and capital letters to designate properties, then we can represent this hierarchy as follows, where the subscript attached to a function indicates its proper level in the hierarchy:

> .   .   .   .
>
> .   .   .   .
>
> .   .   .   .
>
> type 3: F_3, G_3, H_3, . . .
>
> type 2: F_2, G_2, H_2, . . .
>
> type 1: F_1, G_1, H_1, . . .
>
> type 0: a, b, c, . . . , x, y, z

Only a function of type 1 can significantly be predicated of an individual, and in general, a function of type i can be significantly predicated of a function of type j if and only if $i = j + 1$.

The preceding hierarchy presents a rough 'picture' of the simple theory of logical types. Now the ramified theory proceeds to divide each type above level zero into a further hierarchy. Thus all functions of type 1, which may significantly be predicated of individuals, are divided into different *orders* in the following fashion.

All propositional functions of type 1 which contain either no quantifiers or else quantifiers on individual variables only are said to be *first-order* functions. For example, $F_1(x)$ and $(y)[F_1(y) \supset G_1(x)]$ are first-order functions of type 1. First-order functions will have a left superscript 1 attached to indicate their position in the hierarchy of orders. Thus all first-order functions of type 1 may be listed as $^1F_1$, $^1G_1$, $^1H_1$, ... Next, all propositional functions of type 1 which contain quantifiers on first-order functions but no quantifiers on any other functions are *second-order* functions. Examples of second-order functions of type 1 are $(^1F_1)[^1F_1(x) \equiv {}^1F_1(a)]$ and $(\exists^1G_1)(\exists y)[^1G_1(y) \supset {}^1H_1(x)]$. Second-order functions will have a left superscript 2 attached, and all second-order functions of type 1 may be listed as $^2F_1$, $^2G_1$, $^2H_1$, . . . In general, an nth order function of type 1 will contain quantifiers on functions of order $n - 1$, but no quantifiers on functions of order m where $m \geq n$.

The ramified theory of logical types can be described compendiously by means of the following two dimensional array:

	Order 1	*Order* 2	*Order* 3	. . .
	. . .	.	.	
	. .	.	.	
	.	.	.	
type 3:	$^1F_3$, $^1G_3$, $^1H_3$, . . . ;	$^2F_3$, $^2G_3$, $^2H_3$, ... ;	$^3F_3$, $^3G_3$, $^3H_3$, ... ;	. . .
type 2:	$^1F_2$, $^1G_2$, $^1H_2$, . . . ;	$^2F_2$, $^2G_2$, $^2H_2$, ... ;	$^3F_2$, $^3G_2$, $^3H_2$, ... ;	. . .
type 1:	$^1F_1$, $^1G_1$, $^1H_1$, . . . ;	$^2F_1$, $^2G_1$, $^2H_1$, ... ;	$^3F_1$, $^3G_1$, $^3H_1$, ... ;	. . .

Just as the simple hierarchy of types prevents us from speaking about all functions or properties, permitting us to speak only about all functions of individuals, or all functions of functions of individuals, or etc., so the hierarchy of orders prevents us from speaking about all functions or properties of a given type, permitting us to speak only about all first-order functions of a given type, or all second-order functions of a given type, etc. Thus we cannot, according to the ramified theory of types, say that Bob has all of Al's good qualities, which would ordinarily be symbolized as

$$(F_1)\{[G_2(F_1)\cdot F_1(a)] \supset F_1(b)\}$$

Instead, we can say that Bob has all of Al's good *first-order* qualities, symbolized as

$$(^1F_1)\{[^1G_2(^1F_1)\cdot^1F_1(a)] \supset {}^1F_1(b)\}$$

or that Bob has all of Al's good *second-order* qualities, symbolized as

$$(^2F_1)\{[^1G_2(^2F_1)\cdot^2F_1(a)] \supset {}^2F_1(b)\}$$

or that Bob has all of Al's good n^{th} order qualities, for any specified n. It should be noticed that the property of having all of Al's first-order properties, symbolized by the function

$$(^1F_1)[^1F_1(a) \supset {}^1F_1(x)]$$

is a *second-order* property.

The preceding formulation of the ramified theory of logical types is crude, but it suffices to eliminate the Grelling paradox. In Case 1 the step from (2) to (3) is rejected on the grounds that the function 'Het' is of higher order than the function variable 'ψ' and may not be instantiated in its place. In Case 2 the step from (1) to (2) is likewise rejected on the grounds that the function 'Het' is of higher order than the function variable 'ϕ' and may not be instantiated in its place.

Another feature of the ramified theory of logical types is that it divides *propositions* into a hierarchy of propositions of different orders. Just as any function (of any type) is a first-order function if it makes no reference to any totality of functions of that type (i.e., contains no quantifier on any function variable of that type), so any proposition is said to be a *first-order proposition* if it makes no reference to any totality of propositions (i.e., contains no quantifier on any propositional variable). In general, a proposition is of order $n + 1$ if it contains a quantifier on a propositional variable of order n but contains no quantifier on any propositional variable of order m where $m \geq n$.[5] The restric-

---

[5] In *Principia Mathematica*, propositions are also divided into different orders on the basis of differences in the orders of the functions they contain. But we shall ignore that (dubious) subtlety in the present exposition.

tion here is that we can never refer to *all* propositions, but only to all propositions of this or that specified order. Thus we cannot say that 'None of the propositions uttered by Smith tends to incriminate him', which we might partially symbolize as

$$(p)[(\text{Smith utters } p) \supset \sim(p \text{ tends to incriminate Smith})]$$

but can say instead either that 'None of the first-order propositions uttered by Smith tends to incriminate him', or that 'None of the second-order propositions uttered by Smith tends to incriminate him', or etc. We would partially symbolize the second of these alternative propositions as

$$(^2p)[(\text{Smith utters } ^2p) \supset \sim(^2p \text{ tends to incriminate Smith})]$$

That proposition contains a quantifier on a propositional variable of order 2, and is therefore a proposition of order 3.

By dividing propositions into different orders and permitting reference only to propositions of some specified order or orders, the ramified theory of logical types effectively prevents the paradox of the liar. Any version of that paradox involves the assertion that *all propositions satisfying a certain condition are false*, where the assertion itself is a proposition which satisfies that condition. (The condition in question might be *being asserted by the speaker*, or *being written in a specified location*, or *being uttered by a Cretan*, or etc.) The paradox is fully explicit when the assertion in question is the *only* proposition which satisfies the specified condition, for in that case if it is true then it is false, and if it is false then it is true. Such a contradiction is prevented by the ramified theory of logical types in the following way. The assertion can refer only to all propositions of a certain order, so that it can assert only for some specified n that *all n^{th} order propositions satisfying a certain condition are false*. But no paradox can arise here, because the italicized sentence expresses a proposition of order $n + 1$, and even if it satisfies the specified condition, it is not an nth order proposition and therefore does not assert its own falsehood.

The ramified theory of logical types, including both the hierarchy of types and the hierarchy of orders, was recommended by Russell and Whitehead not only for 'its ability to solve certain contradictions', but also for having 'a certain consonance with common sense which makes it inherently credible'.[6] They claimed to have deduced the theory from what they called the 'vicious-circle principle', of which one of their formulations was: 'Whatever involves *all* of a collection must not be one of the collection'.[7] But that principle is not obvious, and their putative deduction is not convincing.[8] The chief merit of the theory of logical types, at least of its ramified version, would seem to be its prevention of the paradoxes.

There are difficulties as well as advantages entailed by the ramified theory of logical types. One of these concerns the notion of identity, which was discussed on pages 158ff. and 171. The usual definition of identity (of individuals) is

$$(x = y) = \mathrm{df} \ (F_1)[F_1(x) \equiv F_1(y)]$$

from which definition all of the usual properties of the identity relation can be deduced. But that definition violates the ramified theory of logical types, since in it reference is made to *all* functions of type 1. Were we to replace it by the definition

$$(x = y) = \mathrm{df} \ (^1F_1)[^1F_1(x) \equiv {}^1F_1(y)]$$

which provides that x and y are identical if they have all of their *first-order* properties in common, the possibility arises that x and y might be identical (in this sense) and nevertheless have different *second-order* properties. It should be clear that for any n, defining identity as the sharing of all properties of order n would permit "identical" individuals to differ with respect to properties of order m where $m > n$. If we accept the restrictions of the ramified theory of logical types, then we cannot define the identity relation, and even if we accept it as primitive or undefined, we could not state all the rules for its usage (as enunciated on pages 159–161).

[6] *Principia Mathematica* by A. N. Whitehead and B. Russell, Introduction to the first edition, Chapter II.

[7] *Ibid.*

[8] In his 'Foundations of Mathematics', F. P. Ramsey remarked on the 'rather sloppy way' in which the type theory was deduced from the 'vicious-circle principle' (p. 356, p. 24 of reprint), and challenged the validity of that principle itself, holding that '. . . we may refer to a man as the tallest in a group, thus identifying him by means of a totality of which he is himself a member without there being any vicious circle' (p. 368, p. 41 of reprint).

Other disadvantages of the ramified theory of logical types are more technical, and will merely be mentioned. Mathematicians wish to establish their theorems for *all* functions (of numbers), but they cannot do so if they permit themselves to be bound by the hierarchy of orders. Moreover, certain existence theorems in analysis, such as that of the Least Upper Bound, cannot be proved within the restrictions of the ramified theory of types. The Cantorean theory of the infinite, which is basic to nearly all of modern mathematics, cannot be established within the rigid framework of the ramified type theory. And even the principle of mathematical induction must be abandoned in its full generality, for its complete statement is prevented by the ramified theory of logical types.

To relax the excessive restrictions of the hierarchy of orders the 'Axiom of Reducibility' was introduced. That axiom asserts that to any function of any order and any type there corresponds a formally equivalent *first-order* function of the same type (two functions are *formally equivalent* when for any admissible argument they are either both true or both false). In the presence of this axiom, the identity relation *can* be satisfactorily defined in terms of first-order functions, and all of the disadvantages mentioned in the preceding paragraph disappear. The question naturally arises: does the Axiom of Reducibility relax the restrictions of the ramified theory of logical types sufficiently to permit the reintroduction of the paradoxes? It seems clear that if to a logical system like that of *Principia Mathematica*, which contains both the ramified type theory and the Axiom of Reducibility, *all* of the semantical terms such as 'true', 'false', and 'designates' are added, and names for all functions are added also, then at least some of the paradoxes reappear.[9] On the other hand, if the names of *some* functions are left out, then even in the presence of the semantical terms the paradoxes do not seem to be derivable even with the aid of the Axiom of Reducibility.[10]

It may not be out of place here to indicate briefly how the 'levels

[9] Cf. the author's article on 'The Inconsistency or Redundancy of *Principia Mathematica*' in *Philosophy and Phenomenological Research*, vol. XI, no. 2 (December 1950), pp. 190–199.

[10] Cf. the review of the preceding article by Alonzo Church in *The Journal of Symbolic Logic*, vol. XVI, no. 2 (June 1951), pp. 154–155.

of language' method of avoiding the semantical paradoxes[11] is remarkably similar to the ramified type theory's hierarchy of orders.[12] Confining our remarks to the Grelling paradox, we note that it does not arise in an object language (like the extended function calculus, for example) when we assume that there are in it no symbols which designate symbols. Nor does it arise in the metalanguage of that object language. Since the metalanguage contains synonyms for all symbols of the object language and names for all symbols of the object language, as well as its own variables and the name relation (which we write as 'Des'), the symbol 'Het' can be defined in it. By definition:

$$\text{Het}(v) \cdot \equiv \; : \cdot \; (\exists \phi) : v \text{Des} \phi \cdot v \text{Des} \psi \; \equiv_{\psi} \psi = \phi \cdot \sim \phi(v)$$

Yet the Grelling cannot be derived in the metalanguage, because although there is a symbol for the function Het there is no symbol for the name of that function. In other words, in the metalanguage, although we could substitute 'Het' for 'ϕ', we cannot substitute ' 'Het' ' for 'v' because ' 'Het' ' is not a symbol of the metalanguage.

So far there are no complications. The paradox does not arise in the object language because it contains no names for the symbols in it; and it does not arise in the metalanguage because there is no name for the function symbol 'Het' in that language. The *threat* of the Grelling only arises in the meta-metalanguage. *If* certain safeguards or refinements of the levels of language theory are ignored, the paradox seems to be derivable. Ignoring those safeguards, we have, by definition, in the meta-metalanguage,

$$\text{Het}(v) \cdot \equiv \; : \cdot \; (\exists \phi) : v \text{Des} \phi \cdot v \text{Des} \psi \; \equiv_{\psi} \psi = \phi \cdot \sim \phi(v)$$

Since the meta-metalanguage *does* contain a name for the function symbol 'Het', we substitute that name, ' 'Het' ', for the variable 'v' and obtain the contradiction as in our first derivation.

The way in which the safeguards of the levels of language theory serve to prevent this contradiction makes it very similar to the theory

[11] First suggested by Bertrand Russell in his Introduction to L. Wittgenstein's *Tractatus logico-philosophicus* (London and New York, 1922), p. 23.

[12] The remainder of this appendix is reprinted by permission from 'The Inconsistency or Redundancy of *Principia Mathematica*', *Philosophy and Phenomenological Research*, vol. XI. Copyright 1950 by the University of Buffalo.

of orders. The definition of Het in the meta-metalanguage which was written above requires the addition of subscripts to resolve its ambiguity. Once these ambiguities are pointed out and resolved, the contradiction vanishes.

In the first place, the meta-metalanguage contains two symbols for the name relation, 'Des$_1$' and 'Des$_2$'.[13] The first of these is the meta-metalanguage's synonym for the name relation in the metalanguage. The full sentence.

$$v\mathrm{Des}_1\phi$$

asserts that the function symbol denoted by 'v' is a symbol of the object language and designates the function ϕ. The second has no synonym in the metalanguage. The full sentence

$$v\mathrm{Des}_2\phi$$

asserts that the function symbol denoted by 'v' is a symbol of the metalanguage and designates the function ϕ. These are quite different, since we assume in this discussion that although every symbol of the object language has a synonym in the metalanguage, there are no symbols common to the two languages.

And in the second place, the meta-metalanguage contains two symbols 'Het$_1$' and 'Het$_2$', between whose meanings there is significant difference. The first of these is the meta-metalanguage's synonym for the function symbol 'Het' of the metalanguage. The full sentence

$$\mathrm{Het}_1(v)$$

asserts that the function symbol denoted by 'v' is a symbol of the object language and has the property of designating in the object language a property which it does not possess. The second has no synonym in the metalanguage. The full sentence

$$\mathrm{Het}_2(v)$$

asserts that the function symbol denoted by 'v' is a symbol of the metalanguage and has the property of designating in the metalanguage a

---

[13] As was suggested by Ramsey in a somewhat different context. *Op. cit.*, p. 370, in reprint, p. 43.

property which it does not possess. Their definitions are different:

$$\text{Het}_1(v) = \text{df} \ (\exists\phi){:}v\text{Des}_1\phi{\cdot}v\text{Des}_1\psi \equiv_\psi \psi = \phi{\cdot}\sim\phi(v)$$

and

$$\text{Het}_2(v) = \text{df} \ (\exists\phi){:}v\text{Des}_2\phi{\cdot}v\text{Des}_2\psi \equiv_\psi \psi = \phi{\cdot}\sim\phi(v)$$

It is clear that we cannot define Het_1 in terms of Des_2 because the values of the arguments of the two functions are terms of different languages, of the object language for Het_1 and of the metalanguage for Des_2. The same consideration suffices to show that Het_2 cannot be defined in terms of Des_1.

No version of the Grelling can be derived from the definition of Het_1, because the only values of its arguments are terms of the object language, and there is no term of the object language analogous to either 'Het_1' or 'Het_2'. The only possibility lies in the direction of deriving a contradiction from the definition of Het_2, and this is thwarted by something remarkably like *Principia's* theory of orders.

In the definition of Het_2 we cannot substitute for 'v' the name of the symbol for that function, because although the function symbol 'Het_2' occurs in the meta-metalanguage, no *name* of that function symbol does. The best we can do is to substitute the meta-metalanguage's name of the function symbol of the metalanguage which is synonymous with 'Het_1', for which we *do* have a name in the meta-metalanguage (call it ' 'Het' '). Making the substitution, we have

$$\text{Het}_2(\text{'Het'}){\cdot} \equiv : {\cdot}(\exists\phi){:}\text{'Het'}\text{Des}_2\phi{\cdot}\text{'Het'}\text{Des}_2\psi \equiv_\psi \psi = \phi{\cdot}\sim\phi(\text{'Het'})$$

If we endeavor to deduce a contradiction from this equivalence by an argument parallel to earlier versions, we are unable to do so. There is a choice of function symbol to substitute for the generalized function variable 'ψ', for there are two function symbols in our meta-metalanguage that look promising: 'Het_1' and 'Het_2'.

If we substitute 'Het_1', we obtain

$$\text{Het}_2(\text{'Het'}){\cdot} \supset {:}\text{'Het'}\text{Des}_2\phi{\cdot}\text{'Het'}\text{Des}_2\text{Het}_1 \equiv \text{Het}_1 = \phi{\cdot}\sim\phi(\text{'Het'})$$

Since ' 'Het' ' is the meta-metalanguage's name for the function symbol of the metalanguage which is synonymous with 'Het_1', we have

$$\text{'Het'}\text{Des}_2\text{Het}_1{\cdot}\text{'Het'}\text{Des}_2\text{Het}_1 \equiv \text{Het}_1 = \phi$$

and consequently

$$\text{Het}_2(\text{'Het'}) \supset \sim\text{Het}_1(\text{'Het'})$$

But this is no part of any contradiction, being antecedently known on independent grounds; for if any term satisfies Het_2 it is in the metalanguage and not in the object language, while only terms of the object language satisfy Het_1.

On the other hand, if we substitute 'Het$_2$', we obtain

$$\text{Het}_2(\text{'Het'}) \supset \text{:'Het'Des}_2\phi\cdot\text{'Het'Des}_2\text{Het}_2 \equiv \text{Het}_2 = \phi\cdot\sim\phi(\text{'Het'})$$

From this, *if* ' 'Het'Des$_2$Het$_2$' were true, we should indeed be able to obtain a contradiction. But ' 'Het'Des$_2$Het$_2$' is *not* true, because the argument ' 'Het' ' denotes a symbol of the metalanguage while the property denoted by the argument 'Het$_2$' is not denoted by any symbol of the metalanguage. In other words, ' 'Het'Des$_2$Het$_2$' is false because 'Het$_2$' is a symbol of the meta-metalanguage which has no synonym in the metalanguage.

This is very like the theory of orders, because the contradiction is evaded by arranging that certain symbols of the meta-metalanguage are defined *over certain ranges*. Thus 'Des$_1$' is defined over a narrower range than 'Des$_2$', and 'Het$_1$' is defined over a narrower range than 'Het$_2$'; Des$_1$ and Het$_1$ being satisfied only by symbols of the object language, Des$_2$ and Het$_2$ being satisfied only by symbols of the metalanguage, which is a wider and more inclusive language. Not only is the levels of language theory remarkably analogous to the theory of orders, but where each metalanguage is conceived as actually containing the object language with which it deals,[14] it can be identified with the Russellian theory of orders *as applied to symbols* rather than to the functions they denote.

In spite of the indicated similarities, there are fundamental differences between the two. Most significant is that unlike the ramified type theory, the levels of language device for avoiding the paradoxes does not jeopardize the derivation of any parts of classical mathematics, so that no need arises for any analogue to the reducibility axiom.

[14] This conception is recommended by A. Tarski in his 'Semantic Conception of Truth', *Philosophy and Phenomenological Research*, vol. IV (1944), pp. 341–375. Reprinted in H. Feigl and W. Sellars, *Readings in Philosophical Analysis* (New York, 1949), pp. 52–84. Cf. especially p. 350, in reprint, pp. 60–61.

SOLUTIONS
TO
SELECTED
EXERCISES

Exercises on page 14:

1. **F**   2. **T**   13. **F**   18. **T**   20. **F**

Exercises on page 17–18:

I.   1. **T**   2. **F**   13. **F**   18. **F**   20. **T**

II.   5. $\sim A \supset \sim(C \vee D)$ 10. $(A \supset \sim C) \cdot (\sim C \supset D)$
  15. $(\sim A \cdot \sim C) \supset \sim(A \cdot C)$

Exercises on pages 25–27:

I.   1. Valid.   5. Invalid—shown by row 2.
  10. Valid.   19. Invalid—shown by rows 4, 6, 8, 12.
  20. Valid.

II.   1. Invalid—shown by row 1.   5. Valid.
  10. Invalid—shown by row 3.   15. Invalid—shown by row 12.

Exercises on page 32:

I.   1. Contingent—**F** in row 1, **T** in row 2.
  5. Tautologous.   8. Contradictory.

II.   4. Not equivalent—shown by rows 6 and 8.
  8. Equivalent.

Exercises on pages 36–41:

I. **1.** 3. 2, Simp.   **5.** 4. 3, Simp.   **10.** 7. 1, 6, M.T.
        4. 1, 3, M.P.   5. 2, 4, M.P.   8. 2, 6, M.T.
        5. 3, Simp.   6. 4, Simp.   9. 7, 8, Conj.
        6. 4, 5, M.P.   7. 6, Add.   10. 3, 9, M.P.
        7. 6, Simp.   8. 1, 7, M.P.   11. 4, 10, C.D.
        8. 7, Add.   9. 8, 5, H.S.   12. 5, 11, D.D.

II. **1.** 1. $(A \lor G) \supset S$
        2. $A \cdot T$ $/ \therefore S$
        3. A 2, Simp.
        4. $A \lor G$ 3, Add.
        5. S 1, 4, M.P.

     5. 1. $(\sim K \cdot P) \supset (B \lor R)$
        2. $\sim K \supset (B \supset D)$
        3. $K \lor (R \supset E)$
        4. $\sim K \cdot P$ $/ \therefore D \lor E$
        5. $\sim K$ 4, Simp.
        6. $B \supset D$ 2, 5, M.P.
        7. $R \supset E$ 3, 5, D.S.
        8. $(B \supset D) \cdot (R \supset E)$ 6, 7, Conj.
        9. $B \lor R$ 1, 4, M.P.
       10. $D \lor E$ 8, 9, C.D.

    10. 1. $T \lor (E \supset D)$
        2. $T \supset C$
        3. $(E \supset G) \supset (D \supset I)$
        4. $(\sim T \cdot \sim C) \supset (D \supset G)$
        5. $\sim C$
        6. $\sim I \lor \sim G$ $/ \therefore \sim D \lor \sim E$
        7. $\sim T$ 2, 5, M.T.
        8. $E \supset D$ 1, 7, D.S.
        9. $\sim T \cdot \sim C$ 7, 5, Conj.
       10. $D \supset G$ 4, 9, M.P.
       11. $E \supset G$ 8, 10, H.S.
       12. $D \supset I$ 3, 11, M.P.
       13. $(D \supset I) \cdot (E \supset G)$ 12, 11, Conj.
       14. $\sim D \lor \sim E$ 13, 6, D.D.

Exercises on pages 46–51:

I. 1. 3. 2, Add.
       4. 3, De M.
       5. 1, 4, M.T.
       6. 5, De M.
       7. 6, Com.
       8. 7, Simp.

    5. 4. 1, Exp.
       5. 2, Impl.
       6. 5, Taut.
       7. 4, 6, M.T.
       8. 7, De M.
       9. 3, 8, D.D.
      10. 9, Impl.

   10. 3. 2, Assoc.
       4. 3, Simp.
       5. 1, Assoc.
       6. 5, 4, D.S.
       7. 6, Dist.
       8. 7, Simp.
       9. 4, 8, Conj.
      10. 9, Dist.
      11. 2, Com.
      12. 11, Simp.
      13. 10, 12, D.S.

II. 1. 1. $S \supset G$
       2. $\sim S \supset E$ /∴ $G \vee E$
       3. $\sim G \supset \sim S$ 1, Trans.
       4. $\sim G \supset E$ 3, 2, H.S.
       5. $\sim\sim G \vee E$ 4, Impl.
       6. $G \vee E$ 5, D.N.

    5. 1. $(G \cdot L) \vee (W \cdot T)$
       2. $\sim G$ /∴ T
       3. $\sim G \vee \sim L$ 2, Add.
       4. $\sim(G \cdot L)$ 3, De M.
       5. $W \cdot T$ 1, 4, D.S.

      6. $T \cdot W$　　　　5, Com.

      7. T　　　　　6, Simp.

10.　1. $B \lor T$

    2. $(B \lor C) \supset (L \cdot M)$

    3. $\sim L$　　　$/ \therefore T$

    4. $\sim L \lor \sim M$　　　3, Add.

    5. $\sim(L \cdot M)$　　　4, De M.

    6. $\sim(B \lor C)$　　　2, 5, M.T.

    7. $\sim B \cdot \sim C$　　　6, De M.

    8. $\sim B$　　　7, Simp.

    9. T　　　1, 8, D.S.

15.　1. $(W \supset M) \cdot (I \supset E)$

    2. $W \lor I$

    3. $(W \supset \sim E) \cdot (I \supset \sim M)$　　$/ \therefore E \equiv \sim M$

    4. $M \lor E$　　　　　　　1, 2, C.D.

    5. $\sim E \lor \sim M$　　　　　3, 2, C.D.

    6. $E \supset \sim M$　　　　　5, Impl.

    7. $\sim \sim M \lor E$　　　　　4, D. N.

    8. $\sim M \supset E$　　　　　7, Impl.

    9. $(E \supset \sim M) \cdot (\sim M \supset E)$　　　6, 8, Conj.

   10. $E \equiv \sim M$　　　　　9, Equiv.

25.　1. $(A \lor B) \supset [(C \lor E) \supset (\sim P \cdot V)]$

    2. $(\sim P \lor \sim N) \supset U$　　$/ \therefore A \supset (C \supset U)$

    3. $\sim(A \lor B) \lor [(C \lor E) \supset (\sim P \cdot V)]$　　　　　1, Impl.

    4. $[(C \lor E) \supset (\sim P \cdot V)] \lor \sim(A \lor B)$　　　　　3, Com.

    5. $[(C \lor E) \supset (\sim P \cdot V)] \lor (\sim A \cdot \sim B)$　　　　　4, De M.

    6. $\{[(C \lor E) \supset (\sim P \cdot V)] \lor \sim A\} \cdot \{[(C \lor E) \supset$

       $(\sim P \cdot V)] \lor \sim B\}$　　　　　5, Dist.

    7. $[(C \lor E) \supset (\sim P \cdot V)] \lor \sim A$　　　　　6, Simp.

    8. $[\sim(C \lor E) \lor (\sim P \cdot V)] \lor \sim A$　　　　　7, Impl.

    9. $\sim(C \lor E) \lor [(\sim P \cdot V) \lor \sim A]$　　　　　8, Assoc.

   10. $[(\sim P \cdot V) \lor \sim A] \lor \sim(C \lor E)$　　　　　9, Com.

   11. $[(\sim P \cdot V) \lor \sim A] \lor (\sim C \cdot \sim E)$　　　　　10, De M.

   12. $\{[(\sim P \cdot V) \lor \sim A] \lor \sim C\} \cdot \{[(\sim P \cdot V) \lor \sim A] \lor \sim E\}$　　11, Dist.

   13. $[(\sim P \cdot V) \lor \sim A] \lor \sim C$　　　　　12, Simp.

   14. $(\sim P \cdot V) \lor (\sim A \lor \sim C)$　　　　　13, Assoc.

   15. $(\sim A \lor \sim C) \lor (\sim P \cdot V)$　　　　　14, Com.

   16. $[(\sim A \lor \sim C) \lor \sim P] \cdot [(\sim A \lor \sim C) \lor V]$　　　　　15, Dist.

17. $(\sim A \vee \sim C) \vee \sim P$ 16, Simp.
18. $[(\sim A \vee \sim C) \vee \sim P] \vee \sim N$ 17, Add.
19. $(\sim A \vee \sim C) \vee (\sim P \vee \sim N)$ 18, Assoc.
20. $\sim(A \cdot C) \vee (\sim P \vee \sim N)$ 19, De M.
21. $(A \cdot C) \supset (\sim P \vee \sim N)$ 20, Impl.
22. $(A \cdot C) \supset U$ 21, 2, H.S.
23. $A \supset (C \supset U)$ 22, Exp.

Exercises on page 53:

1.

A	B	C	D
F	T	F	F

5.

T	U	V	W	X
T	T	T	T	F

or

F	F	T	F	T

10.

W	X	Y	Z	A	B
F	F	F	T	T	T

Exercises on page 61:

23.
1. $E \supset S$
2. $E \supset (S \supset N)$
3. $S \supset (N \supset F)$ /∴ $E \supset F$
4. E /∴ F (C.P.)
5. $S \supset N$ 2, 4, M.P.
6. S 1, 4, M.P.
7. N 5, 6, M.P.
8. $N \supset F$ 3, 6, M.P.
9. F 8, 7, M.P.

25.
1. $(A \vee B) \supset [(C \vee E) \supset (\sim P \cdot V)]$
2. $(\sim P \vee \sim N) \supset U$ /∴ $A \supset (C \supset U)$
3. A /∴ $C \supset U$ (C.P.)
4. C /∴ U (C.P.)
5. $A \vee B$ 3, Add.
6. $(C \vee E) \supset (\sim P \cdot V)$ 1, 5, M.P.
7. $C \vee E$ 4, Add.
8. $\sim P \cdot V$ 6, 7, M.P.
9. $\sim P$ 8, Simp.
10. $\sim P \vee \sim N$ 9, Add.
11. U 2, 10, M.P.

Exercises on page 65:

3.   1. $(H \supset I) \cdot (J \supset K)$

     2. $(I \vee K) \supset L$

     3. $\sim L$ $/ \therefore \sim (H \vee J)$

     4. $\sim (I \vee K)$ 2, 3, M.T.   4'. $\sim\sim(H \vee J)$ I.P.

     5. $\sim I \cdot \sim K$ 4, De M.   5'. $H \vee J$ 4', D.N.

     6. $\sim I$ 5, Simp.   6'. $I \vee K$ 1, 5', C.D.

     7. $H \supset I$ 1, Simp.   7'. L 2, 6', M.P.

     8. $\sim H$ 7, 6, M.T.   8'. $L \cdot \sim L$ 7', 3, Conj.

     9. $(J \supset K) \cdot (H \supset I)$ 1, Com.

   10. $J \supset K$ 9, Simp.

   11. $\sim K \cdot \sim I$ 5, Com.

   12. $\sim K$ 11, Simp.

   13. $\sim J$ 10, 12, M.T.

   14. $\sim H \cdot \sim J$ 8, 13, Conj.

   15. $\sim (H \vee J)$ 14, De M.

5.   1. $(V \supset \sim W) \cdot (X \supset Y)$

     2. $(\sim W \supset Z) \cdot (Y \supset \sim A)$

     3. $(Z \supset \sim B) \cdot (\sim A \supset C)$

     4. $V \cdot X$ $/ \therefore \sim B \cdot C$

     5. $V \supset \sim W$ 1, Simp.   5'. $\sim (\sim B \cdot C)$ I.P.

     6. V 4, Simp.   6'. $\sim\sim B \vee \sim C$ 5', De M.

     7. $\sim W$ 5, 6, M.P.   7'. $\sim Z \vee \sim\sim A$ 3, 6', D.D.

     8. $\sim W \supset Z$ 2, Simp.   8'. $\sim\sim W \vee \sim Y$ 2, 7', D.D.

     9. Z 8, 7, M.P.   9'. $\sim V \vee \sim X$ 1, 8', D.D.

   10. $Z \supset \sim B$ 3, Simp.   10'. $\sim (V \cdot X)$ 9', De M.

   11. $\sim B$ 10, 9, M.P.   11'. $(V \cdot X) \cdot \sim (V \cdot X)$ 4, 10', Conj.

   12. $(X \supset Y) \cdot (V \supset W)$ 1, Com.

   13. $X \supset Y$ 12, Simp.

   14. $X \cdot V$ 4, Com.

   15. X 14, Simp.

   16. Y 13, 15, M.P.

   17. $(Y \supset \sim A) \cdot (\sim W \supset Z)$ 2, Com.

   18. $Y \supset \sim A$ 17, Simp.

   19. $\sim A$ 18, 16, M.P.

   20. $(\sim A \supset C) \cdot (Z \supset \sim B)$ 3, Com.

   21. $\sim A \supset C$ 20, Simp.

   22. C 21, 19, M.P.

   23. $\sim B \cdot C$ 11, 22, Conj.

Exercises on pages 67–68:

I.   1.   1. P $/ \therefore Q \supset P$ (C.P.)
        2. $P \vee \sim Q$ 1, Add.
        3. $\sim Q \vee P$ 2, Com.
        4. $Q \supset P$ 3, Impl.

   5.   1. $\sim\sim P$ $/ \therefore P$ (C.P.)
        2. P 1, D.N.

  10.   1. $A \supset B$ $/ \therefore A \supset (A{\cdot}B)$ (C.P.)
        2. A $/ \therefore A{\cdot}B$ (C.P.)
        3. B 1, 2, M.P.
        4. $A{\cdot}B$ 2, 3, Conj.

  15.   1. $A \supset (B{\cdot}C)$ $/ \therefore [B \supset (D{\cdot}E)] \supset (A \supset D)$ (C.P.)
        2. $B \supset (D{\cdot}E)$ $/ \therefore A \supset D$ (C.P.)
        3. A $/ \therefore D$ (C.P.)
        4. $B{\cdot}C$ 1, 3, M.P.
        5. B 4, Simp.
        6. $D{\cdot}E$ 2, 5, M.P.
        7. D 6, Simp.

  20.   1. $P \supset Q$ $/ \therefore \sim(Q{\cdot}R) \supset \sim(R{\cdot}P)$ (C.P.)
        2. $\sim(Q{\cdot}R)$ $/ \therefore \sim(R{\cdot}P)$ (C.P.)
        3. $\sim Q \vee \sim R$ 2, De M.
        4. $Q \supset \sim R$ 3, Impl.
        5. $P \supset \sim R$ 1, 4, H.S.
        6. $\sim P \vee \sim R$ 5, Impl.
        7. $\sim R \vee \sim P$ 6, Com.
        8. $\sim(R{\cdot}P)$ 7, De M.

II.   1.   1. $\sim[(A \supset B) \vee (A \supset \sim B)]$ $/ \therefore (A \supset B) \vee (A \supset \sim B)$ (I.P.)
        2. $\sim(A \supset B){\cdot}\sim(A \supset \sim B)$ 1, De M.
        3. $\sim(\sim A \vee B){\cdot}\sim(\sim A \vee \sim B)$ 2, Impl.
        4. $(\sim\sim A{\cdot}\sim B){\cdot}(\sim\sim A{\cdot}\sim\sim B)$ 3, De M.
        5. $(\sim\sim A{\cdot}\sim B){\cdot}(\sim\sim B{\cdot}\sim\sim A)$ 4, Com.
        6. $[(\sim\sim A{\cdot}\sim B){\cdot}\sim\sim B]{\cdot}\sim\sim A$ 5, Assoc.
        7. $[\sim\sim A{\cdot}(\sim B{\cdot}\sim\sim B)]{\cdot}\sim\sim A$ 6, Assoc.
        8. $[(\sim B{\cdot}\sim\sim B){\cdot}\sim\sim A]{\cdot}\sim\sim A$ 7, Com.
        9. $(\sim B{\cdot}\sim\sim B){\cdot}(\sim\sim A{\cdot}\sim\sim A)$ 8, Assoc.
      10. $\sim B{\cdot}\sim\sim B$ 9, Simp.

5. 1. ~[(A ⊃ B) v (~A ⊃ C)]   / ∴ (A ⊃ B) v (~A ⊃ C)   (I.P.)
2. ~(A ⊃ B)·~(~A ⊃ C)   1, De M.
3. ~(~A v B)·~(~~A v C)   2, Impl.
4. (~~A·~B)·(~~~A·~C)   3, De M.
5. ~~A·[~B·(~~~~A·~C)]   4, Assoc.
6. ~~A·[(~~~~A·~C)·~B]   5, Com.
7. ~~A·[~~~~A·(~C·~B)]   6, Assoc.
8. (~~A·~~~~A)·(~C·~B)   7, Assoc.
9. ~~A·~~~~A   8, Simp.

10. 1. ~~[(A ⊃ ~A)·(~A ⊃ A)]   / ∴ ~[(A ⊃ ~A)·(~A ⊃ A)]
                                                            (I.P.)

2. (A ⊃ ~A)·(~A ⊃ A)   1, D.N.
3. (~A v ~A)·(~~A v A)   2, Impl.
4. (~A v ~A)·(~~A v ~~A)   3, D.N.
5. ~A·~~A   4, Taut.

Exercises on pages 79–80:

5. (x)[Sx ⊃ Ex]
10. (x)[Dx ⊃ Bx]
15. (x)[Cx ⊃ (~Wx v Sx)]
20. (x)[(Ix·Ux) ⊃ (Px v Fx)]
25. (x)[(Ax·Ox) ⊃ (Dx ⊃ ~Rx)]
29. (x)[(Hx·Tx) ⊃ Gx]
30. (x)[(Hx·Gx) ⊃ Tx]

Exercises on pages 89–91:

1. 1. (x)[Ax ⊃ Bx]
2. ~Bc   / ∴ ~Ac
3. Ac ⊃ Bc   1, **UI**
4. ~Ac   3, 2, M.T.

5. 1. (x)[Lx ⊃ Mx]
2. (∃x)[Lx·Nx]   / ∴ (∃x)[Nx·Mx]
3. La·Na   2, **EI**
4. La ⊃ Ma   1, **UI**
5. La   3, Simp.
6. Ma   4, 5, M.P.
7. Na·La   3, Com.

8. Na 7, Simp.

9. $Na \cdot Ma$ 8, 6, Conj.

10. $(\exists x)[Nx \cdot Mx]$ 9, **EG**

10. 1. $(x)[Dx \supset Ex]$

2. $(x)[Ex \supset Fx]$

3. $(x)[Fx \supset Gx]$ / $\therefore$ $(x)[Dx \supset Gx]$

4. $Dy \supset Ey$ 1, **UI**

5. $Ey \supset Fy$ 2, **UI**

6. $Fy \supset Gy$ 3, **UI**

7. $Dy \supset Fy$ 4, 5, H.S.

8. $Dy \supset Gy$ 7, 6, H.S.

9. $(x)[Dx \supset Gx]$ 8, **UG**

15. 1. $(x)[(Bx \lor Vx) \supset (Ox \cdot Dx)]$ / $\therefore$ $(x)[Bx \supset Dx]$

2. By

3. $(By \lor Vy) \supset (Oy \cdot Dy)$ 1, **UI**

4. $By \lor Vy$ 2, Add.

5. $Oy \cdot Dy$ 3, 4, M.P.

6. $Dy \cdot Oy$ 5, Com.

7. Dy 6, Simp.

8. $By \supset Dy$ 2–7, C.P.

9. $(x)[Bx \supset Dx]$ 8, **UG**

20. 1. $(x)\{(Bx \lor Wx) \supset [(Ax \lor Fx) \supset Sx]\}$ / $\therefore$ $(x)[Bx \supset (Ax \supset Sx)]$

2. By

3. Ay

4. $(By \lor Wy) \supset [(Ay \lor Fy) \supset Sy]$ 1, **UI**

5. $By \lor Wy$ 2, Add

6. $(Ay \lor Fy) \supset Sy$ 4, 5, M.P.

7. $Ay \lor Fy$ 3, Add.

8. Sy 6, 7, M.P.

9. $Ay \supset Sy$ 3–8, C.P.

10. $By \supset (Ay \supset Sy)$ 2–9, C.P.

11. $(x)[Bx \supset (Ax \supset Sx)]$ 10, **UG**

25. 1. $(x)[(Mx \cdot Cx) \supset (Gx \supset \sim Dx)]$

2. $(x)[(Mx \cdot Rx) \supset Cx]$

3. $(x)[(Cx \cdot \sim Dx) \supset Ex]$

4. $(x)[(Mx \cdot Ex) \supset Gx]$ / $\therefore$ $(x)[(Mx \cdot Rx) \supset (Ex \equiv Gx)]$

    5. *My·Ry*

    6. *(My·Ry) ⊃ Cy*   2, **UI**

    7. *Cy*   6, 5, M.P.

    8. *My*   5, Simp.

    9. *My·Cy*   8, 7, Conj.

  10. *(My·Cy) ⊃ (Gy ⊃ ∼Dy)*   1, UI

  11. *Gy ⊃ ∼Dy*   10, 9, M.P.

  12. *(Cy·∼Dy) ⊃ Ey*   3, UI

  13. *Cy ⊃ (∼Dy ⊃ Ey)*   12, Exp.

  14. *∼Dy ⊃ Ey*   13, 7, M.P.

  15. *Gy ⊃ Ey*   11, 14, H.S.

  16. *(My·Ey) ⊃ Gy*   4, UI

  17. *My ⊃ (Ey ⊃ Gy)*   16, Exp.

  18. *Ey ⊃ Gy*   17, 8, M.P.

  19. *(Ey ⊃ Gy)·(Gy ⊃ Ey)*   18, 15, Conj.

  20. *Ey ≡ Gy*   19, Equiv.

  21. *(My·Ry) ⊃ (Ey ≡ Gy)*   5–20, C.P.

  22. *(x)[(Mx·Rx) ⊃ (Ex ≡ Gx)]*   21, **UG**

Exercises on pages 95–97:

I. **3.** *(x)[Ex ⊃ Fx]*   &boxed{a}   *Ea ⊃ Fa*

          (∃x)[Gx·∼Fx]   *Ga·∼Fa*

	Ea	*Fa*	*Ga*
	F	**F**	**T**

∴ *(∃x)[Ex·∼Gx]*   ∴ *Ea·∼Ga*

7. *(x)[Sx ⊃ Ix]*   &boxed{a, b} *(Sa⊃Ia)·(Sb ⊃ Ib)*

    (∃x)[Px·Ix]   *(Pa·Ia) v (Pb·Ib)*

    (∃x)[Px·∼Ix]   *(Pa·∼Ia) v (Pb·∼Ib)*

∴ *(x)[Sx ⊃ ∼Px]*   ∴ *(Sa ⊃ ∼Pa)·(Sb ⊃ ∼Pb)*

	Sa	*Sb*	*Ia*	*Ib*	*Pa*	*Pb*
	T	**F**	**T**	**F**	**T**	**T**
or	**F**	**T**	**F**	**T**	**T**	**T**

8. *(x)[Sx ⊃ Ix]*   &boxed{a, b, c} *(Sa ⊃ Ia)·(Sb ⊃ Ib)·(Sc ⊃ Ic)*

    (∃x)[Px·Ix]   *(Pa·Ia) v (Pb·Ib) v (Pc·Ic)*

    (∃x)[Px·∼Ix]   *(Pa·∼Ia) v (Pb·∼Ib) v (Pc·∼Ic)*

∴ *(x)[Sx ⊃ Px]*   ∴ *(Sa ⊃ Pa)·(Sb ⊃ Pb)·(Sc ⊃ Pc)*

	Sa	*Sb*	*Sc*	*Ia*	*Ib*	*Ic*	*Pa*	*Pb*	*Pc*
	T	**F**	**T**	**T**	**F**	**T**	**F**	**T**	**T**
or	**T**	**F**	**F**	**T**	**F**	**T**	**F**	**T**	**T**

II. 7. $(x)[(Ax \vee Wx) \supset Vx]$ $\boxed{a, b}$ $[(Aa \vee Wa) \supset Va]\cdot[(Ab \vee Wb) \supset Vb]$
$(\exists x)[Ax \cdot Fx]$ $[Aa \cdot Fa] \vee [Ab \cdot Fb]$
$(\exists x)[Ax \cdot Tx]$ $[Aa \cdot Ta] \vee [Ab \cdot Tb]$
$(x)[Tx \supset Vx]$ $[Ta \supset Va]\cdot[Tb \supset Vb]$
$\therefore (\exists x)[Fx \cdot Tx]$ $\therefore [Fa \cdot Ta] \vee [Fb \cdot Tb]$

Aa	Ab	Wa	Wb	Va	Vb	Fa	Fb	Ta	Tb
T	T	T	T	T	T	T	F	F	T

or any of 7 other truth value assignments.

8. 1. $(x)[(Ax \vee Wx) \supset Vx]$
   2. $(\exists x)[Ax \cdot Fx]$
   3. $(\exists x)[Ax \cdot Tx]$
   4. $(x)[Vx \supset Tx]$ $/ \therefore (\exists x)[Fx \cdot Tx]$
   5. $Aa \cdot Fa$ 2, **EI**
   6. Aa 5, Simp.
   7. $Aa \vee Wa$ 6, Add.
   8. $(Aa \vee Wa) \supset Va$ 1, **UI**
   9. Va 8, 7, M.P.
  10. $Va \supset Ta$ 4, **UI**
  11. Ta 10, 9, M.P.
  12. $Fa \cdot Aa$ 5, Com.
  13. Fa 12, Simp.
  14. $Fa \cdot Ta$ 13, 11, Conj.
  15. $(\exists x)[Fx \cdot Tx]$ 14, **EG**

12. 1. $(x)\{[Ax \cdot (Ux \vee Ix)] \supset \sim(Hx \vee Cx)\}$
   2. $(\exists x)[Ax \cdot (Ix \cdot Bx)]$
   3. $(x)[(Ax \cdot Wx) \supset (\sim Hx \supset Dx)]$
   4. $(x)[Ax \supset Wx]$
   5. $(\exists x)[Wx \cdot Hx]$ $/ \therefore (\exists x)[Ax \cdot Dx]$
   6. $Aa \cdot (Ia \cdot Ba)$ 2, **EI**
   7. Aa 6, Simp.
   8. $(Ia \cdot Ba) \cdot Aa$ 6, Com.
   9. $Ia \cdot Ba$ 8, Simp.
  10. Ia 9, Simp.
  11. $Ia \vee Ua$ 10, Add.
  12. $Ua \vee Ia$ 11, Com.
  13. $Aa \cdot (Ua \vee Ia)$ 7, 12, Conj.
  14. $[Aa \cdot (Ua \vee Ia)] \supset (Ha \vee Ca)$ 1, **UI**

15. $\sim(Ha \text{ v } Ca)$ 14, 13, M.P.

16. $\sim Ha \cdot \sim Ca$ 15, De M.

17. $\sim Ha$ 16, Simp.

18. $Aa \supset Wa$ 4, **UI**

19. Wa 18, 7, M.P.

20. $Aa \cdot Wa$ 7, 19, Conj.

21. $(Aa \cdot Wa) \supset (\sim Ha \supset Da)$ 3, **UI**

22. $\sim Ha \supset Da$ 21, 20, M.P.

23. Da 22, 17, M.P.

24. $Aa \cdot Da$ 7, 23, Conj.

25. $(\exists x)[Ax \cdot Dx]$ 24, **EG**

13. $(x)\{[Cx \cdot (Lx \text{ v } Rx)] \supset \sim(Ex \text{ v } Ax)\}$ $\boxed{a, b}$

$(\exists x)[Cx \cdot (Wx \cdot Lx)]$

$(x)[(Cx \cdot Px) \supset (\sim Ex \supset Dx)]$

$(x)[Cx \supset Px]$

$(\exists x)[Px \cdot Ex]$

∴ $(\exists x)[Cx \cdot \sim Dx]$

$\{[Ca \cdot (La \text{ v } Ra)] \supset \sim(Ea \text{ v } Aa)\} \cdot \{[Cb \cdot (Lb \text{ v } Rb)] \supset \sim(Eb \text{ v } Ab)\}$

$[Ca \cdot (Wa \cdot La)] \text{ v } [Cb \cdot (Wb \cdot Lb)]$

$[(Ca \cdot Pa) \supset (\sim Ea \supset Da)] \cdot [(Cb \cdot Pb) \supset (\sim Eb \supset Db)]$

$[Ca \supset Pa] \cdot [Cb \supset Pb]$

$[Pa \cdot Ea] \text{ v } [Pb \cdot Eb]$

∴ $[Ca \cdot \sim Da] \text{ v } [Cb \cdot \sim Db]$

Ca	Cb	La	Lb	Ra	Rb	Ea	Eb	Aa	Ab	Wa	Wb	Pa	Pb	Da	Db
T	F	T	T	T	F	T	F	T	T	T	T	T	T	T	T

or any of 127 other truth value assignments.

Exercises on pages 102–103:

7. $(x)\{(Bx \cdot Yx) \supset [(y)[(Yy \cdot By) \supset Ry] \supset Rx]\}$

9. $(x)[(Ox \cdot Px) \supset (Cx \text{ v } Mx)] \supset [(\exists y)(Cy \cdot Py) \text{ v } (\exists z)(Mz \cdot Pz)]$

14. $(x)\{(Sx \cdot Wx) \supset [(y)(Wy \supset Fy) \supset Fx]\}$

18. $[(\exists x)(Ex \cdot Lx) \cdot (\exists y)(Py \cdot \sim Fy)] \supset (\exists z)(Ez \cdot \sim Sz)$

Exercises on pages 116–118:

3. The use of **UG** at line 4 is wrong, because ν ('x') occurs free in the assumption '$Fx \equiv Gy$' within whose scope the premiss $\Phi\nu$ ('$Fx \equiv Gy$') lies.

6. There are three mistakes here:

   a) the use of **UG** at line 5 is wrong, because ν ('z') does not occur free in $\Phi\nu$ ('$(\exists x)[(Fx \cdot Gz) \supset Hy]$') at all places that μ ('y') occurs free in $\Phi\mu$ ('$(\exists x)[(Fx \cdot Gy) \supset Hy]$').

   b) the use of **UG** at line 5 is wrong, because the variable ν ('z') occurs free in line 2 within whose scope $\Phi\nu$ ('$(\exists x)[(Fx \cdot Gz) \supset Hy]$') lies.

   c) the use of **UI** at line 7 is wrong, because ν ('x') does not occur free in $\Phi\nu$ ('$(\exists x)[(Fx \cdot Gx) \supset Hx]$') at all places that μ ('y') occurs free in $\Phi\mu$ ('$(\exists x)[(Fx \cdot Gy) \supset Hy]$').

9. There are three (or four) mistakes here:

   Line 3, '$Fx \cdot Gy$', is claimed at line 5 to be a $\Phi\nu$ corresponding to the $\Phi\mu$ ('$Fx \cdot Gx$') in line 1. This claim is false regardless of whether we take ν to be 'x' or to be 'y'. So in either case we note that

   a) the use of **EI** at line 5 is wrong, because ν ('x **or** 'y') does not occur free in $\Phi\nu$ ('$Fx \cdot Gy$') at all places that μ ('x') occurs free in $\Phi\mu$ ('$Fx \cdot Gx$').

   If we take ν in $\Phi\nu$ ('$Fx \cdot Gy$') to be 'x', then we note that

   b) the use of **EI** at line 5 is wrong, because ν ('x') occurs free in p ('Fx'), the last line lying within the scope of the assumption $\Phi\nu$ ('$Fx \cdot Gy$').

   In any case, there are two additional mistakes present:

   c) the use of **EI** at line 8 is wrong, because ν ('x') occurs free in line 5 which precedes $\Phi\nu$ ('$\sim Fx \cdot Gx$').

   d) the use of **EI** at line 8 is wrong, because ν ('x') occurs free in p ('$\sim Fx$'), the last line lying within the scope of the assumption $\Phi\nu$ ('$\sim Fx \cdot Gx$').

Exercises on pages 120–122:

4.
1. $(\exists x)Gx \supset (y)[Cy \supset Gy]$
2. $(\exists x)[Px \cdot Tx] \supset (y)[Gy \supset Ty]$ / ∴ $(\exists x)[Px \cdot (Tx \cdot Gx)] \supset (y)[Cy \supset Ty]$

┌─► 3. $(\exists x)[Px \cdot (Tx \cdot Gx)]$
│ ┌─► 4. $Pu \cdot (Tu \cdot Gu)$
│ │   5. Gu 4, Simp.
│ │   6. $(\exists x)Gx$ 5, **EG**
│ │   7. $Pu \cdot Tu$ 4, Simp.
│ │   8. $(\exists x)[Px \cdot Tx]$ 7, **EG**
│ │   9. $(y)[Cy \supset Gy]$ 1, 6, M.P.
│ │   10. $(y)[Gy \supset Ty]$ 2, 8, M.P.
│ │   11. $Cw \supset Gw$ 9, **UI**
│ │   12. $Gw \supset Tw$ 10, **UI**
│ │   13. $Cw \supset Tw$ 11, 12, H.S.
│ │   14. $(y)[Cy \supset Ty]$ 13, **UG**
│   15. $(y)[Cy \supset Ty]$ 3, 4–14, **EI**
  16. $(\exists x)[Px \cdot (Tx \cdot Gx)] \supset (y)[Cy \supset Ty]$ 3–15, C.P.

8.
1. $(x)[Rx \supset (Sx \lor Mx)]$
2. $(x)[(Ux \cdot Rx) \supset \sim Sx]$ / ∴ $(x)[Ux \supset Rx] \supset (y)[Uy \supset My]$

┌─► 3. $(x)[Ux \supset Rx]$
│ ┌─► 4. Uz
│ │   5. $Uz \supset Rz$ 3, **UI**
│ │   6. Rz 5, 4, M.P.
│ │   7. $Uz \cdot Rz$ 4, 6, Conj.
│ │   8. $(Uz \cdot Rz) \supset \sim Sz$ 2, **UI**
│ │   9. $\sim Sz$ 8, 7, M.P.
│ │   10. $Rz \supset (Sz \lor Mz)$ 1, **UI**
│ │   11. $Sz \lor Mz$ 10, 6, M.P.
│ │   12. Mz 11, 9, D.S.
│   13. $Uz \supset Mz$ 4–12, C.P.
│   14. $(y)[Uy \supset My]$ 13, **UG**
  15. $(x)[Ux \supset Rx] \supset (y)[Uy \supset My]$ 3–14, C.P.

12.
1. $(x)\{Lx \supset [(y)(Py \supset Vy) \supset Mx]\}$
2. $(\exists z)(Pz \cdot Vz) \supset (y)(Py \supset Vy)$ / ∴ $(\exists x)Lx \supset [(\exists z)(Pz \cdot Vz) \supset (\exists y)My]$

3. $(\exists x)Lx$
4. $(\exists z)(Pz \cdot Vz)$
5. $(y)(Py \supset Vy)$ 2, 4, M.P.
6. Lu
7. $Lu \supset [(y)(Py \supset Vy) \supset Mu]$ 1, **UI**
8. $(y)(Py \supset Vy) \supset Mu$ 7, 6, M.P.
9. Mu 8, 5, M.P.
10. $(\exists y)My$ 9, **EG**
11. $(\exists y)My$ 3, 6–10, **EI**
12. $(\exists z)(Pz \cdot Vz) \supset (\exists y)My$ 4–11, C.P.
13. $(\exists x)Lx \supset [(\exists z)(Pz \cdot Vz) \supset (\exists y)My]$ 3–12, C.P.

Exercises on page 130:

4.
1. $\sim(\exists x)(Fx \supset Gx)$
2. $(x)\sim(Fx \supset Gx)$ 1, **QN**
3. $\sim(Fy \supset Gy)$ 2, UI
4. $Fy \cdot \sim Gy$ 3, Impl.
5. Fy 4, Simp.
6. $(\exists x)Fx$ 5, **EG**
7. $\sim Gy$ 5, Simp.
8. $(x)\sim Gx$ 7, **UG**
9. $\sim(\exists x)Gx$ 8, QN
10. $(\exists x)Fx \cdot \sim(\exists x)Gx$ 6, 9, Conj.
11. $\sim(\exists x)(Fx \supset Gx) \supset [(\exists x)Fx \cdot \sim(\exists x)Gx]$ 1–10, C.P.
12. $\sim[(\exists x)Fx \cdot \sim(\exists x)Gx] \supset (\exists x)(Fx \supset Gx)$ 11, Trans., D.N.
13. $[(\exists x)Fx \supset (\exists x)Gx] \supset (\exists x)(Fx \supset Gx)$ 12, Impl.

8.
1. $(\exists x)(Fx \vee Q)$
2. $Fx \vee Q$
3. $\sim Q$
4. Fx 2, 3, D.S.
5. $(\exists x)Fx$ 4, **EG**
6. $\sim Q \supset (\exists x)Fx$ 3–5, C.P.
7. $Q \vee (\exists x)Fx$ 6, Impl., D.N.
8. $(\exists x)Fx \vee Q$ 7, Com.
9. $(\exists x)Fx \vee Q$ 1, 2–8, **EI**
10. $(\exists x)(Fx \vee Q) \supset$
$[(\exists x)Fx \vee Q]$ 1–9, C.P.

1. $\sim(\exists x)(Fx \vee Q)$
2. $(x)\sim(Fx \vee Q)$ 1, **QN**
3. $\sim(Fx \vee Q)$ 2, **UI**
4. $\sim Fx \cdot \sim Q$ 3, DeM.
5. $\sim Fx$ 4, Simp.
6. $(x)\sim Fx$ 5, **UG**
7. $\sim(\exists x)Fx$ 6, **QN**
8. $\sim Q$ 4, Simp.
9. $\sim(\exists x)Fx \cdot \sim Q$ 7, 8, Conj.
10. $\sim[(\exists x)Fx \vee Q]$ 9, De M.
11. $\sim(\exists x)(Fx \vee Q) \supset$
$\sim[(\exists x)Fx \vee Q]$ 1–10, C.P.
12. $[(\exists x)Fx \vee Q] \supset$
$(\exists x)(Fx \vee Q)$ 11, Trans.

12.

1.	$\sim(\exists x)(Fx \text{ v } Gx)$	
2.	$(x)\sim(Fx \text{ v } Gx)$	1, **QN**
3.	$\sim(Fx \text{ v } Gx)$	2, **UI**
4.	$\sim Fx \cdot \sim Gx$	3, De M.
5.	$\sim Fx$	4, Simp.
6.	$\sim Gx$	4, Simp.
7.	$(x)\sim Fx$	5, **UG**
8.	$(x)\sim Gx$	6, **UG**
9.	$(x)\sim Fx \cdot (x)\sim Gx$	7, 8, Conj.
10.	$\sim(\exists x)Fx \cdot \sim(\exists x)Gx$	9, **QN**
11.	$\sim[(\exists x)Fx \text{ v } (\exists x)Gx]$	10, De M.
12.	$\sim(\exists x)(Fx \text{ v } Gx) \supset \sim[(\exists x)Fx \text{ v } (\exists x)Gx]$	1–11, C.P.
13.	$[(\exists x)Fx \text{ v } (\exists x)Gx] \supset (\exists x)(Fx \text{ v } Gx)$	12, Trans.
14.	$(\exists x)(Fx \text{ v } Gx)$	
15.	$Fy \text{ v } Gy$	
16.	$\sim(\exists x)Fx$	
17.	$(x)\sim Fx$	16, **QN**
18.	$\sim Fy$	17, **UI**
19.	Gy	15, 18, D.S.
20.	$(\exists x)Gx$	19, **EG**
21.	$\sim(\exists x)Fx \supset (\exists x)Gx$	16–20, C.P.
22.	$(\exists x)Fx \text{ v } (\exists x)Gx$	21, Impl., D.N.
23.	$(\exists x)Fx \text{ v } (\exists x)Gx$	14, 15–22, **EI**
24.	$(\exists x)(Fx \text{ v } Gx) \supset [(\exists x)Fx \text{ v } (\exists x)Gx]$	14–23, C.P.
25.	$\{13\} \cdot \{24\}$	13, 24, Conj.
26.	$[(\exists x)Fx \text{ v } (\exists x)Gx] \equiv (\exists x)(Fx \text{ v } Gx)$	25, Equiv.

Exercises on pages 144–147:

I.   5. All things come to him who waits.

10. A person is judged by the company he keeps.

15. It's an ill wind that blows nobody any good.

20. No one borrows everything from everybody.

25. Where ignorance is bliss 'tis folly to be wise.

II.   5. $(x)[Rx \supset (\exists y)(Ty \cdot Hxy)]$

10. $(x)\{Px \supset [(\exists y)Axy \supset (z)(Pz \supset Ezx)]\}$

15. $(x)\{Px \supset \{(Ey)\{Dy \cdot Hxy \cdot (z)[(Pz \cdot Vzx) \supset Byz]\} \supset (\exists u)(Nu \cdot Mxu)]\}$

20. $(\exists x)\{Sx \cdot (y)[Py \supset (\exists z)Byzx]\}$

25. $(x)\{Sx \supset (y)\{Py \supset (\exists z)[(\exists w)Bwzx \cdot \sim Byzx]\}\}$

Exercises on pages 149–151:

4.
1. $(x)\{(\exists y)(Byb \cdot Lxyb) \supset Fx\}$
2. $(\exists x)(Cxb \cdot Lxab)$ $/ \therefore (x)(Cxb \supset \sim Fx) \supset \sim Bab$

    3. $(x)(Cxb \supset \sim Fx)$
    4. $Cxb \cdot Lxab$
    5. $Cxb \supset \sim Fx$ 3, **UI**
    6. Cxb 4, Simp.
    7. $\sim Fx$ 5, 6, M.P.
    8. $(\exists y)(Byb \cdot Lxyb) \supset Fx$ 1, **UI**
    9. $\sim(\exists y)(Byb \cdot Lxyb)$ 8, 7, M.T.
   10. $(y)(\sim Byb \lor \sim Lxyb)$ 9, **QN**, De M.
   11. $\sim Bab \lor \sim Lxab$ 10, **UI**
   12. $Lxab$ 4, Simp.
   13. $\sim Bab$ 11, 12, Com., D.N., D.S.
   14. $\sim Bab$ 2, 4–13, **EI**
   15. $3 \supset 14$ 3–14, C.P.

6.
1. $(x)\{(\exists y)[(\exists z)(Gz \cdot \sim Rz \cdot Sxzy)] \supset Cx\}$
2. $(z)[(Wz \cdot Orz) \supset (Slzr \lor Smzr)]$ $/ \therefore (\exists z)(Wz \cdot Orz \cdot Gz \cdot \sim Rz)$
                                       $\supset [(u)(\sim Smur) \supset Cl]$

    3. $(\exists z)(Wz \cdot Orz \cdot Gz \cdot \sim Rz)$
    4. $(u)(\sim Smur)$
    5. $Wz \cdot Orz \cdot Gz \cdot \sim Rz$
    6. $Wz \cdot Orz$ 5, Simp.
    7. $(Wz \cdot Orz) \supset (Slzr \lor Smzr)$ 2, **UI**
    8. $Slzr \lor Smzr$ 7, 6, M.P.
    9. $\sim Smzr$ 4, **UI**
   10. $Slzr$ 8, 9, Com., D.S.
   11. $Gz \cdot \sim Rz$ 5, Simp.
   12. $Gz \cdot \sim Rz \cdot Slzr$ 11, 10, Conj.
   13. $(\exists z)(Gz \cdot \sim Rz \cdot Slzr)$ 12, **EG**
   14. $(\exists y)[(\exists z)(Gz \cdot \sim Rz \cdot Slzy)]$ 13, **EG**
   15. $(\exists y)[(\exists z)(Gz \cdot \sim Rz \cdot Slzy)] \supset Cl$ 1, **UI**
   16. Cl 15, 14, M.P.
   17. Cl 3, 5–16, **EI**
   18. $4 \supset 17$ 4–17, C.P.
   19. $3 \supset [18]$ 3–18, C.P.

9.
1. $(x)[(Px \cdot \sim Rxx) \supset (y)(Py \supset \sim Ryx)]$
2. $(y)\{Py \supset (x)[(Px \cdot \sim Ryx) \supset \sim Hyx]\}$ $/ \therefore (x)\{[Px \cdot (z)(Pz \supset \sim Rxz)]$
                                      $\supset (y)(Py \supset \sim Hyx)\}$

3. $Px \cdot (z)(Pz \supset \sim Rxz)$
4. Py
5. $(z)(Pz \supset \sim Rxz)$ 3, Simp.
6. $Px \supset \sim Rxx$ 5, **UI**
7. Px 3, Simp.
8. $\sim Rxx$ 6, 7, M.P.
9. $Px \cdot \sim Rxx$ 7, 8, Conj.
10. $(Px \cdot \sim Rxx) \supset (y)(Py \supset \sim Ryx)$ 1, **UI**
11. $(y)(Py \supset \sim Ryx)$ 10, 9, M.P.
12. $Py \supset \sim Ryx$ 11, **UI**
13. $\sim Ryx$ 12, 4, M.P.
14. $Px \cdot \sim Ryx$ 7, 13, Conj.
15. $Py \supset (x)[(Px \cdot \sim Ryx) \supset \sim Hyx]$ 2, **UI**
16. $(x)[(Px \cdot \sim Ryx) \supset \sim Hyx]$ 15, 4, M.P.
17. $(Px \cdot \sim Ryx) \supset \sim Hyx$ 16, **UI**
18. $\sim Hyx$ 17, 14, M.P.

19. $4 \supset 18$ 4–18, C.P.
20. $(y)(19)$ 19, **UG**

21. $3 \supset 20$ 3–20, C.P.
22. $(x)\{21\}$ 21, **UG**

Exercises on pages 157–158:

3.   1. $(x)[Fx \supset (y)(Sy \supset Oxy)]$ /∴ $(y)[Sy \supset (x)(Fx \supset \sim Oyx)]$
    2. $(x)(y)(Oxy \supset \sim Oyx)$ (auxiliary premiss)
    3. Sy
    4. Fx
    5. $Fx \supset (y)(Sy \supset Oxy)$ 1, **UI**
    6. $(y)(Sy \supset Oxy)$ 5, 4, M.P.
    7. $Sy \supset Oxy$ 6, **UI**
    8. Oxy 7, 3, M.P.
    9. $(y)(Oxy \supset \sim Oyx)$ 2, **UI**
   10. $Oxy \supset \sim Oyx$ 9, **UI**
   11. $\sim Oyx$ 10, 8, M.P.

   12. $Fx \supset \sim Oyx$ 4–11, C.P.
   13. $(x)(Fx \supset \sim Oyx)$ 12, **UG**

   14. $Sy \supset (x)(Fx \supset \sim Oyx)$ 3–13, C.P.
   15. $(y)[Sy \supset (x)(Fx \supset \sim Oyx)]$ 14, **UG**

5.   1. $(x)\{\{Px \cdot (\exists y)[Py \cdot (\exists z)(Cz \cdot Cyz) \cdot Nxy]\} \supset Ux\}$ /∴ $(x)\{[Px \cdot (\exists z)$
                                                     $(Bz \cdot Cxz)] \supset Ux\}$

    2. $(z)(Bz \supset Cz)$ } (additional premisses)
    3. $(x)(Nxx)$

374

4. $Px \cdot (\exists z)(Bz \cdot Cxz)$
5. $(\exists z)(Bz \cdot Cxz)$ 4, Simp.
6. $Bz \cdot Cxz$
7. Bz 6, Simp.
8. $Bz \supset Cz$ 2, **UI**
9. Cz 8, 7, M.P.
10. Cxz 6, Simp.
11. $Cz \cdot Cxz$ 9, 10, Conj.
12. $(\exists z)(Cz \cdot Cxz)$ 11, **EG**
13. Px 4, Simp.
14. Nxx 3, **UI**
15. $Px \cdot (\exists z)(Cz \cdot Cxz) \cdot Nxx$ 13, 12, 14, Conj.
16. $(\exists y)[Py \cdot (\exists z)(Cz \cdot Cyz) \cdot Nxy]$ 15, **EG**
17. $Px \cdot (\exists y)[Py \cdot (\exists z)(Cz \cdot Cyz) \cdot Nxy]$ 13, 16, Conj.
18. $\{Px \cdot (\exists y)[Py \cdot (\exists z)(Cz \cdot Cyz) \cdot Nxy]\} \supset Ux$ 1, **UI**
19. Ux 18, 17, M.P.
20. Ux 5, 6–19, **EI**

21. $[Px \cdot (\exists z)(Bz \cdot Cxz)] \supset Ux$ 4–20, C.P.
22. $(x)\{[Px \cdot (\exists z)(Bz \cdot Cxz)] \supset Ux\}$ 21, **UG**

7. 1. $(x)[Vx \supset (y)(Oyx \supset \sim Ixy)]$
2. $(y)(x)[(Rx \cdot Oyx) \supset Tyx]$ / $\therefore$ $(y)[(\exists x)(Vx \cdot Oyx) \supset (\exists x)(Tyx \cdot \sim Ixy)]$
3. $(x)(Vx \supset Rx)$ (auxiliary premiss)
4. $(\exists x)(Vx \cdot Oyx)$
5. $Vx \cdot Oyx$
6. Vx 5, Simp.
7. $Vx \supset Rx$ 3, **UI**
8. Rx 7, 6, M.P.
9. Oyx 5, Simp.
10. $Rx \cdot Oyx$ 8, 9, Conj.
11. $(x)[(Rx \cdot Oyx) \supset Tyx]$ 2, **UI**
12. $(Rx \cdot Oyx) \supset Tyx$ 11, **UI**
13. Tyx 12, 10, M.P.
14. $Vx \supset (y)(Oyx \supset \sim Ixy)$ 1, **UI**
15. $(y)(Oyx \supset \sim Ixy)$ 14, 6, M.P.
16. $Oyx \supset \sim Ixy$ 15, **UI**
17. $\sim Ixy$ 16, 9, M.P.
18. $Tyx \cdot \sim Ixy$ 17, 13, Conj.
19. $(\exists x)(Tyx \cdot \sim Ixy)$ 18, **EG**
20. $(\exists x)(Tyx \cdot \sim Ixy)$ 4, 5–19, **EI**

21. $(\exists x)(Vx \cdot Oyx) \supset (\exists x)(Tyx \cdot \sim Ixy)$ 4–20, C.P.
22. $(y)[(\exists x)(Vx \cdot Oyx) \supset (\exists x)(Tyx \cdot \sim Ixy)]$ 21, **UG**

Exercises on pages 168–169:

2. 1. $(\exists x)\{Px \cdot Sx \cdot (y)[(Py \cdot Sy) \supset x=y] \cdot Lx\}$ $/ \therefore (x)[(Px \cdot Sx) \supset Lx]$

    2. $Pz \cdot Sz$

    3. $Px \cdot Sx \cdot (y)[(Py \cdot Sy) \supset x=y] \cdot Lx$

    4. $(y)[(Py \cdot Sy) \supset x=y]$ 3, Simp.

    5. $(Pz \cdot Sz) \supset x=z$ 4, **UI**

    6. $x=z$ 5, 2, M.P.

    7. Lx 3, Simp.

    8. Lz 6, 7, Id.

    9. Lz 1, 3–8, **EI**

   10. $(Pz \cdot Sz) \supset Lz$ 2–9, C.P.

   11. $(x)[(Px \cdot Sx) \supset Lx]$ 10, **UG**

4. 1. $(\exists x)\{Px \cdot (y)[(Py \cdot x \neq y) \supset Fxy] \cdot Sx\}$ $/ \therefore (y)[(Py \cdot {\sim} Sy) \supset (\exists x)(Px \cdot Fxy)]$

    2. $Py \cdot {\sim} Sy$

    3. $Px \cdot (y)[(Py \cdot x \neq y) \supset Fxy] \cdot Sx$

    4. Sx 3, Simp.

    5. ${\sim} Sy$ 2, Simp.

    6. $x \neq y$ 4, 5, Id.

    7. Py 2, Simp.

    8. $Py \cdot x \neq y$ 7, 6, Conj.

    9. $(y)[(Py \cdot x \neq y) \supset Fxy]$ 3, Simp.

   10. $(Py \cdot x \neq y) \supset Fxy$ 9, **UI**

   11. Fxy 10, 8, M.P.

   12. Px 3, Simp.

   13. $Px \cdot Fxy$ 12, 11, Conj.

   14. $(\exists x)(Px \cdot Fxy)$ 13, **EG**

   15. $(\exists x)(Px \cdot Fxy)$ 1, 3–14, **EI**

   16. $(Py \cdot {\sim} Sy) \supset (\exists x)(Px \cdot Fxy)$ 2–15, C.P.

   17. $(y)[(Py \cdot {\sim} Sy) \supset (\exists x)(Px \cdot Fxy)]$ 16, **UG**

6. 1. $(x)\{Fx \supset (y)[(Fy \cdot Lxy) \supset Sxy]\}$
          $/ \therefore (\exists x)\{Fx \cdot (y)[(Fy \cdot x \neq y) \supset Lxy]\} \supset (\exists x)\{Fx \cdot (y)[(Fy \cdot x \neq y) \supset Sxy]\}$

  2. $(\exists x)\{Fx \cdot (y)[(Fy \cdot x \neq y) \supset Lxy]\}$

  3. $Fx \cdot (y)[(Fy \cdot x \neq y) \supset Lxy]$

4.	Fx	3, Simp.
5.	$(y)[(Fy \cdot x \neq y) \supset Lxy]$	3, Simp.
6.	$Fx \supset (y)[(Fy \cdot Lxy) \supset Sxy]$	1, **UI**
7.	$(y)[(Fy \cdot Lxy) \supset Sxy]$	6, 4, M.P.
8.	$(Fy \cdot Lxy) \supset Sxy$	7, **UI**
9.	$(Fy \cdot x \neq y) \supset Lxy$	5, **UI**
10.	$Lxy \supset (Fy \supset Sxy)$	8, Com., Exp.
11.	$(Fy \cdot x \neq y) \supset (Fy \supset Sxy)$	9, 10, H.S.
12.	$(Fy \cdot x \neq y \cdot Fy) \supset Sxy$	11, Exp.
13.	$(Fy \cdot x \neq y) \supset Sxy$	12, Com., Taut.
14.	$(y)[(Fy \cdot x \neq y) \supset Sxy]$	13, **UG**
15.	$Fx \cdot (y)[(Fy \cdot x \neq y) \supset Sxy]$	4, 14, Conj.
16.	$(\exists x)\{Fx \cdot (y)[(Fy \cdot x \neq y) \supset Sxy]\}$	15, **EG**
17.	$(\exists x)\{Fx \cdot (y)[(Fy \cdot x \neq y) \supset Sxy]\}$	2, 3–16, **EI**
18.	$2 \supset 17$	2–17, C.P.

Exercises on pages 175–176:

I. 3. $(x)(y)[x \neq y \supset (\exists F)(Fx \cdot \sim Fy)]$

     6. $(\exists x)\{Fxd \cdot (y)(Fyd \supset x = y) \cdot (G)[(Gx \cdot \mathbf{F}G) \supset Gd] \cdot (H)[(Hx \cdot \mathbf{V}H) \supset \sim Hd]\}$

     9. $(x)\{[Mx \cdot (F)(\mathbf{V}F \supset Fx)] \supset Vx\} \cdot (\exists x)[Mx \cdot Vx \cdot (\exists F)(\mathbf{V}F \cdot \sim Fx)]$

II. 2.

1. $(\exists x)(\exists F)Fx$		
2. $(\exists F)Fx$		
3. Fx		
4. $(\exists x)Fx$	3, **EG**	
5. $(\exists F)(\exists x)Fx$	4, **EG**	
6. $(\exists F)(\exists x)Fx$	2, 3–5, **EI**	
7. $(\exists F)(\exists x)Fx$	1, 2–6, **EI**	
8. $1 \supset 7$	1–7, C.P.	

1. $(\exists F)(\exists x)Fx$		
2. $(\exists x)Fx$		
3. Fx		
4. $(\exists F)Fx$	3, **EG**	
5. $(\exists x)(\exists F)Fx$	4, **EG**	
6. $(\exists x)(\exists F)Fx$	2, 3–5, **EI**	
7. $(\exists x)(\exists F)Fx$	1, 2–6, **EI**	
8. $1 \supset 7$	1–7, C.P.	

6.

1. $(x)(y)(z)[(Rxy \cdot Ryz) \supset Rxz] \cdot (x)\sim Rxx$
2. $(x)(y)(z)[(Rxy \cdot Ryz) \supset Rxz]$ 1, Simp.
3. $(y)(z)[(Rxy \cdot Ryz) \supset Rxz]$ 2, **UI**
4. $(z)[(Rxy \cdot Ryz) \supset Rxz]$ 3, **UI**
5. $(Rxy \cdot Ryx) \supset Rxx$ 4, **UI**
6. $(x)\sim Rxx$ 1, Simp.
7. $\sim Rxx$ 6, **UI**
8. $\sim(Rxy \cdot Ryx)$ 5, 7, M.T.
9. $\sim Rxy \text{ v} \sim Ryx$ 8, De M.
10. $Rxy \supset \sim Ryx$ 9, Impl.
11. $(y)(Rxy \supset \sim Ryx)$ 10, **UG**
12. $(x)(y)(Rxy \supset \sim Ryx)$ 11, **UG**
13. $\{1\} \supset 12$ 1–12, C.P.
14. $(R)\{13\}$ 13, **UG**

10.

1. $(x)(y)[(x=y) \equiv (F)(Fx \equiv Fy)]$ $/ \therefore (x)(x=x)$
2. Fx
3. $\sim\sim Fx$ 2, D.N.
4. Fx 3, D.N.
5. $Fx \supset Fx$ 2–4, C.P.
6. $(Fx \supset Fx) \cdot (Fx \supset Fx)$ 5, Taut.
7. $Fx \equiv Fx$ 6, Equiv.
8. $(F)(Fx \equiv Fx)$ 7, **UG**
9. $(y)[(x=y) \equiv (F)(Fx \equiv Fy)]$ 1, **UI**
10. $(x=x) \equiv (F)(Fx \equiv Fx)$ 9, **UI**
11. $[(x=x) \supset (F)(Fx \equiv Fx)] \cdot$
    $[(F)(Fx \equiv Fx) \supset (x=x)]$ 10, Equiv.
12. $(F)(Fx \equiv Fx) \supset (x=x)$ 11, Simp.
13. $x=x$ 12, 8, M.P.
14. $(x)(x=x)$ 13, **UG**

Exercises on page 201:

2. *wff*   4. *wff*   8. NO

Exercises on page 204:

2. $\sim((\sim(\sim(P)))\cdot(\sim(P)))$
5. $\sim((P)\cdot(\sim(\sim((Q)\cdot(\sim(P))))))$
8. $\sim((\sim((P)\cdot(\sim((P)\cdot(Q)))))\cdot(\sim(\sim((P)\cdot(\sim(Q))))))$

Exercises on page 206:

1. $f_2(P,Q)$ is expressed as $\sim(P\cdot\sim Q)$
   $f_6(P,Q)$ is expressed as $\sim(P\cdot Q)\cdot\sim(P\cdot\sim Q)$
   $f_{11}(P,Q)$ is expressed as $\sim(P\cdot Q)\cdot\sim(P\cdot\sim Q)\cdot\sim(\sim P\cdot Q)$

Exercises on page 211:

1. $S(v,\sim)$ is functionally complete, for it contains the same '$\sim$' as does R.S., and the '·' of R.S. is definable in $S(v,\sim)$ as $P\cdot Q = \mathrm{df} \sim(\sim P \,v \sim Q)$. Hence any truth function expressible in R.S. is expressible in $S(v,\sim)$, whose functional completeness now follows from that of R.S.

2. $S(\supset,\cdot)$ is functionally incomplete, for it contains no *wff* that can express a truth function whose value is *false* when all its arguments have the value *true*. Proof by strong induction on the number of symbols in the *wff* $g(P,Q,R, \ldots)$ of $S(\supset,\cdot)$.

   α) If $g(P,Q,R, \ldots)$ contains just one symbol it is either P or Q or R or . . . . If these are all *true* then $g(P,Q,R, \ldots)$ cannot have the value *false*.

   β) Assume that any *wff* containing $<m$ symbols cannot be *false* when all its arguments are *true*. Now consider any *wff* $g(P,Q,R, \ldots)$ containing exactly m symbols ($m > 1$). It must be either $g_1(P,Q,R, \ldots) \supset g_2(P,Q,R, \ldots)$ or $g_1(P,Q,R, \ldots)\cdot g_2(P,Q,R, \ldots)$. But $g_1(P,Q,R, \ldots)$ and $g_2(P,Q,R, \ldots)$ each contains $<m$ symbols, hence they must have the value *true* if all their arguments are *true*. And because $\mathbf{T} \supset \mathbf{T}$ and $\mathbf{T}\cdot\mathbf{T}$ are both $\mathbf{T}$, $g(P,Q,R, \ldots)$ cannot be *false* when all of its arguments have the value *true*. Hence no *wff* of $S(\supset,\cdot)$ can be *false* when its arguments are all *true*, so $S(\supset,\cdot)$ is functionally incomplete.

6. $S(\supset,+)$ is functionally complete, for the '$\sim$' of R.S. is definable in $S(\supset,+)$ as $\sim P = \mathrm{df}\ P + (P \supset P)$, and the '·' of R.S. is then definable in $S(\supset,+)$ as

$P \cdot Q = \mathrm{df} \sim [P \supset (P + Q)]$. Hence any truth function expressible in R.S. is expressible in $S(\supset, +)$, whose functional completeness now follows from that of R.S.

Exercises on pages 230–231:

Th. 6. $\vdash (R \sim \sim P) \supset (PR)$

| *Proof:* | $\vdash \sim \sim P \supset P$ | Th. 2 |
| | $\vdash (R \sim \sim P) \supset (PR)$ | DR 3 |

DR 6. $P \supset Q, Q \supset R \vdash P \supset R$

Proof:	$P \supset P$	Th. 7
	$P \supset Q$	pr.
	$Q \supset R$	pr.
	$P \supset R$	DR 5

Th. 10. $\vdash (PQ)R \supset P(QR)$

Proof:	$\vdash (PQ)R \supset PQ$	Ax. 2
	$\vdash PQ \supset P$	Ax. 2
	$\vdash (PQ)R \supset P$	DR 6
	$\vdash PQ \supset QP$	Th. 8
	$\vdash QP \supset Q$	Ax. 2
	$\vdash PQ \supset Q$	DR 6
	$\vdash (PQ)R \supset QR$	DR 7, Cor. 1
	$\vdash (PQ)R \supset P(QR)$	DR 8

DR 10. $P \supset R, Q \supset R \vdash (P \vee Q) \supset R$

Proof:	$P \supset R$	pr.
	$Q \supset R$	pr.
	$(P \vee Q) \supset (R \vee R)$	DR 9
	$\sim R \supset \sim R \sim R$	Ax. 1
	$[\sim R \supset \sim R \sim R] \supset [\sim (\sim R \sim R) \supset \sim \sim R]$	Th. 5
	$\sim (\sim R \sim R) \supset \sim \sim R$	R 1
	$(R \vee R) \supset \sim \sim R$	df.
	$\sim \sim R \supset R$	Th. 2
	$(P \vee Q) \supset R$	DR 5

Th. 14. $\vdash [PQ \supset R] \supset [P \supset (Q \supset R)]$

   Proof: $\vdash \sim\sim(Q\sim R) \supset (Q\sim R)$ Th. 2

            $\vdash P\sim\sim(Q\sim R) \supset P(Q\sim R)$ DR 7, Cor. 2

            $\vdash P(Q\sim R) \supset (PQ)\sim R$ Th. 10, Cor.

            $\vdash P\sim\sim(Q\sim R) \supset (PQ)\sim R$ DR 6

            $\vdash \{P\sim\sim(Q\sim R) \supset (PQ)\sim R\} \supset$

                            $\{\sim[(PQ)\sim R] \supset \sim[P\sim\sim(Q\sim R)]$ Th. 5

            $\vdash \sim[(PQ)\sim R] \supset \sim[P\sim\sim(Q\sim R)]$ R 1

            $\vdash [PQ \supset R] \supset [P \supset (Q \supset R)]$ df.

Exercises on pages 234–235:

Th. 17, Cor. $\vdash P \supset (P \vee Q)$

   Proof: $\vdash P \supset (Q \vee P)$ Th. 17

            $\vdash (Q \vee P) \supset (P \vee Q)$ Th. 11

            $\vdash P \supset (P \vee Q)$ DR 6

DR 14. $P, Q \vdash PQ$

   Proof: $P \supset (Q \supset PQ)$ Th. 15

            P pr.

            $Q \supset (PQ)$ R 1

            Q pr.

            PQ R 1

Exercises on page 237:

DR 20. $(P \supset Q)\cdot(R \supset S), P \vee R \vdash Q \vee S$

   Proof: $(P \supset Q)\cdot(R \supset S)$ pr.

            $P \supset Q$ DR 19

            $R \supset S$ DR 19, Cor.

            $(P \vee R) \supset (Q \vee S)$ DR 9

            $P \vee R$ pr.

            $Q \vee S$ R 1

Th. 30. $\vdash P(Q \vee R) \equiv PQ \vee PR$

   Proof: $\vdash PQ \supset P$ Ax. 2

            $\vdash PR \supset P$ Ax. 2

            $\vdash (PQ \vee PR) \supset P$ DR 10

$\vdash PQ \supset QP$	Th. 8
$\vdash QP \supset Q$	Ax. 2
$\vdash PQ \supset Q$	DR 6
$\vdash PR \supset RP$	Th. 8
$\vdash RP \supset R$	Ax. 2
$\vdash PR \supset R$	DR 6
$\vdash (PQ \vee PR) \supset (Q \vee R)$	DR 9
$\vdash (PQ \vee PR) \supset P(Q \vee R)$	DR 8
$\vdash P(Q \vee R) \supset (Q \vee R)P$	Th. 8
$\vdash (Q \vee R)P \supset QP \vee RP$	Th. 18
$\vdash P(Q \vee R) \supset QP \vee RP$	DR 6
$\vdash QP \equiv PQ$	Th. 21
$\vdash P(Q \vee R) \supset PQ \vee RP$	MT IV, Cor.
$\vdash RP \equiv PR$	Th. 21
$\vdash P(Q \vee R) \supset PQ \vee PR$	MT IV, Cor.
$\vdash P(Q \vee R) \equiv PQ \vee PR$	DR 14, df.

Exercises on page 265:

1. 1. $CApp p$

2. $CpApq$

3. $CApqAqp$

4. $CCpqCArpArq$

Exercises on page 267:

2. $P{\downarrow}P{:}{\downarrow}{:}P{\downarrow}P.{\downarrow}.P{\downarrow}P{:}.{\downarrow}{:}.P{\downarrow}P{:}{\downarrow}{:}P{\downarrow}P.{\downarrow}.P{\downarrow}P$

6. $P|Q.|.P|Q{:}|{:}P|P$

8. $P{\downarrow}P{:}{\downarrow}{:}P{\downarrow}P.{\downarrow}.P{\downarrow}P{:}.{\downarrow}{:}.P{\downarrow}P{:}{\downarrow}{:}P{\downarrow}P.{\downarrow}.P{\downarrow}P$

Exercises on pages 290–296:

Th. 4. $\vdash (x)(P \supset Q) \supset [(\exists x)P \supset (\exists x)Q]$

Proof:

$(x)(P \supset Q) \vdash (x)(P \supset Q) \supset (P \supset Q)$	P 5
$(x)(P \supset Q) \vdash (x)(P \supset Q)$	premiss
$(x)(P \supset Q) \vdash P \supset Q$	R 1
$(x)(P \supset Q) \vdash {\sim}Q \supset {\sim}P$	℗
$(x)(P \supset Q) \vdash (x)({\sim}Q \supset {\sim}P)$	R 2
$(x)(P \supset Q) \vdash (x){\sim}Q \supset (x){\sim}P$	DR 5
$(x)(P \supset Q) \vdash {\sim}(x){\sim}P \supset {\sim}(x){\sim}Q$	℗

$(x)(P \supset Q) \vdash (\exists x)P \supset (\exists x)Q$ df.

$\vdash (x)(P \supset Q) \supset [(\exists x)P \supset (\exists x)Q]$ D.T.

Th. 13. $\vdash (\exists x)(P \cdot Q) \supset (\exists x)P \cdot (\exists x)Q$

Proof: $\vdash [(x) \sim P \vee (x) \sim Q] \supset (x)(\sim P \vee \sim Q)$ Th. 10

$\vdash \sim(x)(\sim P \vee \sim Q) \supset \sim[(x) \sim P \vee (x) \sim Q]$ $\textcircled{P}$

$\vdash \sim(x) \sim(P \cdot Q) \supset [\sim(x) \sim P \cdot \sim(x) \sim Q]$ Duality

Theorem and S.T.

$\vdash (\exists x)(P \cdot Q) \supset (\exists x)P \cdot (\exists x)Q$ df.

Th. 21. $\vdash (x)(P \supset Q) \equiv (\exists x)P \supset Q$

Proof: $\vdash (x)(\sim Q \supset \sim P) \equiv \sim Q \supset (x) \sim P$ Th. 20

$\vdash (x)(P \supset Q) \equiv \sim(x) \sim P \supset \sim\sim Q$ $\textcircled{P}$ and S.T.

$\vdash (x)(P \supset Q) \equiv \sim(x) \sim P \supset Q$ $\textcircled{P}$ and S.T.

$\vdash (x)(P \supset Q) \equiv (\exists x)P \supset Q$ df.

DR 6. $P \supset Q \vdash (\exists x)P \supset Q$

Proof: $P \supset Q$ premiss

$(x)(P \supset Q)$ R 2

$(\exists x)P \supset Q$ Th. 21 and S.T.

Exercises on page 305:

2. $(\exists x)(w)(z)(\exists u)(\exists v)(t)\{[F(u,v) \supset [G(t) \vee H(y)]] \cdot [[G(x) \vee H(y)] \supset F(w,z)]\}$

4. $(\exists y)(x)(\exists z)(w)[F(x,y) \supset F(z,w)]$

Exercises on page 307:

1. $(\exists t)(x)(y)(z)\{\{[H(x) \vee H(y)] \vee H(z)\} \cdot \sim[D(t) \cdot \sim D(t)]\}$

3. $(\exists t)(y)(z)(\exists x)\{[G(x,y) \vee F(z)] \cdot \sim[D(t) \cdot \sim D(t)]\}$

Exercises on page 311:

1. $(\exists x)(\exists z)(y)[F(x,y) \vee G(z)]$

3. $(\exists w)(\exists x)(\exists y)(t)\{\{[F(x,y) \cdot \sim[D(w) \cdot \sim D(w)]] \supset H(w,x)\} \supset H(w,t)\}$

Exercises on page 332:

2. p 6. $(p \cdot q) \vee r$ 10. $p \vee \bar{p}$

Exercises on pages 340–341:

Th. 2.   There is at most one entity 1 in **C** such that $\alpha \cap 1 = \alpha$

  Proof: Suppose there are entities 1_1 and 1_2 such that $\alpha \cap 1_1 = \alpha$, $\alpha \cap 1_2 = \alpha$.
Then $1_1 \cap 1_2 = 1_1$ and $1_2 \cap 1_1 = 1_2$. $1_1 \cap 1_2 = 1_2 \cap 1_1$ by Ax. 6.
Hence $1_1 = 1_2$ by two substitutions of equals for equals.

Th. 7. $0 \neq 1$

  Proof: Suppose $0 = 1$. Then by Ax. 10 there is an α in **C** such that $\alpha \neq 0$
and $\alpha \neq 1$. However,

$$\alpha \cap 1 = \alpha \cap 0 \qquad \text{by assumption that } 0 = 1.$$
$$\alpha = \alpha \cap 0 \qquad \text{Ax. 4}$$
$$\alpha = 0 \qquad \text{Th. 6}$$

contrary to $\alpha \neq 0$. Therefore supposition that $0 = 1$ must be false,
so $0 \neq 1$.

Th. 12. $\alpha \cup (\beta \cup \gamma) = (\alpha \cup \beta) \cup \gamma$

  Proof: Lemma 1. $\alpha \cup (\alpha \cap \beta) = \alpha$

    Proof: $\alpha \cup (\alpha \cap \beta) = (\alpha \cap 1) \cup (\alpha \cap \beta) \qquad \text{Ax. 4}$
$$= \alpha \cap (1 \cup \beta) \qquad \text{Ax. 8}$$
$$= \alpha \cap (\beta \cup 1) \qquad \text{Ax. 5}$$
$$= \alpha \cap 1 \qquad \text{Th. 5}$$
$$= \alpha \qquad \text{Ax. 4}$$

  Lemma 2. $\alpha \cap (\alpha \cup \beta) = \alpha$

    Proof: $\alpha \cap (\alpha \cup \beta) = (\alpha \cup 0) \cap (\alpha \cup \beta) \qquad \text{Ax. 3}$
$$= \alpha \cup (0 \cap \beta) \qquad \text{Ax. 7}$$
$$= \alpha \cup (\beta \cap 0) \qquad \text{Ax. 6}$$
$$= \alpha \cup 0 \qquad \text{Th. 6}$$
$$= \alpha \qquad \text{Ax. 3}$$

  Lemma 3. If $\alpha \cap \gamma = \alpha$ and $\beta \cap \gamma = \beta$ then $(\alpha \cup \beta) \cap \gamma = \alpha \cup \beta$

    Proof: $(\alpha \cup \beta) \cap \gamma = \gamma \cap (\alpha \cup \beta) \qquad \text{Ax. 6}$
$$= (\gamma \cap \alpha) \cup (\gamma \cap \beta) \qquad \text{Ax. 8}$$
$$= (\alpha \cap \gamma) \cup (\beta \cap \gamma) \qquad \text{Ax. 6}$$
$$= \alpha \cup \beta \qquad \text{hypothesis}$$

A. $\alpha \cap [\alpha \cup (\beta \cup \gamma)] = \alpha$ L. 2

  $\beta \cap [\alpha \cup (\beta \cup \gamma)] = (\beta \cap \alpha) \cup [\beta \cap (\beta \cup \gamma)]$ Ax. 8

  $\qquad\qquad\qquad = (\beta \cap \alpha) \cup \beta$ L. 2

  $\qquad\qquad\qquad = \beta \cup (\beta \cap \alpha)$ Ax. 5

B. $\beta \cap [\alpha \cup (\beta \cup \gamma)] = \beta$ L. 1

C. $(\alpha \cup \beta) \cap [\alpha \cup (\beta \cup \gamma)] = \alpha \cup \beta$ by L. 3 from $A, B.$

  $\gamma \cap [\alpha \cup (\beta \cup \gamma)] = \gamma \cap [(\beta \cup \gamma) \cup \alpha]$ Ax. 5

  $\qquad\qquad\qquad = [\gamma \cap (\beta \cup \gamma)] \cup (\gamma \cap \alpha)$ Ax. 8

  $\qquad\qquad\qquad = [\gamma \cap (\gamma \cup \beta)] \cup (\gamma \cap \alpha)$ Ax. 5

  $\qquad\qquad\qquad = \gamma \cup (\gamma \cap \alpha)$ L. 2

D. $\gamma \cap [\alpha \cup (\beta \cup \gamma)] = \gamma$ L. 1

E. $[(\alpha \cup \beta) \cup \gamma] \cap [\alpha \cup (\beta \cup \gamma)] = (\alpha \cup \beta) \cup \gamma$ by L. 3 from $C, D.$

  $\alpha \cap [(\alpha \cup \beta) \cup \gamma] = [\alpha \cap (\alpha \cup \beta)] \cup (\alpha \cap \gamma)$ Ax. 8

  $\qquad\qquad\qquad = \alpha \cup (\alpha \cap \gamma)$ L. 2

F. $\alpha \cap [(\alpha \cup \beta) \cup \gamma] = \alpha$ L. 1

  $\beta \cap [(\alpha \cup \beta) \cup \gamma] = [\beta \cap (\alpha \cup \beta)] \cup (\beta \cap \gamma)$ Ax. 8

  $\qquad\qquad\qquad = [\beta \cap (\beta \cup \alpha)] \cup (\beta \cap \gamma)$ Ax. 5

  $\qquad\qquad\qquad = \beta \cup (\beta \cap \gamma)$ L. 2

G. $\beta \cap [(\alpha \cup \beta) \cup \gamma] = \beta$ L. 1

  $\gamma \cap [(\alpha \cup \beta) \cup \gamma] = \gamma \cap [\gamma \cup (\alpha \cup \beta)]$ Ax. 5

H. $\gamma \cap [(\alpha \cup \beta) \cup \gamma] = \gamma$ L. 2

I. $(\beta \cup \gamma) \cap [(\alpha \cup \beta) \cup \gamma] = \beta \cup \gamma$ by L. 3 from $G, H.$

J. $[\alpha \cup (\beta \cup \gamma)] \cap [(\alpha \cup \beta) \cup \gamma] = \alpha \cup (\beta \cup \gamma)$ by L. 3 from $F, I.$

  $\alpha \cup (\beta \cup \gamma) = [\alpha \cup (\beta \cup \gamma)] \cap [(\alpha \cup \beta) \cup \gamma]$ $J.$

  $\qquad\qquad\qquad = [(\alpha \cup \beta) \cup \gamma] \cap [\alpha \cup (\beta \cup \gamma)]$ Ax. 6

  $\alpha \cup (\beta \cup \gamma) = (\alpha \cup \beta) \cup \gamma$ $E.$

Th. 20.   If $\alpha \cap \beta \neq 0$ and $\beta \cap -\gamma = 0$, then $\alpha \cap \gamma \neq 0$

  Proof: $(\alpha \cap \gamma) \cap \beta = \alpha \cap (\gamma \cap \beta)$ Th. 13

  $\qquad\qquad\qquad = \alpha \cap (\beta \cap \gamma)$ Ax. 6

  $\qquad\qquad\qquad = (\alpha \cap \beta) \cap \gamma$ Th. 13

  $\qquad\qquad\qquad = [(\alpha \cap \beta) \cap \gamma] \cup 0$ Ax. 3

  $\qquad\qquad\qquad = [(\alpha \cap \beta) \cap \gamma] \cup (\alpha \cap 0)$ Th. 6

  $\qquad\qquad\qquad = [(\alpha \cap \beta) \cap \gamma] \cup [\alpha \cap (\beta \cap -\gamma)]$ hypothesis

  $\qquad\qquad\qquad = [(\alpha \cap \beta) \cap \gamma] \cup [(\alpha \cap \beta) \cap -\gamma]$ Th. 13

  $\qquad\qquad\qquad = \alpha \cap \beta$ Th. 11

  $(\alpha \cap \gamma) \cap \beta \neq 0$ hypothesis

  $\alpha \cap \gamma \neq 0$ Th. 10

SPECIAL
SYMBOLS

	PAGE
·	10, 199f., 251, 260–264
∼	11, 199f.
v	12, 202
( )	13, 199f.
⊃	16, 202, 251
≡	29f., 202, 251
(x)	73
∃	74
Φ	75, 106
Ψ	77f., 106f.
⌐→	86
μ	106
ν	106
=	159, 171, 334, 341
≠	162, 337, 341
=df	171
'	164
·	198, 279
∼	198, 250, 279
( )	198, 279
f(P)	204
⊃	208, 280
α	208

	PAGE
β	208
$+$	211
$\vdash$	214, 215, 283
S^*	235
$\mathbf{v}$	250, 280
$\vert_{\overline{HA}}$	252
N	264
C	264
K	264
A	264
$\vert$	266
$\downarrow$	266
$\vert_{\overline{N}}$	268
∃	280
■	280
F'	283
F°	283
Ⓟ	279
W^*	291
$W^\triangle$	293
(Qx)	302
(Q^*x)	299, 310
S^c	315
$\{\ \}$	316
Γ	316
$\subset$	316, 339, 341
Λ	317, 335
$\bar{p}$	325
$\cup$	334, 341
$\cap$	334, 341
$\bar{\alpha}$	334, 341
0	335, 341
1	335, 341
V	335
$\hat{x}(Fx)$	341

INDEX

A proposition, 75–78, 295, 333, 337, 339

a.f.P., 283–84

Abbreviation, 7, 202, 280

Absorption, law of, 335

Ackermann, Wilhelm, 95*n*., 283; *see also* Hilbert-Ackermann system

Add., 36

Addition
of classes, 333–34
principle of, 36, 118–19, 237

Affirmative proposition
particular, 75–78
singular, 71–72
universal, 75–78

Affirming the consequent, fallacy of, 24

Affirmo, 75

Algebra
Boolean, 339–342
of classes, *see* Appendix B

Algebraic operations on statements, *see* Appendix A

Alpha case, 208

Alternation, 11

Alternative, 11
denial, 266
interpretations, 185, 342–44
methods of proving completeness, 252
systems and notations, *see* Chapter 8

Analogy, logical, 19

Analytic, 215, 216, 315

Analytical geometry, 186

And, 9, 78, 131–32

Anderson, Alan Ross, vi

Angell, Richard B., vi

Antecedent, 14

Apodosis, 15

Apparent variable, 98*n*.

Arbitrarily selected
individual, 81–82, 98
triangle, 81

Argument, 2–4, 5, 7, 193, 194, 212–213
and conditional statement, 30, 58, 65, 331

389

Argument (*Cont.*)
   extra-systematic, 182
   mathematical sense of, 204
Argument form, 19–25, 31, 331
Aristides, 129
Aristotle, ix, 7, 72, 133
Assignment of truth values, 51–52, 68–69
Assoc., 42
Associated
   conditional, 30, 58, 64, 331
   propositional formula, 283
   quantifier-free formula, 283
Association
   to the left, 203
   principles of, 42, 231, 237, 238, 239, 326, 334
Assumption of limited scope, 86–88, 112, 114
Asymmetrical relations, 151, 153
Aut, 12
Axinn, Sidney, vi
Axiom; *see also* Chapter 6
   of H.A., 251
   of N, 268
   of P.M., 256
   of R.S., 212
   of RS₁, 282
   of Boolean algebra, 340
   of reducibility, 352, 356

Balboa, 27
Baldwin, James Mark, 1*n*.
Ball, W. W. Rouse, 184*n*.
Ballard, Kaith Emerson, vi
Bar, 325, 334
Barbee, Mrs, W. L., vii, 57*n*.
Base of a system, 189
Beard, Robert W., vi
Bergmann, Gustav, xi
Bernays, Paul, 95*n*., 256
Bernstein, B. A., 268*n*.
Beta case, 208

Biconditional, 29
Binary, *see* Dyadic
Binding of free variables, 105, 109–11, 114–16, 126; *see also* **EG**; **UG**
Boole, George, 329
Boolean
   algebra, 339–42
   expansion, 329–32, 336–37
Booth, John Wilkes, 158, 164
Bound
   least upper, 352
   occurrence of a variable, 98, 282
Branching theory of types, 347
Brutus, 158
Bunge, Mario, vi
Bures, Charles E., vi
Burks, Arthur W., xii, 265*n*.
Butts, Robert E., vi

C.D., 36
C.P., 60–61, 84–89
cwff, 305, 315–16
Caesar, 158
Calculus
   extended function, 324, 353
   first-order function, *see* Chapter 9
   predicate, 277*n*.
   propositional, 194, 342–44; *see also* Chapters 7 and 8
   sentential, 194
Cantorean theory of the infinite, 352
Canty, John Thomas, 247*n*.
Carnap, Rudolf, xii, 172*n*.
Carroll, Lewis, 159
Castor and Pollux, 9–10
Categorical
   proposition, 333, 337
   syllogism, 338, 339
Church, A., 309*n*., 352*n*.
Circle, vicious, 179, 181
Clark, George A., vi
Class, *see* Appendix B
Clemens, Samuel, *see* Twain, Mark

Closed, 305, 315

Closure, 315

Com., 42

Commutation, principles of, 42, 118–19, 237, 238, 239, 326, 334

Complement, 334, 335

Completeness
  deductive, 188–89, 190, 217, 238–39, 252–53, 311–24
  expressive, 187, 201
  functional, 201, 204–208, 265–67
  of the method of deduction, 246
  of the 'natural deduction' apparatus, 323

Compound statement, 9–10, 71, 195

Conclusion, 3, 4

Conditional
  proof, 58–61, 64, 65, 66, 84–89, 238, 288, 298
  statement, 14, 15, 16, 17, 30, 58, 65, 66, 202, 331–32

Conj., 36

Conjunct, 9

Conjunction, 9, 10
  principle of, 36, 119, 228, 231, 234, 236

Conjunctive normal form, 328
  Boolean, 330–32, 337

Consequent, 15

Consistency, 68–70, 187–190, 215–16, 283–85, 317, 318, 319

Constant
  individual, 72, 279, 318, 321
  predicate, 278
  propositional, 278

Constructive dilemma, 36, 57, 237

Contingent, 28, 69

Contradiction, 28, 62, 63, 66, 68, 69, 172, 173, 197; see also Appendix C

Contradictory, 11, 28, 75, 77, 338

Contraries, 75, 77–78

Convention
  of association to the left, 203

governing '∼', 13, 203, 280

governing '·', 202–203, 280

governing 'Φμ' and 'Φν', 108

governing juxtaposition, 279–80

governing order of precedence, 203, 280

governing order of statement variables, 19, 27

Conversion, 338

Copi, David M., xii

Copi, Irving M., iii*n*., 165*n*.

Cortez, 28

Costa, Filippo, vi

Cox, Kendall B., vi

Curl symbol, 11, 13

Curry, Haskell B., vi, 264*n*.

D.D., 36

D.N., 42

D.S., 36

D.T., 234, 288

Dagger function, 266–67

Dangling variables, 101, 102

Decision problem, 245

Deduction, 177
  method of, 246–47; see also Chapter 3
  natural, 81, 106–116, 129, 298–302, 323
  theorem, 229, 231–234, 288–290, 316

Deductive
  argument, 4
  completeness, 188–89, 217, 238–47, 252–53, 311–24
  system, see Chapter 6; Appendix B

Defined term, 181

Definite description, 158, 164–68

Definition, 177–79, 180–81
  circular, 178, 179
  contextual, 165
  explicit, 165
  formal, 171

Definition (*Cont.*)
  of identity, 171, 351
  inductive, 200, 281
  in use, 165
  of material implication, 17, 30
  recursive, 200, 250, 268, 281
De M., 42
Demonstration, 122–130
  in H.A., 252
  in R.S., 214–215
  in RS₁, 282
De Morgan, Augustus, 30, 133
  his theorems, 30, 42, 57, 237, 295,
    325–26, 335
Denial, 11, 75
  alternative, 266
  joint, 266
Denoting, 165, 167
Denying the antecedent, fallacy of, 25
Derived rule of inference, 214
Descartes, 72
Description, definite, 158, 164–67
Destructive dilemma, 36, 237
Dilemma, 36, 237
Disjunct, 11
Disjunction, 11, 12–13, 14, 202
Disjunctive normal form, 328
  Boolean, 329–332, 337
Disjunctive syllogism, 12–13, 20, 21,
    36, 237
Dist., 42
Distribution, principles of, 42, 119,
    234, 237–38, 240, 326, 334
Dodgson, Charles Lutwidge, *see* Car-
    roll, Lewis
Dot symbols, 10, 11, 202–203, 260–64
Double negation, principle of, 29, 42,
    227, 228, 235, 237, 238, 325, 335
Dual, 293–95
Duality, 293–95
Dyadic
  relations, 132, 151–157
  functions, 206

E proposition, 75–78, 295, 333, 337
EG, 82, 105, 109–11, 128, 147, 298
EI, 83–4, 103–104, 111–14, 128–129,
    147, 148, 299–302
Effectiveness, 44, 200, 215
Einstein, 183
Elementary valid argument form, 34,
    35–36
Eliot, George, 160
Empty class, 335
Enthymeme, 155–57
Epistemological paradoxes, 345
Equiv., 42
Equivalence
  formal, 352
  logical, 29, 42
  material, 29, 42, 202, 237
Euclid, 62, 179–184
Euclidean geometry, 179–184, 190,
    192, 248–49
Evans, Mary Ann, *see* Eliot, George
Exceptive statements, 161
Excluded middle, 227
Exclusive
  classes, 336
  disjunction, 12, 13, 211
Exhaustive classes, 336
Existential
  generalization, 82, 105, 109–110;
    see also **EG**
  instantiation, 83–84, 111–14; *see also*
    EI
  quantifier, 74, 99–100
Exp., 43
Expansion
  Boolean, 329–32, 336–37
  law of, 336
Exportation, principle of, 44, 58, 59,
    231, 237
Expressive completeness, 187, 201
Extended function calculus, 324, 353
Extensionality, principle of, 42; *see also*
    Substitution theorems

Factors, 238–39
Fallacy
    of affirming the consequent, 24
    of denying the antecedent, 24, 25
Falzone, Joseph, iv, vii
Farber, Marvin, xii
Feigl, H., 356n.
First-order
    function, 348, 352
    function calculus, see Chapter 9
    proposition, 349–50
Form
    argument, 19–21
    Boolean normal, 329–32, 336
    normal, 302–311, 328, 329
    prenex normal, 302–305
    Skolem normal, 307–11
    statement, 27, 30–31
    of valid categorical syllogism, 338–39
Formal
    deductive system, 184–190
    definition, 171
    nature of validity, 21
    proof of validity, 33–36, 41–46, 88, 105
    truth, 27
Formula, 184–86
    quantifier-free, 283
    of type R, 307
    well-formed, 191–194, 198–201, 281
Free occurrence of a variable, 98, 126, 282
Freeing of bound variables, 105–106, 107–109, 111–14; see also EI; UI
Frege, G., 165n., 260
Function
    calculus, see Chapter 9
    monadic, 205
    orders of, 348
    propositional, 73, 97–8, 103–108, 134
    singulary, 205
    truth, 204–207
    unary, 205
Functional completeness, 201, 204–208, 265–67

Gale, Richard, vi
Galileo, 177
Gamma, 316
Gardner, Martin, 329n.
General proposition, 70–78, 91–92, 97–102
Generality
    advantage of, 185–86
    limited, 140
    unlimited, 140
Generalization, 73
    existential, 82, 105, 109–110; see also EG
    universal, 81–82, 103–104, 114–116; see also UG
Gentzen, Gerhard, iii, 81n.
Geometry, 81, 179–185, 190, 248–49
Gödel, K., 313n., 324n.
Gould, J. A., 165n.
Grant, U. S., 131–32
Grelling, Kurt, 345, 346, 349, 353, 355

H.A., 250–259
H.S., 36
Hailperin, Theodore, viii
Heath, Thomas L., 182n., 184n.
Heijenoort, John van, viii
Henkin, Leon, xiii, 312n.
Henle, Paul, xiv
Henry, O., 159
Hereditary, 54, 217
Heterological, see Appendix C
Hierarchy
    of logical types, 173, 347–48
    of orders, 348
    of propositions, 349–350
Hilbert, 283
Hilbert-Ackermann system, 250–259

Horseshoe symbol, 16
Huntington, E. V., 340*n*.
Hypothetical
statement, 14
syllogism, 22, 23, 36, 56, 230, 236

I proposition, 75–78, 295, 333, 337–38
I.P., 62
Id., 159, 161
Identity, 152, 158–68
definition of, 171, 351
of indiscernibles, 159
principle of, 159, 161
If, *see* Implication
Ikezawa, Michael, 238*n*.
Immediate inference, 338
Impl., 42
Implicans, 14
Implicate, 15
Implication, 14, 15, 16–17, 22, 29
Implicative statement, 14
Implicit relations, 138–39
Impredicable, 172, 173–74, 345
Inclusion, 333, 339, 341
Inclusive disjunction, 12
Incompleteness of a set of rules, 54–58
Inconsistent, 68–70, 187, 189, 311,
317; *see also* Contradiction
Independence of axioms, 183, 188,
217–23
Independent variable, 204
Indirect proof, 62–65, 66, 88, 238
Indiscernibles, identity of, 159
Individual, 72
arbitrarily selected, 81–82, 98
constant, 72, 279, 318, 321
symbol, 279
variable, 72, 98, 279
Induction
strong, 209–211
weak, 208, 209
Inductive
argument, 4

definition, 200, 281
Inference
immediate, 338
mediate, 338
rules of, 34, 35–36, 41, 45, 81–82
Inferring, 2
Initially placed, 302
Instance, substitution, 20, 27, 35, 73,
74, 97, 98
Instantiation, 73
existential, 83–84, 105, 111–114; *see
also* **EI**
universal, 80–81, 107–109, 167; *see
also* **UI**
Interchange of bound variables, 297
Interpretation, 196, 198, 201, 313–
314, 321
alternative, 185, 342–344
normal, 194, 201, 313–315, 321
proof of consistency, 188
proof of independence, 188
Intersection, 334
Intransitive relations, 152
Invalid, 4, 19, 20
argument form, 20–21
Invalidity, proof of, 51, 52, 91–95
Iota, 164
Irreflexive relations, 152–153

Jaśkowski, Stanislaw, 81*n*.
Johnson, Samuel, 276
Johnstone, Henry W., iv
Joint denial, 266
Jørgensen, J., 268*n*.
Justification, 34, 44, 225
Juxtaposition, 279–280

Kalish, Donald, iv
Kepler, 177
Klemke, E. D., ix

Lambda, 316
Langford, C. H., xiv, 264*n*.

Language, 6, 7, 193, 195–96
  levels of, 195–96, 352–56
  object, 195–97, 352–56
Lean, Martin E., xiii
Least upper bound, 352
Leblanc, Hugues, iiin., iv, vii, 111n.
Leibniz, 159
Levels of language, 195–97, 352–56
Lewis, C. I., 264n.
Liar paradox, 197; *see also* Appendix C
Limited
  generality, 140
  scope of an assumption, 86–88, 105, 113, 114
Lincoln, 131–32, 143, 158, 164
Lobachevsky, 183, 248
Logic
  definition, 1
  science of, 177
  study of, 1, 2
  task of deductive, 4
Logical
  analogy, 19, 20
  equivalence, 29, 30, 42
  proof, 190
  sum, 239, 240, 334
  truth, 122–130, 312, 314
  types, 173–74; *see also* Appendix C
Logistic system, 190–194; *see also* Chapters 7, 8, 9 *passim*
Lower function calculus, 277
Lukasiewicz, J., x, 197n., 249, 260, 264

M.P., 35, 36
M.T., 36
Magel, Charles R., vii
Many-valued logics, 249
Marsh, Robert Charles, 173n.
Material
  equivalence, 29, 42, 202, 237
  implication, 17, 22, 23, 29, 42, 202, 237

Mathematical induction, 208–211, 352
Matrix 305
Max, 55
Maximal, 320
McNaughton, Robert, vii, xii
Mediate inference, 338
Metalanguage, 195–97, 353–356
Meta-metalanguage, 353–356
Metatheorem, 208
Meyer, Rene S., ix
Middle, excluded, 227
Min, 55
Model, 54, 217, 313, 315
  system of logic, 250, 259
Modus
  Ponens, 22, 35, 36, 213, 236, 269
  Tollens, 22, 23, 36, 237
Monadic function, 205
Moore, John Dennis, iv, vii
Morgan, Douglas N., vii
Mu, 106
Multiplication of classes, 334
Multiply general propositions, 97–102
Myers, C. Mason, vii

N, 267–276
Nakhnikian, George, xii
Napoleon, 175
Natural deduction, 81, 106–116, 129, 298–302, 323
Negation, 11, 74, 325
  quantifier, 124
Negative proposition
  particular, 75
  singular, 73
  universal, 75
nEgO, 75
Nelson, L., 345n.
Newton, 178
Nicod, J. G. P., 267–276
Non-Euclidean geometry, 183, 190
Nonreflexive relations, 152–53
Nonsymmetrical relations, 151–52

Nontransitive relations, 152

Normal form, 302–311, 328
  Boolean, 329–332, 336
  conjunctive, 328
  disjunctive, 328
  prenex, 302–305
  Skolem, 308–311

Normal interpretation, 194, 201, 313–315, 321

Nu, 106

Null class, 335–337

Numerals, Arabic and Roman, 8

Numerical propositions, 163

O proposition, 75, 77–78, 295, 333, 337–38

Object language, 195–97, 352–56

Obverse, 338

Operators, 198, 208
  stroke and dagger, 265–67

Opposition, square of, 74, 77, 295

Or, 11, 12, 13

Order
  of functions, 348
  of precedence, 203, 261, 280
  of propositions, 349–350
  of quantifiers, 137

P.M., 256

Paradox
  of the liar, 197; *see also* Appendix C
  of material implication, 29

Parallel postulate, 183, 190

Parentheses, 13, 72*n.*, 203, 260–64

Parenthesis-free notation, 264–65

Parry, W. T., iii, iv, vii

Part, well formed, 281

Particular propositions, 75–77

Peirce, Charles, 1, 266*n.*
  his law, 69

Pfeiffer, John E., 329*n.*

Phi, 77, 106–107

Placed, initially, 302

Plato, 132–33, 170

Plus symbol, 211

Polish notation, 257–58

Pollux, *see* Castor and Pollux

Ponens, see Modus Ponens

Porte, J., vii

Porter, William Sidney, *see* Henry, O.

Possible nonempty universe, 91–95, 312–14

Post, E. L., 187, 246*n.*, 249
  criterion for consistency, 187, 216–17, 285

Postulate, *see* Axiom

Prawitz, Dag, iv

Precedence, order of, 203, 261, 280

Predicable, 172

Predicate
  calculus, 277*n.*
  constant, 278
  symbol, 279
  term, 72, 333
  variable, 279

Prefix, 305

Premiss, 3, 4
  suppressed, 155

Prenex normal form, 302–305

Primitive symbols, 198

Principia Mathematica, 256, 349*n.*, 351*n.*, 352

Proclus, 182

Product of classes, 334

Proof
  conditional, 58–61, 64–66, 84–89, 238, 288, 298–99
  of consistency, 188, 216–17, 283–85
  of deductive completeness, 238–247, 252–53, 311–324
  of functional completeness, 204–208
  of functional incompleteness, 210
  of incompleteness of rules, 54–58
  of independence of axioms, 188, 217–223
  indirect, 62–65, 66, 88, 238

of invalidity, 51, 52, 91–95
  in R.S., 225–27
  reductio ad absurdum, 62–65, 66, 68–70
  shorter, 118–120
  of tautology, 65–67
  of validity, 33–36, 41–46
Properties, 72
  of different orders, 347
  of formal deductive systems, 187–190
  predicable and impredicable, 172
  of properties, 169–175
  of relations, 151–157
Property variable, 169–175
Proposition, 2, 3, 6; *see also* Statement
  categorical, 333, 337
  general, 71–78, 91–92
  multiply general, 97–102
  numerical, 163
  orders of, 349–350
  relational, 132, 134, 138
  singly general, 97
  singular, 71–73
  subject-predicate, 75–77, 78
Propositional
  calculus, 194; *see also* Chapters 7 and 8
  constant, 278
  function, 73, 97–98, 103–108, 134
  symbol, 198, 278
  variable, 199, 278
Protasis, 14
Psi, 77, 106–107
Psychology, 2
Punctuation, 13, 260–265
Putnam, Ruth Mathers, ix
Pythagoras, 179, 180

QN, 124
Quantification, 73, 99–100; *see also* Chapter 9
  order of, 137

rules, 80–84, 103–116; *see also* **EG**; **EI**; **UG**; **UI**
  words, 142
Quantifier
  existential, 74, 99–100
  initially placed, 302
  negation, 124
  rank, 307–308
  scope, 76, 99–100, 302
  universal, 73, 99–100, 281
Quantifier-free formula, 283
Quaternary relations, 132
Quine, Willard Van Orman, 173*n*., 266*n*., 268*n*.

R.S., 201, 342–344
RS$_1$, 277
RS$_1$*, 318
Ramified theory of types, *see* Appendix C
Ramsey, F. P., 345, 346, 351*n*., 354*n*.
Rank, 307–308
Real variable, 98*n*.
Reasoning, 2
Recursive
  definition, 200, 250, 268, 281
  rule, 250, 268, 281
Reducibility axiom, 352, 356
Reductio ad absurdum, 62, 63, 68–70, 183
Redundance, 43, 188
  in punctuation, 261
  of P.M. postulates, 256
Reflexive relations, 152–53
Refutation by logical analogy, 19, 20
Regression, 179, 181
Relations, *see* Chapter 5
Remnant, Peter, vii
Replacement, rule of, 42; *see also* Substitution theorems
Restricted function calculus, 277
Riemann, 183, 248
Rigor, 184–86, 190–94
Rockefeller, 5, 19

Roffe, Peggy Fingard, vii
Rosser, J. Barkley, xi, 201n., 249
Rowe, William, vii
Rule
    of conditional proof, 58–61, 64, 65,
        66, 84–89, 238, 288, 298
    derived, 214–15
    of indirect proof, 62–65
    of inference, 34, 35–36, 41, 45, 81–
        82
    quantification, 80–84, 103–116; see
        also **EG**; **EI**; **UG**; **UI**
    recursive, 250, 268, 281
    of replacement, 42
    H.A., 251–52
    N, 268
    R.S., 213
    RS₁, 282
Russell, Bertrand, xii, 165, 172n., 173,
    256n., 350, 351n., 353n., 356

S.T., 291
Saccheri, Gerolamo, 183
Satisfiable, 314
    simultaneously, 318
Satisfy, 314
Scharle, Thomas W., 268n.
Schema, 208, 209
Schönfinkel, Moses, 95n.
Science
    of geometry, 179–185, 190, 248–49
    as organized knowledge, 177
    of reasoning, 2
Scope
    of an assumption, 86–88, 112, 114
    of operator symbols, 203–204, 280
    of a quantifier, 76, 99–100, 302
Scott, Sir Walter, 158, 164
Second-order
    functions, 348
    propositions, 349–350
Self-evidence, 182
Sellars, W., 356n.

Semantical, 193–94, 196, 204
    paradoxes, 197; see also Appendix C
    terms, 352
Sentential calculus, see Calculus, prop-
    ositional
Set, 316
Shannon, Claude E., 329n.
Sheffer, H. M., 266n.
Simons, Leo, ix, 54n.
Simp., 36
Simple
    class terms, 336
    statement, 9–10, 71
    theory of types, 173–74; see also
        Appendix C
Simplification, principle of, 36, 119,
    237
Simultaneously satisfiable, 318
Singly general proposition, 97
Singular proposition, 71–73
Singulary function, 205
Skolem normal form, 308–311
Slater, John G., iiin.
Socrates, 3, 71, 72, 110, 133, 169, 170
Spinoza, 180
Square of opposition, 75, 77, 295
Statement
    contingent, 28, 69
    contradictory, 28
    form, 27, 30, 31
    simple and compound, 8
    tautologous, 28
    truth-functionally compound, 10
    variable, 19
Strawson, P. F., 165n.
Strengthened rule of conditional
    proof, 84–89
Stroke function, 265–67
Stroll, Avrum, vii
Strong
    disjunction, 12, 202
    induction, 209–211
Subclass, 336

Subcontraries, 75, 77
Subject term, 72, 333
Subject-predicate propositions, 75, 77, 333
Subset, 316
Substitution instance, 20, 27, 35, 73, 74, 97, 98
Substitution theorems, 235, 291
Sum, logical, 239, 240, 334
Summand, 240
Syllogism
  categorical, 338, 339
  disjunctive, 12–13, 20, 21, 36, 237
  hypothetical, 22, 55, 230, 236
Symmetrical relations, 151
Syntactical, 193–94, 196
  variable, 279
Syntax language, 196
System
  deductive, *see* Chapter 6
  logistic, 190–197; *see also* Chapters 7, 8, 9 *passim*

Table
  three-valued, 55–58, 218–222
  truth, 11, 21–24, 28–32, 68–70, 241, 246
Tarski, A., 356*n*.
Taut., 43
Tautologous, 28
Tautology, 28, 66
  principles of, 43, 237, 326, 334
  proof of, 65–67
  and validity, 30–31, 58–59, 65
Temporal words, 142–43
Terms, 72, 177–79, 189, 333, 336
  predicate, 72, 333
  simple class, 336
  subject, 72, 333
Ternary, *see* Triadic
Tetradic relations, 132
The, 148, 164–168

The form
  of an argument, 19–21
  of a statement, 27
Theorem, *see* Chapter 6
Thing, 72
Thomson, J. F., vii
Three-valued
  logic, 249
  truth tables, 55–58, 218–222
Tilde, 11
Todhunter, 180*n*.
Tollens, see Modus Tollens
Totally reflexive relations, 152–53
Trans., 42
Transitive relations, 152
Transposition, principle of, 42, 228, 237
Triadic
  functions, 206
  relations, 132
Truth, 4–6
  formal, 27
  function, 204–208
  functionally compound statement, 10, 41
  hereditary, 54
  logical, 122–130
  necessary, 27
  table, 11, 21–24, 28–32, 68–70, 241, 246
  unconditional, 66
  value, 10, 51, 55, 68–70
Turing, A. M., 264*n*.
Turquette, A. R., xi, 249
Twain, Mark, 159
Two-valued logic, 249
Types, logical, 173–74; *see also* Appendix C

UG, 81–82, 114–116, 129, 298–299
UI, 80–81, 107–109, 128, 298
Unary function, 205
Undefined terms, 180–181

Union, 334
Universal
  class, 335
  generalization, 81, 114–116; *see also* **UG**
  instantiation, 80, 107–109; *see also* **UI**
  proposition, 75
  quantifier, 73, 99, 281
  quantification, 74, 99–100
Universe, possible nonempty, 91–95, 312–314

Valid, 4, 20, 104, 193, 314
  and tautologous, 31, 58
Validity
  conditional proof of, 58–61, 64, 65, 84–88
  formal proof of, 33–36, 41–45, 105
  formal nature of, 21
  indirect proof of, 62–64, 66
  semantical and syntactical, 193–94, 196
  and tautology, 30–31, 58–59, 65
Variable
  apparent, 98*n*.
  binding, 105, 126; *see also* **EG**; **UG**
  bound occurrence, 98, 282
  dangling, 101, 102
  free occurrence, 98, 126
  freeing, 105, 107–109, 111–14; *see also* **EI**; **UI**
  independent, 204

  individual, 72, 98, 279
  interchange of bound, 297
  predicate, 279
  property, 169–175
  propositional, 199, 278
  real, 98*n*.
  statement, 19
  syntactical, 279
Vee symbol, 12, 202, 250, 280
Vel, 12
Vicious circle, 179
  principle, 351

wff, 193–94, 198–200, 250, 268, 281
Warren, Don W., 265*n*.
Weak
  disjunction, 12, 202
  induction, 208–209
Wedge symbol, 12, 202, 250, 280
Well formed
  formula, 191–194, 198–200, 281
  part, 281
Whitehead, Alfred North, 8, 173*n*., 256*n*., 350, 351*n*.
Wittgenstein, L., 353*n*.
Workman, Rollin, vii, xii
Wright, Jesse, 265*n*.

Yields symbol, 214, 228

Zermelo, E., 173*n*.
Ziff, Paul, xii